A SYSTEMATIC
REGIONAL GEOGRAPHY

General Editor

J. F. UNSTEAD, M.A., D.Sc.

VOLUME V
MONSOON ASIA

A SYSTEMATIC REGIONAL GEOGRAPHY

Volume I
THE BRITISH ISLES

Volume II
EUROPE

Volume III
A WORLD SURVEY—From the Human Aspect

Volume IV
AUSTRALIA, NEW ZEALAND AND THE
SOUTHWEST PACIFIC

Volume V
MONSOON ASIA

A SYSTEMATIC
REGIONAL GEOGRAPHY

VOLUME V

MONSOON ASIA

E. H. G. DOBBY, B.A., Ph.D.

*Formerly Professor of Geography, University of Malaya
and University College of Ghana*

UNIVERSITY OF LONDON PRESS LTD
WARWICK SQUARE, LONDON, E.C.4

Copyright © 1961 by E. H. G. Dobby

UNIVERSITY OF LONDON PRESS LTD
Warwick Square, LONDON E.C.4

SHOWROOMS OVERSEAS

41 Shortland Street, AUCKLAND C.1, New Zealand
425 Little Collins Street, MELBOURNE, Victoria, Australia
429 Kent Street, SYDNEY, New South Wales, Australia

REPRESENTATIVE IN WEST AFRICA

Mr Leslie Smith, B.A., P.O. Box 62, IBADAN, Nigeria

AGENTS OVERSEAS

Brazil   Dr J. E. Bloch, Caixa Postal 8675, SÃo PAULO

Canada   Clarke, Irwin & Co. Ltd, Clarwin House, 791 St Clair Avenue West,
TORONTO 10

Egypt and the   Dino Judah Nahum, 44 Sharia Sherif Pasha, CAIRO (P.O. Box 940)
Sudan

The Far East   Donald Moore Ltd, Macdonald House, Orchard Road, SINGAPORE 9
(P.O. Box 1742)
with branches in
Hong Kong   707 Gt China House, Queen's Road Central
Japan   Shimura Building, 4–1 Kojimachi, Chiyoda-ku,
TOKYO
Malaya   Great Eastern Life Building, Ampang Road,
KUALA LUMPUR
represented in
Indonesia   by Gunung Agung, Kwitang 13, DJAKARTA

India   Orient Longmans Private Ltd, 17 Chittaranjan Avenue, CALCUTTA 13
(P.O. Box 2146)
with branches at
Nicol Road, Ballard Estate, BOMBAY 1 (P.O. Box 704)
36A Mount Road, MADRAS 2 (P.O. Box 310)
24/1 Kanson House, Asaf Ali Road, NEW DELHI 1

East Pakistan   Mr N. Mahmood, Orient Longmans Private Ltd,
17 Nazimuddin Road, DACCA

West Pakistan   Longmans Green & Co. Ltd, Hayat House, 14 Hall Road, LAHORE

South Africa   Mr H. B. Timmins, 109 Long Street CAPE TOWN (P. O. Box 94)

Printed & Bound in England for the University of London Press Ltd
by Hazell Watson & Viney Ltd, Aylesbury and Slough

Preface

IN THIS BOOK I have attempted to use my experience of working in Asia to express a geographer's point of view on some parts of Asia for higher schools and colleges. As an examiner for British students and as visiting professor to American universities, I know the special difficulties of Western students when they look closer at the Monsoon Asia of today. Here I assume an elementary acquaintance with geography, yet try to make what I have to say helpful to those of several fields of interest—of international affairs, business and commercial geography as well as of formal studies in Asian geography, history, economics and politics.

My scheme has been first to review the peculiarities of Monsoon Asia as a whole, outlining the setting and its major human influences, than to demonstrate landscape details of its chief regions on different scales. Besides sketch-maps and close-up photographs, I use a selection of air-photographs and extracts from Asian topographic maps to build a sense of being in intimate contact with local realities and "down to earth". The emphasis is agricultural because farming, still the dominant activity of Asians, is critical in their ways of thinking, in their relations with one another and the rest of the world, and in the foundations of what they hope to make of the future. I have gone on to examine the economic and political aspects of national geographies, giving factual data from latest United Nations reports to indicate objectively the new trends and significances which are vital, not merely for international commerce and industry but also for properly appreciating modern Asia's function in the political economy of our quickly changing world.

Written from inside Asia, this up-to-date geography is not focused on any one Asian nation, and it should enable Asian students no less than Western students to see their national problems in relation to those of others.

If the proportion I have given to different Asian regions is uneven, it is partly because the territory, its population and its problems are large and varied, so that selection must be ruthless to be brief.

I wrote this work while at the universities of Malaya, Washington and Ghana, for whose professional hospitality I am most grateful.

E. H. G. DOBBY

Acknowledgements

The author gratefully acknowledges his thanks to the following for permission to reproduce their photographs:

Shell Photographic Unit for Plates 8, 11, 12, 14, 17, 19, 21, 22
British Overseas Airways Corporation for Plates 3, 4, 10, 13, 15, 18, and 24
Government of India Tourist Office for Plate 27
Central Office of Information for Plate 16
Other Plates have been obtained as follows:
from Paul Popper—2, 6, 20, 25
from Radio Times Hulton Picture Library—7, 26
from Educational Publications—23
from Pictorial Press—1, 5
from Lubinski—28
from Selwood—29

The author also acknowledges his general debt to all those who have recorded their studies of Asian life.

Contents

CONTENTS

PART IV
SOUTHERN ASIA

PART V
ECONOMIC AND POLITICAL GEOGRAPHY

Tables

Maps and Diagrams

9

Plates

Part I

Monsoon Asia as a Whole

CHAPTER ONE

Monsoon Asia in the Modern World

BY "MONSOON ASIA" is to be understood the territory of the countries from West Pakistan through India, Burma, Siam, Indochina and Eastern China as far as the Gulf of Chihli and the off-shore island groups of Japan, the Philippines, Indonesia and Ceylon. The monsoon condition does not, of course, obtain throughout this area, but to use the boundaries of these countries as its limit has statistical convenience. Monsoon Asia is thus the southern and eastern part of Asia, and its features have been described as "the golden fringe to a beggar's mantle" and as "the golden crescent". It includes less than a seventh of the world's land surface, yet contains half of humanity and nearly a third of the world's cultivated land, ranking as the most important of regions. Within such a sweep of the globe, a great variety of terrain and landscape types are to be found. Monsoon Asia cannot be summarised in a few sentences. We will question whether it is *all* subject to "the monsoon", "fertile" or "golden", but its peoples are Asians who have a daily life and a cultural pattern so distinctive that they seem different, romantic and strange to the rest of the world, even though some Asians seem equally different and strange to the others.

OLD AND NEW

The distinctiveness is long-standing. The world's oldest civilisations (of North India and North China) are identified with Monsoon Asia, their very antiquity being an element in the complexities of problems arising there today. In speech, colour and physique the people differ considerably from those of surrounding regions; they also differ greatly from place to place inside their "Oriental World". Among millions of them, dress, food habits, domestic manners, social customs and modes of farming remain much as they have been for millennia, and largely peculiar to the Orient. The self-contained peasant and the rural way of life in small villages persists and forms one of the major contrasts with the Western World, where urbanisation, commercial farming and industry set the characteristic pattern. Its landscape is dominated by cereal farming in contrast to W. Europe, where grass covers much of the used land and is the

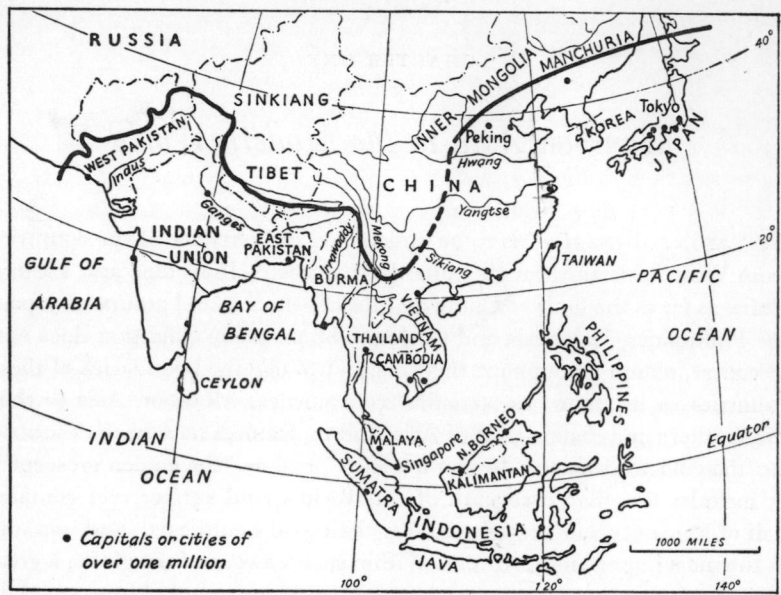

FIG. 1—Monsoon Asia: the heavy line indicates the extent of the region

basis of animal farming. Cotton is the usual textile fibre in the East, wool in the West. Mechanisation sets the standard elsewhere, manual methods are still a feature of the East. The West is a world of metals in wide and everyday application: Monsoon Asia is the home of a "vegetable civilisation", where wood and plant materials have been the basis of everyday things from houses to domestic utensils, farm implements and clothing.

CONTRIBUTIONS TO MANKIND

The attraction and curiosity aroused among Western peoples by Asians are also long-standing. The Greeks and Romans looked upon them as the source of wonderful new things. To curiosity about Asia and interest in its wares may be ascribed even the discovery of America, the march to the "Far West" being a consequence of Turkish and Arabic obstruction on the old ways to the "Far East". The material contributions of Asians to the world as a whole have been so great that there is no excuse for the Westerner to be patronising about the Easterner. Paper, printing and explosives were invented in Monsoon Asia. A whole host of fundamental crops were evolved there, including rice, citrus fruits, soya and spices.

Eastern people were for centuries the major producers of fine textiles (cotton and silk). But equally fundamental have been the West's more recent contributions to the Asian Lands, particularly in transport, bulk trade, hygiene, heavy industry and science; it has also introduced new crops—maize, the rubber tree, tobacco and the peanut. Monsoon Asia has stimulated fashions and ideas in the West; the West has also stamped its ideas of public health, organisations and politics upon the Asian World.

After Europe became changed by its 'Industrial Revolution' and the increasing command of men and material it made possible, the attraction of Monsoon Asia increased. The impact of the European industrial and trading civilisations upon the Oriental World was most pronounced. Many parts of Monsoon Asia became "colonial", whether directly or indirectly ruled; mere handfuls of Europeans could, with their trading and organisation methods, control vast Asian populations. In several cases the Western trading groups "colonised" unwillingly—a necessity imposed upon them in the political vacuum caused by local breakdowns in organisation. Japan and Thailand resisted being colonised, but quickly Westernised themselves.

EFFECTS OF COLONIAL PERIOD

The colonising Westerners, although rarely settling permanently in Asia, injected into Asians those systems of trade and industry which were the basis of their own power. Thereby they revolutionised the economy of Monsoon Asia. Though the change occurred at varying paces from place to place, it brought great Asian cities into being, caused heavy industries to grow up, laid out modern transport systems and ultimately affected almost every corner of Asia. The economic and political development induced by Western innovations in Asia prepared the way for dispensing with Western administrators.

The effects of the colonial association between Europe and Asia went deep. Into the remotest Asian village penetrated cheap machine-made cotton cloth, needles, bicycles, candles; old methods were occluded, novelties introduced. Western medicine changed the Asian rates of birth and of death; millions more people appeared in the old places; new places were opened up by mechanical means, ports flowered into cities and cities became magnets of employment for wages. A march to the Asian cities began and the squalor of industrial slums appeared. In consequence, Monsoon Asia has come to have great contrasts—customs, articles and practices which were old even in Greek times, continue side by side with the most modern facilities. The Oriental World today is one where the ancient and the modern live cheek by jowl, giving rise to a complex struggle of ideas in Asian minds.

The colonial phase of political control from Europe was quite brief. It was at its peak by 1910. It has already ended. Its effects, however, continue, and one feature of Monsoon Asia today is its character as a laboratory of continuous and quickly changing technical and social development and readjustment. The departure of colonial civil servants has left countries which are new but confused with inheritances from ancient ones. Within these countries are modes of living as Western as any in Europe, side by side with other modes far removed in space, time and motive. Town and country in Asia team with difficulties and with conflicts of need. Every issue once faced in the countries of now industrialised Europe is reappearing in the Asian states created by the Western colonisers.

INCREASING NUMBERS

In conjunction there occurred a remarkable expansion of population due to (a) new hygiene standards introduced by the Western powers, (b) law and order, established by the colonists, curbed war—the traditional population control, and (c) the techniques they introduced made possible a great increase in cultivation in places previously unusable. In some parts, the Asian increase has been spectacular: Japanese have multiplied by 10 since 1800, Ceylonese by 8, Filipinos by 9. This proliferation in a long-standing period of peace set foot a great movement of Asians who gravitated from country to town and from one state to more attractive ones. People swarmed to newly opened parts of Asia, producing colonies of foreign Asians and plural societies where the speed and volume of the movement was greater than local societies could absorb by natural miscegenation. By now the proliferation is creating a new problem—of man-made scarcity. The human increase has been faster and continued longer than the increase of food production; a fact which threatens a continuing state of inadequate food.

NEW WORLD IMPORTANCE

The way of life which had been evolved within the Oriental World developed in isolation, partly because resources within Monsoon Asia were for a long time ample in relation to the techniques available. Isolation was enforced by the physically difficult terrain on the landward side and the vast oceanic emptiness seaward. The region was the centre of all the world that they needed to know so far as many generations of Indians, Chinese, Japanese and Javanese were concerned. It became for a while only an appanage to Western industrial and seaborne civilisation, but now assumes a new significance as a complex of self-centred independencies. The countries find themselves to be centres of major internal readjustments and also the focus of major external pressures—the Western democracies from seaward and Russian Communism from landward. The new countries are often mutually jealous, and the new leaders find their countries in the forefront of international affairs with a significance they have not known for over four centuries.

World interest in Monsoon Asia now largely arises because, while at first the development of transport and communications served to make available to the rest of the world their markets and products, they now serve to share the age-old liabilities of Asia with others. The military security of the globe now depends for various reasons on the Oriental World. The economic well-being of the West is now recognised as being imperilled if that half of the world's people living in Asia remains cut off from the general circulation and use of the world's commodities. Transport, communications and the huge numbers of people in Asia make the zone a fulcrum of international political and economic power, causing to some extent a dwarfing of the Western World. For all its tropical setting, Asia had been darkened by ignorance arising largely from remoteness and isolation. Popular education, literacy, the radio and the aeroplane are restoring Asians to knowledge, removing them from twilit faith into the light of stark facts which present problems of proportions alarming in their size at first glance, but reassuring at second examination because they are problems of a kind already known elsewhere, and because their size means that they offer fields of activity which could keep fully employed the whole of the world's people and resources for several generations.

The problems attracting modern interest to Monsoon Asia are of two kinds—those affecting Asians domestically and those affecting people living outside Monsoon Asia.

WHAT ASIANS ASK

Problems chiefly affecting Asians domestically are: How can the age-old practices of the rural areas be brought into line with the modernity of Asian cities and industrial centres? Whence can come the food supplies for the urban areas if rising standards of diet and new forms of land tenure in the countryside cause surpluses to dry up? Can the pressure of population be absorbed by domestic developments alone? Is it possible for the plural societies to be welded into nations? Are the gulfs between the ancient and the modern aspects of Asian economic life bridgeable? Will the principles of nationalism splinter the political units into new ones racially more homogeneous? Why do the present countries now appear as poor and backward after having been prized as colonial jewels? Can local production be extended spatially or intensified enough to keep pace with natural increase and with the demand for higher standards of living? Can the administrative and economic machinery originally established by Westerners be continued in the changed circumstances? Can the political ambitions which Asians learnt from the West be pursued without further destructive revolution? Can the Asian tradition be reconciled with standing at the forefront of world issues? Is it better for Monsoon Asia to look to the older democracies or to Communism for a pattern in political and economic affairs? Will industrialisation relieve internal strains or create more strain?

WHAT THE WORLD ASKS ABOUT ASIA

People living outside Monsoon Asia see the contemporary questions to be: Why are the countries so unstable now that they have achieved independence? What relations can be expected to become established among the new states? Can they on their own acquire the economic and political strength they had in the colonial association? What links will they establish with Europe, the U.S.A. and Russia? Are the conditions within any one country sufficiently like those in the next to be a basis for a regional *bloc*? Will their internal food and population problems lead to policies of expansionism which will produce wars between the Asian states? Have we to expect a great march of hungry hordes from Monsoon Asia to emptier places in Australia, Central Asia and Africa? How is it that "scarcity" is so widespread in Asia's "golden crescent"? Do the new countries have the basis for industrialisation? What effects on European and American interests in commerce and transport will result from changes taking place in Monsoon Asia? What are the potentials for more intensive exploitation of local domestic resources? Why the paradox between the poor, struggling Asian states of today and the alleged grandeur of their ancient past? Are the present boundaries, laid out in the colonial period, likely to change?

The majority of these problems have a material basis. The modern Asian conceives of present issues in physical and material terms taken from Europeans and Americans. Because the majority of Asians are rural people, they have a strong foundation in the hard facts of life, and their materialistic outlook on public affairs must in the long run dominate Asian attitudes and reactions to problems in Monsoon Asia.

Because the geographer is concerned with material things and their associations on the landscape, both locally and regionally, he has a special contribution to make in appraising these issues. His kind of survey of actualities in Asia is a vital preliminary to development and planning as well as to understanding. His conception of the association and relationship between human needs and natural environment is a corrective to those who would introduce a change without carefully estimating the displacements and replacements it will involve in the region's human ecology.

By presenting a survey of Monsoon Asia on these lines, this book hopes to contribute to an understanding of their circumstances and their lines of development, thereby assisting a proper appreciation of the place the new Asian countries has in the modern world.

CHAPTER TWO

Landforms and Physical Patterns

TWO FEATURES dominate Monsoon Asia: it lies south and east of the Tibetan Highlands, which in breadth, altitude and continuity create within the Asian continent a major impediment to human activity; it is broken by bays and gulfs of the Indian and Pacific Oceans in such a way that most parts are within 500 miles of a coast. Both the sea and the massive high interior recur as themes in the variations of historic, economic and political factors among people in Southern and Eastern Asia.

FESTOON OF FOLDS

A third physical feature is a vast festoon of fold mountains arranged partly marginally to and partly subdividing the "Oriental realm". In the Himalayas, these mountains abut the Tibetan Highlands: they change direction and position at the eastern end of the Himalayas to become the Arakan Yoma, and then, intermittently concealed by sea, continue through West Sumatra and South Java, bending north again through Celebes, the Philippines and Japan. This Himalayan-Island Arc in part separates Monsoon Asia from Central Asia, in part marks the Pacific limit of Monsoon Asia and in part divides southern from eastern Monsoon Asia. Youthfulness and erosion characterise the landforms of this feature where mountain building and mountain shaping continue, evidenced by the frequency of earthquakes near the Himalayas and the presence of many volcanic islands. On its southern side is a great "foredeep" or geosyncline, constituting the profound oceanic trenches off Japan and the Philippines, but filled with alluvium south of the Himalayas.

BLOCKS AND PLATEAUX

While the Tibetan Highland is abruptly separated by the Himalayas from southern Monsoon Asia, it has a more gradual transition to the east where many "block uplands" form the broken mountains of South and Central China, whose latitudinal arrangements repeat alignments evident in Tibet. The partially submerged Sunda Shelf underlying Southeast Asia and its islands is a continuation of similar block landforms.

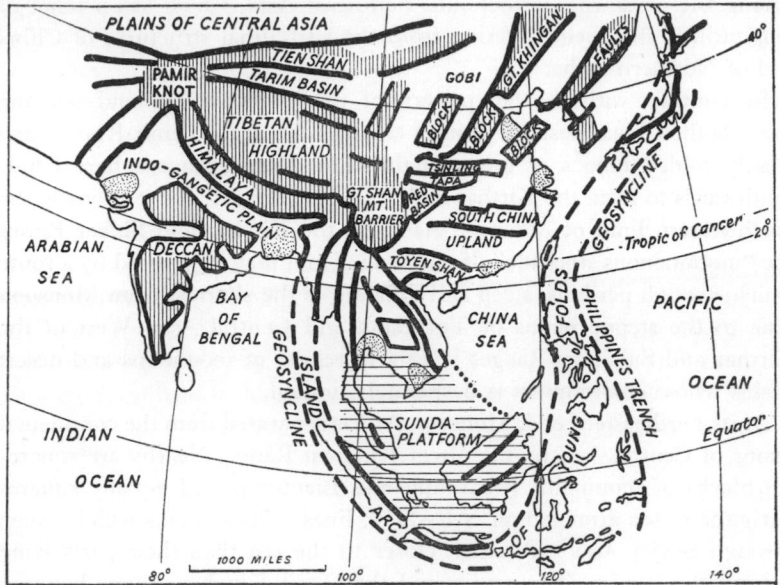

FIG. 2—The structural pattern of Asia

One major physical unit of Monsoon Asia lies south of the festoon of folds—the Deccan tilted plateau, one of the world's oldest physical features, a fragment of the ancient Gondwana continent and related in rocks and structure more to Africa and Australia than to Asia.

The influence of the eastern Tibetan Highland on the landforms of Monsoon Asia is accentuated and extended by rivers. That little-known knot of the Highland where the names Kam Mountains, Upper Hwang Highlands and Great Snowy Mountains are used has altitudes exceeding 20,000 feet over large areas, and gives rise to huge rivers which, though starting close together, terminate thousands of miles apart. From this little-explored mountain knot fan out the Hwang-Ho[1], Yangtse, Mekong, Salween, Irrawaddy and Brahmaputra rivers, whose courses lie within unmapped chasms in a wild, seasonally snowbound, sparsely peopled landscape. The profound gorges of the Salween, Mekong and Yangtse are in places less than 50 miles apart, but their N.–S. lines set a pattern repeated

[1] Atlases and books may render any one place-name with different words or different spellings. The former differences arise from the several languages in use within an Asian state; the latter reflect the several ways of transcribing alphabetically the characters and tones of an Asian language.

23

among the landforms farther into Southeast Asia, which has a relief of longitudinal alignment differing from the latitudinal structures of China and of Northern India.

By contrast with the fan pattern of the Tibetan Highland opening towards the China coast, its western end narrows at the Pamir Knot which closely folded ranges of great height. The Himalayan arc here bends southwards to form the Kirthar and Sulaiman Ranges, conventionally the northwestern limit of Monsoon Asia. By the Khyber and Shikar Passes the "mountainous stockade" of the Pamir Knot may be crossed by a route which, though perilous, steep and difficult, is the shortest from Monsoon Asia to the steppe plains of Turkestan and Central Asia. West of the Kirthar and Sulaiman Ranges is an arid region of mountains and desert basins whose environment is desperately limited.

At its northeastern end, Monsoon Asia is separated from the continental plains of Central Asia by the Great Kinghan Range. Nearby are square-cut blocks of mountains (Shantung and Liaotung) and equally square-cut gulfs of sea arranged on N.E.–S.W. lines. Those plains which sweep through Soviet Asia here reach closer to the sea than their parts lying beyond the Pamirs. The way round the Great Kinghan Range between the coast and the Siberian Plains is both level and short, but located well to the north and subject to climatic extremes greater than elsewhere in Monsoon Asia.

LANDFORM GROUPS

These landforms may be classified thus:

1. The Himalayan-Island Arc of folds, everywhere young, still unstable modelled chiefly by water erosion still going on at a great pace upon the parallel ranges.

(a) Its Kirthar–Himalayas–Arakan section separates a major part of Monsoon Asia from Continental Central Asia. It has sustained high altitudes, much glacial erosion and no active volcanoes. Rivers here commonly run within the trough of a fold, and then traverse a gorge into the next trough, creating a coulisse or trellis pattern. They are violent until they break through the ranges to the plains, where they build large alluvial fans.

(b) Its Andaman–Java–Celebes–Japan section is insular, actively volcanic, and forming an island screen between the continent and the Pacific and Indian Oceans. Rain is the dominant eroding agent and volcanic landforms here are prominent. The islands, elongated as an effect of their structure, have short and violent rivers.

24

2. Continental Monsoon Asia has peninsular combinations of highlands and plains:

(a) The Southern Subcontinent (the territories of Pakistan and India) includes the Indo-Gangetic Alluvial Plain and the Deccan Plateau down-tilting towards the east, the main drainage of both being towards the east. The Tropic of Cancer roughly divides the Subcontinent into (i) A southern triangle mostly the compacted Deccan Plateau thrusting into the Indian Ocean its crystalline rocks, covered here and there by old lava sheets and by sedimentary basins. This triangle has been shaped by prolonged erosion into broad, open and flattened or gently sloping horizons, with several rivers on W.–E. lines. Ceylon, an insular outlier upon a small continental shelf, repeats some Deccan features. Faulted edges form lines of hills round the Deccan, the highest being to the west. These hills (ghats) stand back from the coast to leave narrow, little indented coastal plains of new alluvials. (ii) A northern triangle chiefly of the Indo-Gangetic V-shaped Plain whose materials are river-borne debris eroded from the Himalayas to the north, varying in fineness according to distance from source and from surface. Towards the dry west, wind is an agent moulding the landforms. On the continental margin, mountains rise forbiddingly. Its coastal margins are deltaic, built by streams of great size (the Indus, Ganges and Brahmaputra systems) which originate outside the Plain but flow for hundreds of miles across it.

(b) The highlands of Eastern China, mostly north of the Tropic, form a terrain whose elements are modifications and extensions of those in Continental Tibet. They include horst-like masses of upland built of stratified rocks, and structural basins filled with alluvial materials, reshaped during several phases of erosion. The landscapes are level-topped masses with straight, faulted sides. Erosion and deposition by streams and glaciers account for its modelling, but to the northwest wind has also played a part. The Yangtse divides Eastern China into: (i) The northern section including everything from the Tsin Ling to Korea. Here the blocks are smaller and the alluvial basins larger, with high latitude causing much annual variation in daylight and temperature. Wind is a modelling agent and a series of major faults aligned N.E.–S.W. sets the pattern of uplands, plains and bays. The coasts have alternate stretches of rock-bound and alluvial landscapes. The Wei-Hwang River system passes through the unit in a huge zigzag pattern due to the horst structure. (ii) The southern section has a W.–E. form of sustained upland without clearly defined ranges and of complex formations. Here basin forms are negligible and structural embayments infrequent. The coast has rock-bound, drowned-

25

river indentations of ria type, small compared with the whole unit, which is the largest, most compacted continental unit in the east. Not a single arm of the sea penetrates the mass whose only major break is along the Sikiang, a river which originates and completes its course entirely within the unit. Most streams of this southern section are short, steep and violent, not readily lending themselves to navigation or irrigation. The Yangtse River originates from outside Eastern China and, marginal to both sections, links a series of lake-filled basins.

(c) The highlands of Southeast Asia begin among the Kam and Great Snowy Mountains, extending south of the tropic through the Shan country and the Malay Peninsula with the Annamite Highlands as the eastern and the Arakan Yoma the western limit of the Sunda Platform, which dips to the south, partially inundated by the sea which isolates those parts of it which underlie East Sumatra, North Java and Borneo. Dominated by river erosion, Southeast Asian forms are developed round the fan-shape set by the Irrawaddy, Salween, Chao Praya and Mekong, each with sections of broad alluvial valleys formed within structural depressions. The Chao Praya system differs from the others in rising and ending within Southeast Asia and its régime relates entirely to local climate. Old gneiss, limestone, sandstones and shales are found together within the Sunda Platform, where water erosion often exposes igneous cores of the ancient mountain systems now in advanced denudation. A wide range of rock types is apparent in many depositions. Upon the peninsular portion, the N.–S. alignment of old mountains is strongly marked. The Sunda Platform forms the largest continental shelf round Asia. Long stretches of coast are rocky: that of Annam is the eroded, faulted side of a block, that of Arakan has the alternation typical at the end of folds. The subdivisions are: (i) the more compacted continental part from Burma to Indochina, a rhomboidal mass set askew to latitudes and containing large rivers, and (ii) the insular part, including Malaya, Borneo and islands round the Java Sea, where the rivers are short.

ICE AGES

The effects of those Ice Ages which had a major influence in Europe were slight in Monsoon Asia, which was mostly far from the ice-caps. Ice-caps never extended down Eastern Asia to the latitudes they reached in Western Europe or North America. The effects of the Ice Ages here were: (a) An enlargement of valley glaciers in and from the Himalayan and Eastern Tibetan margins. Elsewhere in Monsoon Asia the moderate altitudes were only lightly dusted with snow even at the depth of the Ice Ages. (b) A lowering of sea-level. The effects of water withdrawn from the sea and locked into ice caps were greater near plains in the tropics and less dramatic in their effects where the coasts were steep. At the middle of the Ice Ages much of the Sunda Platform was exposed to form a continuous continent embracing Sumatra, Borneo and Java. The lowered water-level made little difference to the coastal outline of India, China or Japan, though it probably intensified erosion by their rivers. At the present moment, marine inundation is probably more extensive than at any time during the last million years, but the present deltas are mostly post-glacial, although they show several phases of alluviation as a result of alternating advance and withdrawal of the seas.

SEAS

The water bodies adjoining Monsoon Asia are:

1. The Arabian Sea and the Bay of Bengal are vast triangular oceanic basins mostly below 6,000 feet, part of the much deeper Indian Ocean which strongly influences their character. They have only narrow continental shelves without major embayments penetrating the land. In these seas, islands are scarce and small except for Ceylon.

2. The Straits of Malacca, the Java Sea, Gulf of Siam and the South China Sea are shallow waters, roughly radial in pattern, which have advanced and retreated during successive Ice Ages. More influenced by the land around them than by the Indian and Pacific Oceans, they are abnormally fresh, due to local rivers and heavy rains, and abnormally warm by reason of being shallow and much enclosed. Thickly strewn with small islands, the seas are undergoing major sedimentation.

3. The China Sea and its extension to the Sea of Japan is a maritime corridor lying between East Asia and that arc of volcanic islands from the Philippines through the Ryukyus to Japan. Its water is much influenced by the Pacific Ocean, whose North Equatorial Current presses strongly and continuously through the Philippines. It includes basins of oceanic depth and small seas on the continental shelf. One arm of it penetrates the land masses at the Gulf of Tonkin; another to the north is the complexly reticulated Yellow Sea and its gulfs which break deeply into the continent at latitudes where the sea-water often freezes. The Sea of Japan has the square-cut and deep form of a structural basin edged by faults.

27

LANDFORMS AND ACCESSIBILITY

In human affairs, the consequence of these landforms and dispositions largely turns on accessibility. Their layout in peninsulas implies that access by sea is easier and more general than by land, with even deeper penetration possible along the major rivers. On the other hand, until within the last few centuries this was an access across seas which led to nowhere attractive, so that for a long period it was valueless. Their seaborne accessibility exposes the island screen of Southeast and East Asia to the maximum of whatever influences, natural, economic or political, came from overseas, and their small potential of power left them much at the mercy of water-borne political powers, evident in their recent colonial status, in the intense Westernisation of Japan and in the continued use of them as modern bases by overseas powers. Limited overland accessibility is a feature of the coasts of Malabar, Arakan, Annam, South China and Korea, whose steepness and lack of routes give them no significant hinterlands. The deltas offer an attraction of water-borne access to large hinterlands, besides being themselves highly productive. On the islands, the accessibility is in places neutralised by restricted hinterlands.

From overland, major difficulties of steep, continuous and snowbound heights, mostly rising in seried ranks like multiple stockades, hinder continental access to Monsoon Asia. This inaccessibility is completest round the Tibetan Highland, which has throughout history almost prohibited N.–S. movements between Central Asia and India. At the Pamir Knot the impediment of several ranges is great, but their total width is less than anywhere else so that access is possible though the few passes are high and tortuous; they were easier in the period of foot and horse transport than in the present one of mechanised movement. Even now, in the twentieth century, no road or railway traverses these Pamir routes. The obstruction acted as a deterrent to movement outwards from India, though the economic factor was possibly more prohibitive. There has never been an economic inducement outwards because Indians have been able to obtain more easily from within India such supplies as Central Asia had to offer. The attraction was therefore *into* rather than out of India. Hence the slightly easier passages through Khyber and Bolan have been used for movement from north and west *into* the Indo-Gangetic lowlands.

Similar obstructions forming a maze rather than a wall, lie between Eastern Asia and Central Asia. Adjoining Eastern China stand massive uplands which are greatest and broadest in East Tibet and least near the

Taching Mountains, where, however, the extensive Gobi Desert presents only slightly less of a deterrent to movement. The block structures of Eastern China mean that overland access from the continent faced nothing of the wall-like character of the Himalayas, and they were traversed by the Yangtse, and to a less extent by the Hwang, with all the relative ease of boat traffic. The series of arid despressions of which the Gobi Desert is the easternmost, made possible a not too difficult movement between North China by way of the Kalgan Corridor across the Eurasian Continent and north of the Tibetan Highlands. Movement along this route has had a seasonal character: the extreme winter cold usually prevents caravan transport for four to five months a year. This, too, was a "route of ease" chiefly during the phase of foot transport, and one where the attraction induced has also been one way—from the continent into China. As yet no modern railway traverses this classic caravan route out of China, but a little-used railway goes a short distance from Tientsin into Ordos, another is being built to Lanchow and trunk roads are rapidly being built along these ways.

Southeast Asia has a much shorter boundary to the continent, but its difficulties of overland access are greater. The Salween–Yangtse gorge country provides an alignment apparently leading into Southeast Asia, but the height and the extremely broken terrain make this a difficult approach; the rivers are unusable in the interior for transport. The Arakan Range is a forested barrier of multiple folds impeding movement between India and Southeast Asia and still uncrossed by modern land transport. The Toyen Shan to the east is only a limited landward impediment between China and Vietnam, but there has never been overland movement between India and China through Southeast Asia's mountains, although at that point their distance apart is least. This overland physical obstruction is continued far to the south, where the Malay Peninsula still hinders E.-W. movements, enforcing a major detour by sea. Thus the distance from Canton to Calcutta by sea is more than double that of the direct overland route; the sea route gives them the remoteness of London from New York, while the direct distance gives them the proximity of Manchester and Malta. The widespread use of sea transport by way of Southeast Asia between the Indian and Chinese sections of Monsoon Asia is largely a Western development because before the arrival of Europeans those shallow seas operated to isolate rather than to link.

Though the aeroplane is less bound to the exigencies of landforms and patterns, it is to be noted that the major air routes run almost coastwise between one part and another of Monsoon Asia and there is little sign of them pressing overland into the continent; this is for economic rather than physical reasons.

MINERALS

Of the minerals which lie embedded in the rocks of Monsoon Asia's landforms our knowledge is limited. Since metallic ores are closely associated with igneous rocks, the Deccan Plateau holds much promise, as also do those parts of the Southeastern and Eastern Highlands where erosion has exposed igneous formations. Among the old metamorphosed and sedimentary rocks of the Sunda Platform and the Eastern Highlands must be beds of coal and sedimentary iron as well as the possibility of oil-bearing structures. In the young, unstable and as yet lightly eroded rocks of the Himalayan–Island Arc, the ores are limited and dislocated if present at all, or restricted to small blocks of older rocks involved in the mountain building process.

The Climatic Environment

THE NAME "Monsoon Asia" implies a region with common climate. But "monsoon" has come to be used in many ways: some use the word to mean a type of wind, some to mean violent rain and others a season.

THE MONSOON

Arabs first used their expression "mausin" to mean a season of winds such as occur around the Arabian Sea where for about six months a year they blow as northeasterlies and for the other six months as southwesterlies. Arabs thought of seasons in terms of wind because there were no other significant changes through the year in their warm, arid climate—as natural as for Europeans to think of seasons in terms of varying warmth and cold, variations which set the regime of growth in their part of the world. It is equally natural for people within the tropics to think of seasons in terms of raininess, variations of which dominate their farming. The prolonged association of seaborne Arabs with South and East Asia explains why their word and conception have been accepted and perpetuated all the way from the Red Sea to Japan.

At nearly every point in Monsoon Asia there are two phases of the year, the wind prevailing in one being opposite to that prevailing in the other. Sometimes there is a calms period between these two seasons. This gives a common form to the climate mechanics of Monsoon Asia. Over Southern India the seasons involve southwesterlies and northeasterlies; over Singapore and Mandalay there is an interplay of southerlies and northerlies; over North China, southeasterlies and northwesterlies. Winds do not of themselves constitute a climate, though they are the means of transferring its elements. Not winds but temperature, rainfall and evaporation condition the growth of plants and animals with which human beings live in association. The effects in Monsoon Asia of the seasonally opposed winds differ very widely from point to point according to the origin and character of the moving air rather than to the peculiar seasonal reversal. The climatologist often ignores the winds in assessing the likeness of climates from place to place, and there is, in any case, little value in calculating the mathematical average of wind direction. Hence the "monsoon climate" is much more than "a climate of seasons with opposing winds".

The mechanism which produces these winds is complex, and not fully understood owing to the scarcity of observing stations. Among the influences at work are:

1. A permanent high-pressure belt of anticylones is associated with the Tropic of Capricorn over Northern India and the Pacific. The Thar Desert is a consequence of this, as are the deserts of west coasts in similar latitudes of North Africa.

2. A cold-season anticyclone over Central Asia induces out-flowing cold, continental air from the "frozen heart of Asia", descending into Eastern China and there converging with moist, maritime air outblowing from the North Pacific high-pressure belt. The Tibetan and Himalayan relief systems are high and broad enough largely to isolate Central Asian air from India, which at that season develops its own anticyclone system inducing convergences around it.

3. The Intertropical Front is a phenomenon of the tropical zone, with variations of movement over Monsoon Asia which account for much of the peculiarities of local raininess.

THE INTERTROPICAL FRONT

The Intertropical Front is comparable to the Polar Front of middle latitudes by being the surface of convergence of two distinct masses of air. It shows on the weather chart as a line separating air masses which have developed their chief characteristics in the tropics of the Northern and Southern Hemispheres respectively. At the equinoxes the Front roughly coincides with the Equator, and towards it converge northern air in the form of N.E. Trades and the southern air as S.E. Trades. Off Southeast Asia at these seasons both masses have similar warm, moist air which has passed for long distances over equatorial seas. Convergence under these circumstances is of similar air masses meeting at an angle, and without much twisting due to rotation—that force being negligible near the Equator. Hence the Intertropical Front at that season is the scene of very weak low pressure systems (pressures at their centres are only a millibar or two less than at their outer edges), giving rise to very local storms more convectional than convergent.

As the world's wind-belts shift north in the northern summer, the Intertropical Front is displaced northwards. Southern Hemisphere air penetrating across the Equator becomes deflected into southwesterlies, and

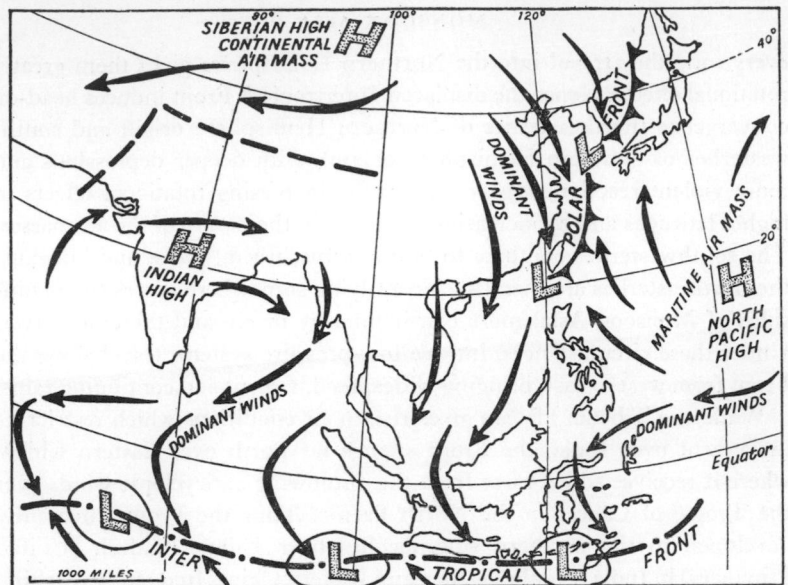

FIG. 3—Air masses and movements over Monsoon Asia at the year-end. 'H' and 'L' are high and low pressure systems, and the heavy broken line indicates the physical barrier of high altitude

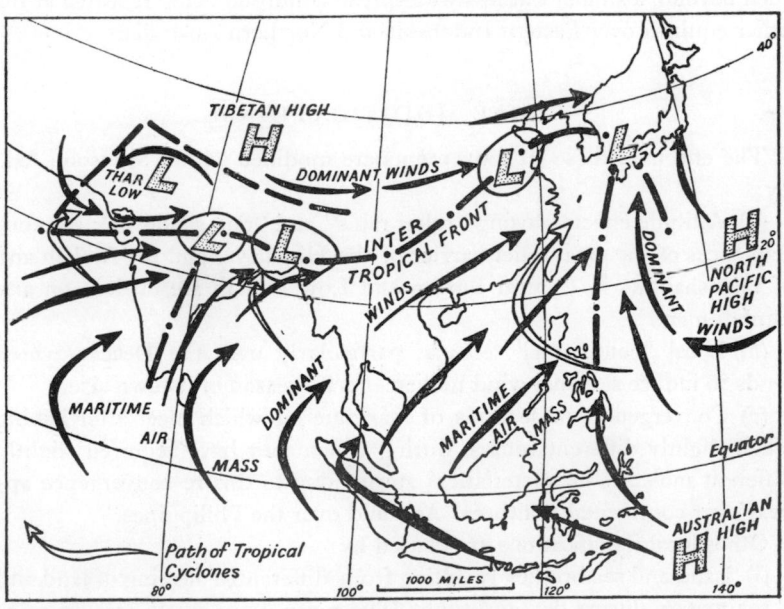

FIG. 4—Air masses and movements over Monsoon Asia at mid-year (the Northern summer)

every mile they travel into the Northern Hemisphere gives them greater rotational effects. Hence the displaced Intertropical Front induces head-on convergence (northeasterlies of Northern Hemisphere origin and south-westerlies of Southern Hemisphere origin), with deeper depressions and more violent reaction, aggravated by the increasing rotational effects in higher latitudes and by increasing contrasts in the nature of the air masses. The southwesterlies continue to be maritime, warm, moist and buoyant; the northeasterlies are then (the Front lying somewhere across the peninsulas of Monsoon Asia) more continental by origin and therefore dryer. Under these circumstances, intense low-pressure systems travel along the Front from west to east, bringing widespread, violent and continuing rains.

While the Tibetan Plateau gives rise to air conditions which restrict its movement over India, the Front swings far north over Eastern China, where it receives added force from the outflowing anticyclonic winds over the Tropic of Cancer in the North Pacific. Thus the Front when fully developed in the northern summer lies over Udhar Pradesh (United Provinces) in India, Southeast Asia and Eastern China, frequently reaching close to Japan and everywhere the occasion of general and heavy rains. After the solstice, the Front is gradually pressed back again to the Equator and then beyond, a similar but less widespread condition being repeated at the other equinox over Eastern Indonesia and Northern Australia.

LOCAL MODIFICATIONS

The effects of these air movements are modified within Monsoon Asia by:

(*a*) Altitude effects causing "relief rains" and "rain shadows"; the consequences of the great relief barrier of the Himalayas and the Arakan and of rain shadows in Central Burma and Lower Siam are evident on any rainfall map.

(*b*) Local "continental" effects, particularly over the Deccan which tends to induce seasonal wind movements by reason of its own size.

(*c*) Convergences of sections of maritime air which meet after having taken slightly different routes, during which they have acquired slightly different moisture characteristics; storms due to this re-convergence appear over continental Southeast Asia and over the Philippines.

Other local modifications are caused by:

(i) Land and sea breezes resulting from differential heating of land and sea masses during day and night. These can cause small, intense rainstorms.

(ii) Mountain and valley breezes resulting from daily differential heating of bare uplands during day and night, producing some storms like those of (i).

(iii) Deflections by relief whereby ground-level winds follow the line of valleys, though the prevailing air movement above them may be quite different. This is common in the Himalayas and mountainous Southeast Asia.

Though Northwestern India and Northern China on the margins of Monsoon Asia resemble one another as zones of dryness and continentality, the former is a self-contained unit, largely isolated from Central Asia, and more subject to interplay between tropical desert and mountain conditions; the latter is dominantly influenced by Siberian air converging with that of the Pacific and by its high latitude.

EFFECTS OF SEASONAL REVERSAL

The seasonal reversal of winds has two major consequences:

1. Over the peninsular parts it means alternate seasons of continental and maritime air, giving rise to alternate dry and wet seasons. This annual wet and dry cycle is less evident on islands, where every wind is maritime to some extent. The season of warm, moist winds is so important for mainland farmers that they have come to look on southerly and easterly aspects from which the rain comes as auspicious and locate their houses accordingly.

2. The alternation of wind facilitates a shuttle movement of sailing ships between certain parts of the region, an effect relative to the standard of skill in handling boats. Thus a shuttle service of sailing ships was easy between Aden and the Indus–Bombay coast of India, between the Coromandel Coast and Burma, between Malaya and South China and between Japan and North China. The pattern of winds impeded a two-way movement between the Strait of Malacca and South India, between Borneo and the Asian mainland and between the Philippines and South China. It made sailing between China and Java easier than between China and India.

While the alternation of wet and dry seasons sets a distinct cycle in Monsoon Asia's farm activities, the character of the farming turns more on the amount of rain and warmth to which growing plants must adjust themselves. Hence the importance of a quantitative analysis of climates based on records of rainfall and temperatures and in relation to crop needs. The Köppen method of analysing and classifying such data takes seasonal quantities into account and underlies the classification given here. Because

35

there are so many pockets of lowland set within upland structures, great local variations occur within each climatic type.

CLIMATIC TYPES

Towards the mountainous margin of this region, high altitudes and continental extremes create climatic conditions (ET and D climatic types) differing from those general in Monsoon Asia, producing great change within short distances and causing farming difficulties. Apart from these, Monsoon Asia is notable for its year-round warmth; frost is insignificant except in Northeastern China and round the Sea of Japan, the line of distinction being roughly the mean January isotherm of 40° which runs along the Tsin Ling and across Honshu. By having a well-marked cold winter, the northeastern region is distinct from the rest. Everywhere the summer temperatures are high, the Thar Desert being remarkable as the hottest part of all Asia at that season when its shade temperatures customarily exceed 120°, as distinct from the rest of the region where summer averages of 85° are general.

The climatic types are classified by Köppen thus:

Afi: Where monthly temperatures always average higher than 65°; the warmest month differs from the coldest by less than 10° and monthly rainfalls always exceed 2·4 inches. These standards mean an equable climate, with very small seasonal variations in both temperature and rainfall. It has abundant rains, is associated with equatorial rain-forest and occurs generally in Southeast Asia.

Aw: Where there is a distinct dry season in localities otherwise having abundant rains. At least one month has an average rainfall of less than 2·4 inches, while monthly temperatures always average over 65°. This type is present over most of the Deccan, in Bengal, Siam and the southern half of Indochina. It is associated with savannah vegetation. An insular variety (*Awi*) is recognisable in East Java.

Amw: This resembles *Aw* in having a dry season, but differs by having a high rainfall and so short a dry season that the ground remains almost continuously damp enough to support rain-forest. It combines features of both *Afi* and *Aw* and occurs on western coasts, as in Malabar, Southwest Ceylon, Coastal Burma and Kra, the Cardamom Mountains of Indochina and North and Central Philippines.

As: A variety of *Aw* in which midsummer is dry and found on the rainshadow coasts of Coromandel and Northeast Ceylon.

Cfa: Where the coldest month averages less than 65° but more than

36

27°, and the warmest month averages 72°. Frozen ground and snow are uncommon. Its driest summer month has more than 1·2 inches of rain, so that there is no distinct dry season. The type occurs round the mouth of the Yangtse, in Northwest Formosa, in South Korea and in Southern Japan.

Cw: Has similar temperatures to *Cfa*, but has a distinct winter drought. This climate occurs in the middle Indo-Gangetic Plain, in Central Burma, Northern Indochina, South China, and from there inland and northward to Shantung and North Korea. In the Ganges Valley is a variety known as *Cwg* in which the hottest month comes before the midsummer rains. In North China is a variety known as *Cws*, whose warmest month exceeds an average of 72°.

Bshw: Here evaporation is always greater than rainfall and no streams can develop. It has an average annual temperature of about 65° and a dry winter. The rainfall is critically small, turning on the great difference in effectiveness between winter and summer rains. It is readily recognisable by the steppe or dry grassland to which it gives rise, and is found in Northwest India and in the rain-shadow zone of Mysore.

Dwa: This is a climate where the coldest month averages below 27°, the warmest above 50°, so that snow and frost normally last for several months of the year. At the same time its summers are warm enough for forests. Its driest winter month averages less than one-tenth the wettest summer month, and its hottest summer month exceeds 72°. It is a feature of the northeastern margins, in Northeastern China and Manchuria.

Thus south of the tropic Monsoon Asia is dominated by warm seasonal rainy climatic types (A); north of it by rainy climates which have greater seasonal changes of temperature, but whose winters are always mild and short (C). Away from these two types and on the boundaries of the region are three others: (*a*) to the southeast, an ever-warm, ever-rainy climate; (*b*) to the northwest, a warm, dry climate; (*c*) to the northeast a climate with severe winters and low summer rains.

PEOPLE'S ADJUSTMENTS

The pattern has several effects on human activities:

(*a*) Travelling between Malaya and Western Pakistan one may see adjustments in crops, diet, clothing and housing associated with a setting which, while continuously warm, varies from wet to arid, in changing combinations of continuous wetness, seasonal wet-and-dryness and continuous dryness. Modifications in relation to temperature chiefly reflect local alti-

37

tudes. The series of changes is summed up as from the umbrella of Malaya to the camel of West Pakistan, from problems of drainage to problems of irrigation, from steep roofs to flat roofs, from forest to desert, from wood to brick and from rice to wheat and millet.

(*b*) From Malaya to Manchuria occur adjustments in crops, diet, clothing and housing related to variations from point to point in temperature, the rainfall being secondary in the changes. The rain effectiveness remains generally high everywhere during seasons of growth, when alone it is relevant. These differences account for the sarong of Malaya versus the furs of Harbin, the verandah versus the kang (a brick bed heated from below), the open wooden hut of the south versus the thick-walled earth or brick-and-tile house of the north, rice versus the short-lived soya, and water versus snow.

DAYLIGHT DIFFERENCES

Seasonal differences of daylight have effects on growing periods and further vary temperature values within Monsoon Asia. Towards the Equator and Southeast Asia, days and nights are nearly equal at all times of the year, adding a further constancy to the equable climate. In the latitudes of Luzon, Rangoon and Bombay, midsummer daylight is 13 hours long and midwinter daylight 11 hours long; in the latitude of Multan (West Pakistan), Delhi and Shanghai the variation is from 14 hours of daylight at midsummer to 10 hours at midwinter; while in the latitude of Hakodate, Mukden and Peking the corresponding daylight periods are 15 hours and 9 hours. The total annual heating effect of varying daylight and of varying angle of incidence to the ground are such that if the total thermal effect at the Equator (Singapore) is taken as 100 units for a year, then from Ceylon to Saigon and Cebu it is 98 units, from Bombay to Akyab and Hanoi 95 units, from Multan to Delhi and Shanghai 88, at Tokyo 84 and at Peking 80 units.

The isohyet is only a partial guide to the qualitative effects of rainfall, although precipitation effectiveness is not easy to estimate because many modifying factors are at work. Heat, sunshine, hardness, steepness and bareness of the ground lower the effectiveness of rains. Low temperatures, much cloud, flat ground and much vegetation increase it. Farmers assess such effectiveness by trial and error in production, for which reason a crop map is a good indicator of rainfall effectiveness in Monsoon Asia.

TYPES OF RAIN

In latitudes of Monsoon Asia south of 10°, the dominant air masses are of the warm, moist type with weak rotational factors in their movements. From these the rain is chiefly convectional, deriving from a local irregularity of heating which establishes an uplift of air and continues to extend by reason of the internal release of heat during precipitation. Convectional storms may also be initiated each day by land and sea breezes, which cause local uplifts and turbulence—and bumpy flying. Hence the rain here occurs in storms which are often violent, concentrated and producing heavy showers from cumulus clouds rather than general rains over a wide area. As a consequence, rainfall is irregular within short distances and deviates widely from the average from year to year. Local farmers are anxious about their water even where the average fall is high.

Farther into the mainland, rains are often from storms arising from frontal convergences of extensive air masses, giving sheet clouds, and rains are more widely distributed. The cyclonic convergences differ in type. There are Intertropical Front convergences to the south, convergences of air masses from Siberia and the North Pacific move over Eastern China, and local convergences arising from tongues of mountain air descending katabatically into the plains of Northwestern India.

Relief rains establish belted isohyetal patterns along the ranges and frequent cloud and mist. Locally they may offset dry seasons and extended latitudinally the belts of forest.

Both convectional and frontal rains occur in conjunction with thunder and lightning, which are more consequential than causal; the lightning charges being a sign of the great energy in the warm, moist, low-latitude maritime air masses common to Southern Monsoon Asia. The electricity results from an ionisation process on particles of air rising rapidly through descending droplets of rain, building up a differential in a cumulus cloud, ultimately equalised by a gigantic spark—the lightning—between one part of the atmosphere and another, or between the atmosphere and the ground. Tropical thunderstorms greatly interfere with radio reception.

TYPHOONS

Typhoons or tropical cyclones are a feature of Monsoon Asia. Each year on an average, 22 of these dangerous revolving wind-storms occur in the China Sea and 10 in the northern Arabian Sea and the Bay of Bengal. In the China

Sea they occur chiefly from July to October, August being the month of greatest risk. In the Bay of Bengal their timing is much the same, but September is the most risky month. In the Arabian Sea there are two typhoon seasons—May/June and October/November. High winds and mountainous seas in typhoons are destructive to shipping and more so to local houses, but typhoons do not normally penetrate far inland, their force and violence being derived from warm, moist maritime air. The danger to aircraft is less than to shipping because the speed of planes enables them to get away from the disturbed centre of typhoons. Starting over the oceans slightly north of latitude 6°, they move westwards, particularly across the Philippines, approaching the Vietnam and South China coasts, and then moving northeastwards to Taiwan and Japan which are very subject to them. Besides winds so tempestuous that they are likely to destroy wind-gauges, typhoons induce tremendous and continuous rainfalls at their centres: 100 inches of rain in four days has been recorded. Great flood damage may occur in rural areas, which in exposed coastal positions also suffer from high seas carrying salt water well inland. Although it is thought such storms begin on fronts, they differ from cyclonic disturbances outside the tropics by having more distinctly circular systems of isobars, very low pressures at their small centres, spiralling winds of at least 75 m.p.h. and torrential rains. The dangers of typhoons have caused an international warning system to be instituted, in Hong Kong and Manila, where both the site and design of houses are chosen to secure protection from the winds, and special harbours have been built to protect the frail local boats.

OCEAN CURRENTS

The seasonal play of wind across Monsoon Asia has a major impact on its water bodies, and gives rise to ocean circulations which accentuate the influence of winds on shipping and may render coasts inaccessible. Most distinctive is the reversing of circulation in the Arabian Sea and the Bay of Bengal, wherein the water moves clockwise in the northern summer and anti-clockwise in the northern winter. These variations have little effect on the adjoining countries, but off Japan the clockwise circulation of the North Pacific undergoes modification by the winds in such a way that the warm Kuro Siwo drifts along the shores of both sides of Japan in the northern summer and only along its southern shores in winter. The result is that only southern Honshu enjoys an amelioration of winter temperature, whereas its northern shores on the Sea of Japan are subject each winter to the cold winds from Northern Siberia and to the cold currents of the Oyashiwo, which then press well south into the Sea of Japan. In the fresher, shallow seas of the Sunda Platform, the water movement is dominated by the seasonal winds and reverses with them, modified only slightly by water from the North Pacific Equatorial Current penetrating through the Philippines, and even more slightly by Bay of Bengal water pressing into the Malacca Strait.

CHAPTER FOUR

Biogeography of Monsoon Asia

VEGETATION

CLIMATE, LANDFORM, vegetation, soils and animal life are closely related to one another: vegetation derives its sustenance from soluble elements in the soil, which in its turn receives from plants its humus content, and animals consume vegetation and add their biological wastes to the soil.

Desert, grassland and forest are present in Monsoon Asia. The dominant is forest, which occurs in a belt along the western edge of the Deccan, in a belt along the Himalayas and fairly continuously from the Indonesian Islands to Northeast China. The rest of India and patches of Southeast Asia have had a cover of savannah, that tall grass with scattered trees which is transitional between forest and desert. North and west of the Thar Desert and north of the Gulf of Chihli are short grasses.

The antiquity of settlement in many parts of the Monsoon Lands has led to major destruction of natural vegetation to make room for cultivation, to the selection by Man of some plants now of economic value and the rejection of others, and to widespread erosion of soil. The dry, bare parts on the Deccan are thought to be the result of over-cultivation, leading quickly to soil erosion by torrential rains. The savannah patches in Siam and Indochina may be similarly man-induced, but the bareness of Eastern China is certainly the result of centuries of cutting. Only in Southeast Asia do large areas of almost virgin forest exist, yet botanists believe primitive people even there have changed that forest slowly by cutting and burning. Beyond the continental boundary of Monsoon Asia appears the tundra of Tibet.

Differentiation of tree type occurs by varying combinations of climatic facts. The equable rains and temperatures of places within 10° of the Equator give rise to the rain-forest, a thick evergreen vegetation of mixed high trees with many epiphytes (plants climbing upon others), lianas (thick, woody creeper plants), and giant ferns. Its seaward fringes are of mangrove, a tree vegetation which tolerates tidal floods. Rain-forest extends into Bengal and as far as Vietnam, but is most prominent in insular South-

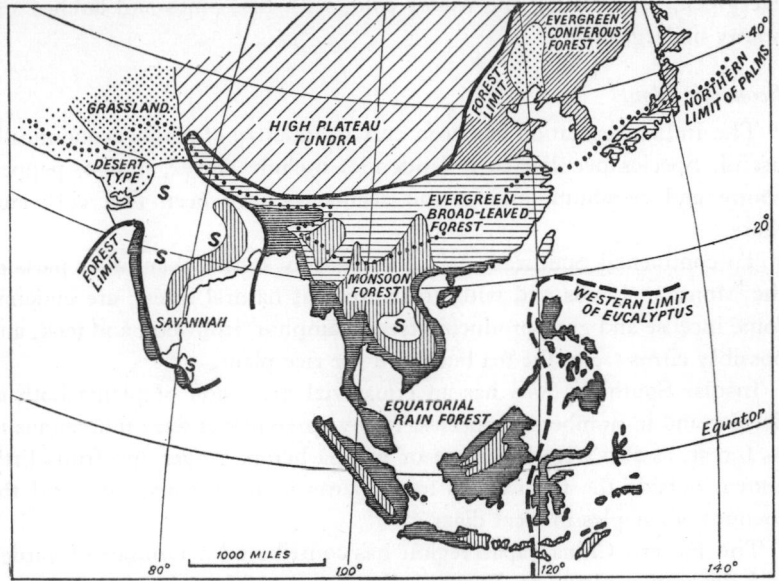

FIG. 5—Distribution of natural vegetation in Asia
("S" represents savannah)

east Asia. A variant under seasonal rains is the monsoon forest, extensive in continental Southeast Asia. It is an open forest, without dense under-growth, of fewer species of broad-leaved trees, deciduous during the dry season when vegetation shrivels to a dead brown until the rains come to cause reinvigoration to a lush green. Ironwood, teak, sal and sandalwood are commercial woods from this forest, which also contains eucalyptus in Eastern Indonesia and the Philippines, whither it came from Australia.

A further variant occurs where the cycle of wet and dry season is com-bined with a great range of temperature. Here the cool winter means greater rain efficiency, so that the trees are predominantly evergreen and at the same time broad-leaved. Among them are rhododendrons, laurels, camelias and magnolias. Associated particularly with China south of the Yangtse, this evergreen, broad-leaved and temperate forest stretches inland to the knot of mountains in the north of continental Southeast Asia, into Korea and South Japan. A mountain belt of it stretches to the west along the Himalayas.

Where winter frosts occur, roughly from the Tsin Ling northwards, and humidity remains adequate, the forest is mixed, largely coniferous and

43

evergreen, yet resisting the winter cold, with firs, pines and larches and scanty undergrowth.

Economic Plants

The Indian vegetation has been very productive of plants economically useful. Species peculiar to it (endemic) include cloves, indigo, pepper, ebony and sesamum, and cotton seems to have been first cultivated there.

To continental Southeast Asia, less densely settled than other parts of the Monsoon Lands and with great areas of natural forest, are endemic some incense and gum-producing trees, camphor, ironwood and teak, and possibly citrus trees, the tea bush and the rice plant.

Insular Southeast Asia has an equatorial profusion of plants both in density and in numbers of species. Many spice plants were indigenous to its forest, as also were the abaca or manila hemp, ginger and fruits little known outside the tropics. Its food plants include yams, sago and the coconut, all staples in local diets.

The Eastern China–Japan region has contributed a number of garden and decorative plants to Europe, directly transferred by sea. From its vegetation have come many economic plants, the most remarkable being the soya bean.

The bamboo is a widespread plant of the Monsoon Lands, prominent round the China Sea and India, but stopping short of the Thar Desert; the use of this woody, tough and flexible member of the grass family in structures and domestic articles has set a distinctive form in Oriental designs. The numerous family of palms is limited chiefly by low temperatures. Palms occur throughout India, but are confined south of the line roughly from Mandalay to the Yangtse mouth and also below lat. 37° in Japan. The nipah, whose fronds serve for thatching and fuel, is limited to insular Southeast Asia, the Arakan–East Pakistan coast and Ceylon. Mangrove, the group of salt-tolerant warmth-loving plants, has great extent along the coasts of Monsoon Asia south of lat. 25°. South of the tropic on the uniformly warm-wet islands are endemic plants whose mode of reproduction is vegetative: the parent stock reproduces itself by a development below ground (by runners or subsurface budding) or artificially by cuttings or slips. This mode perpetually extends the parent asexually without the opportunity of genetic modification which seeds make possible. It is the means of growing bananas, bamboos, yams and rhizomatose plants such as ginger and tapioca.

ANIMALS

Detailed information about the animal distributions in Monsoon Asia are limited. In Southeast and Eastern Asia climbing, gliding and flying animals are common as might be expected from the widespread forest cover. Butterflies and insects are numerous. The thick ground cover restricts the larger creatures, but in India the large, quick-moving mammals, such as the cheetah and tiger, find the more open vegetation to which they are well adapted. In the swampy lowlands of the southeast water-buffaloes are indigenous and domesticated for draught; the zebu type of cattle, both wild and domesticated, are common in the savannah setting of India.

The faunal regions are:

(*a*) Northeast China in whose coniferous woods various types of squirrel, tree-rats, voles, hares and deer occur.

(*b*) South China in whose warmer evergreen forests are many bats, squirrels, bamboo-rats, mongoose, wild pigs and badgers.

(*c*) Continental Southeast Asia has a denser forest in which are tree-shrews, squirrels, porcupines, langurs and muntjak.

(*d*) South India, Malaya and the southeastern islands have extensive rain-forest which supports fruit-eating bats, squirrels, many members of the monkey and gibbon families, elephants, flying lemurs, deer, rhinoceros and tapir. There is nothing to compare with the great herds of wild animals in Africa. Tigers and leopards are few and not important. Since fauna can move and have been steadily deprived of their Asian habitat by cultivation, their distribution is most complex. The ant and insect populations are large, ant-eater animals common and lizard-like creatures numerous.

(*e*) In Northwestern India the semi-desert and grassland setting has a natural fauna of quick-running, leaping and burrowing creatures, but the density is now low.

The mosquito, fly, flea and tick are widespread, functioning as disease vectors for malaria, cholera, plague and typhus, all endemic in Monsoon Asia. While such vectors as individuals have a short life-cycle, the absence of a cold season south of the Yangtse implies an almost continuous re-generation, with a peak at the onset of rains when the flying creatures swarm in spectacular numbers. In Northeast China the long and intense cold season has a limiting effect, offset to some extent among the insects parasitic to human beings by the idleness and indoor living which the season imposes on people.

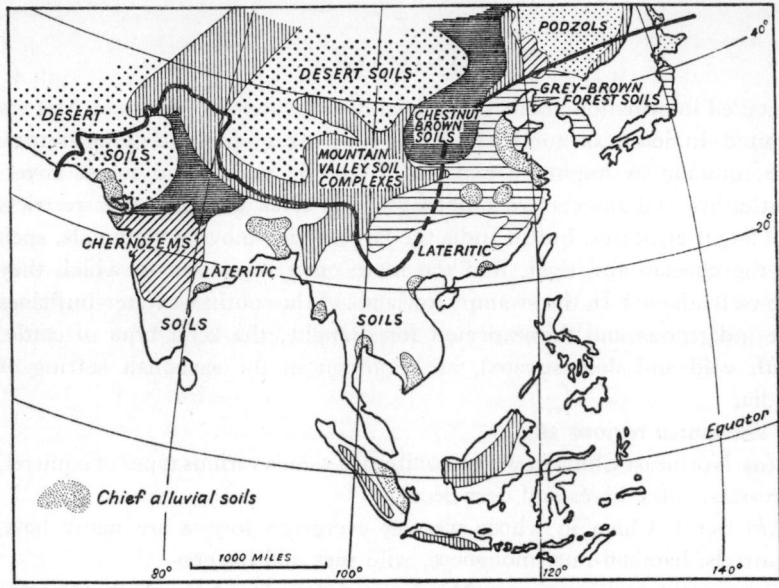

FIG. 6—Types of soil in Monsoon Asia

SOILS

Soils upon which the densest populations and intensest agriculture of the Monsoon Lands have developed are comparatively new alluvials, the result of repeated inundation by rivers and located in the great valleys. Those soils, while graded in detail, are generally clays, dark by reason of their humus content and complexly modified by farming.

Large-scale erosion has taken place following the destruction of natural vegetation south of the Himalayas and in all the hilly country adjoining the alluviated plains of China. Farming on the hills has been done intermittently under pressure from the lowlands, so that much original hill soil has either been carried to valley bottoms or is in process of change and not yet fully matured to its present setting.

The soil types are:

(*a*) The recent alluvials, covering greatest areas in the deltaic plains, in the Lower Ganges and in the North China Plain where level, deep, friable, humus-rich, dark-coloured soils are constantly receiving new silt from regular floods.

(*b*) The highly varied soils of the mountain and valley complexes of the Himalayas, Eastern Tibet, Inner Borneo, Sumatra and Java, where steep topography and change from valley to hill within short distances make any generalisation unrealistic. The forest cover and relief coolness cause much humus irregularly distributed but of continuing fertility value. Volcanic ejecta adds local complexity to these soils.

(c) The most widespread single soil type is the lateritic, evolved under sustained high temperatures and substantial rainfalls which cause chemical changes and leaching, removing much of the silica and leaving clays with a high content of iron oxide, causing a reddish colour. The seasonal raininess leads to a fluctuation of ground-water level in such a way that iron-pan frequently forms a couple of feet below the surface. Often 50 feet thick, lateritic soils contain very little organic matter, which is confined to a few inches of topsoil under long-standing forest, and rapidly leached when the cover is removed. These soils have limited potential, and quickly deteriorate under cultivation. There are several varieties of lateritic soil, depending on the seasonality of rainfalls, the degree of leaching and on the period since vegetation was continuous. While red is the dominant colour, underneath there may be white, yellow or mottled clay materials.

(d) From the Thar Desert northwestwards occur desert soils evolved in arid conditions where no solubles are removed; they accumulate in the upper layer, sometimes as salt or soda crystals inimical to vegetation. Little natural vegetation exists on the surface so that there is no regular renewal of organic matter. The same soil type lies on the boundary of the Monsoon Lands in Northwest China, continuing thence into Gobi.

(e) Between the desert soils and the moister regions both in Northern India (between the desert and lateritic soils) and in Northwest China (between the desert and evergreen coniferous forest) are chestnut brown soils, developed under an originally more grassy and bushy vegetation, having a high organic content, much calcium and moderate moistness, and a half-way stage between excessive accumulation and excessive leaching. Their agricultural potential is high where adequate surface water is available. The type is varied in Shansi and Kansu by being developed on loess materials (blown into position by winds), whereas in Northern India it is upon riverine deposits.

(f) On the central and northwestern Deccan and in a smaller area of Southwest Manchuria are black-earth soils or chernozems, commonly known on the Deccan as "regur" or "cotton soil". Regur is a very dark-coloured soil, retentive of such moisture as may fall, and developed chiefly upon an ancient, dark volcanic rock. This soil once had a savannah vegetation which added organic matter for a long period without noticeable leaching. It has a high potential largely owing to substantial calcium near the surface. Its friable water-holding texture gives its moderate rainfall a high efficiency for farming. The chernozems of Manchuria are continental grassland soils like those in South Russia, but limited in potential by the short growing season.

(g) On the uplands of Eastern China, on either side of the Yangtse, in Shantung, stretching thence into Korea and Northern Japan is a zone where greyish-brown podsolic soils predominate, containing much organic material from the old forest cover: disintegration of humus is slow owing to the cold winter and low rainfall. Unlike true podsols these have become only slightly acid. The distribution is actually very irregular; its flatter, more continuous stretches on the North China Plains have been changed substantially by cultivation.

(h) True podsols cover most of the Manchurian plains with an acid soil derived from under-decomposed forest debris. It is a type apart from the soils usual in Monsoon Asia.

FISH

The fish population off shore from the Monsoon Lands is less known than the animal population, yet fish play a large part in the Asian diet, frequently forming the chief protein intake.

Several oceanographic conditions have helped to give Asian fishing its character. Sunda Platform seas are by shallowness, by proximity to rainy regions and by partially enclosed form, abnormally fresh; they contain a high proportion of land detritus—a major source of fish food. The seas contain many crustacea and sustain a large fish population in which mackerel, bonito, sardine and flat-fish are prominent, mostly caught inshore by shallow-water fishing devices such as traps. The great uniformly-watered gulfs of the Indian Ocean have only small continental shelves and the greatest fish population appears to be on the western side of India, where herring, mackerel and pomfret are commonly caught. Cool currents from the Sea of Japan reach South China in winter, and bring to it a seasonal change which makes for diversity of fishing. Off Japan meet the tropical and arctic waters as on the Great Banks of Newfoundland similarly giving rise to the more fleshy fish, such as cod and flat-fish. Tropical fish are less fleshy, which adversely affects their food value.

Throughout Southeast Asia coral reefs and their aquatic fauna and flora support many fish not commercially exploited. Coral disappears north of Taiwan. Floating seaweeds of many types occur throughout the China Sea which is reportedly extremely rich in plankton, more so than in the Indian

Ocean. This plankton is evidence for supposing that the fish population in the whole of the China Sea is unusually high, though not fully exploited in proportion to its capacity. Landings round the China Sea in 1957 were estimated at ten million tons, while the North Indian Ocean produced little more than two million tons. The most active and motorised sea fisheries are those off Japan and as far south as Luzon; these localities are accessible to the long-distance fishing fleet of Japan. Elsewhere fishing is done by vessels averaging little bigger than a large rowing boat, and limited in range and capacity by using sails or small outboard motors.

Pressure of population towards the low-lying shores and the frequency of lagoons have given rise to much fish cultivation in ponds. In Java, South China and Japan salt-water fish of the carp and prawn types are widely reared in coastal polders. Farther inland fresh-water fish are cultivated among the padifields and swamps. The greatest freshwater fishing is in Cambodia whose lake fish production is greater than the North Sea catch.

Throughout these warm Asian seas, sharks, dolphins, rays, flying fish, turtles, sea-snakes and giant jellyfish are common, and many have local use. There is, however, no reliable estimate of the local catch in these waters. Owing to transport difficulties, the fish in internal commerce is commonly dried, salted or similarly preserved.

CHAPTER FIVE

Peoples, Races and Modes of Living

ON A WORLD POPULATION map, Monsoon Asia stands out today as a region with many large areas of high density. Compared with the Eurasian continent as a whole, it is distinctive by having a density almost everywhere greater than 75 persons per square mile, and that density almost delimits the Monsoon Asia region within whose continental and peninsular sections only minor patches, such as the Thar Desert and the Annamite and Arakan Mountains, have less than that density. Some of the equatorial islands, particularly Borneo and farther east, have extensive areas of scanty population.

HIGH DENSITY

More remarkable are the numerous and large areas where the population exceeds 500 persons per square mile. Densities of this order are general over the maps of India and China. Through industrial Northern Europe there is no equivalent continuous extent anywhere of densities exceeding 500 persons per square mile such as occur all the way from Calcutta to Delhi, in ribbons along the eastern and western coasts of South India, on the North China Plain, along the Yangtse from Shanghai to Hankow, in patches along the South China coast, in the belt from Nagasaki to Tokyo and through much of Java. These areas of sustained high density dwarf those of Europe and the United States in size and, if political strength be judged by compacted voting power, these localities could assert a significance in world affairs and in the United Nations Organisation greater than Europe or the United States of America.

The large high-density areas are unevenly distributed. They are characteristic of North and Eastern India, of North and Eastern China, of South Japan and Java. They are chiefly confined to places adjoining and west of the Bay of Bengal and adjoining the northern portion of the China Sea. That lushly forested terrain of Southeast Asia, from Eastern Tibet through the Malayan Peninsula to the equatorial islands of Sumatra, Borneo and Mindanao, is the thinnest peopled sector of Monsoon Asia—a "green desert"—but even there may be found small, scattered patches of high density. Thus the general distribution of high densities is (*a*) two extensive continental areas, one in Eastern India astride the tropic, and one in Eastern China between lats. 28° and 40°, and (*b*) two smaller insular areas in Java and Japan.

None of these dense zones is itself a national unit or country. The countries are constituted of different proportions of the high-density and low-density sectors. The national population densities vary widely: using 1957 figures, from over 550 persons per square mile in Japan, Taiwan and Korea to 370 per square mile for Ceylon and 324 for India, and to 74 per square mile for Burma.

That the dense populations cover large areas implies that the characteristic is dispersed rural settlement. In China 73% of the people live rurally, taking groups of more than 5,000 persons each to be urban. In India, Ceylon and Korea, nearly 90% of people are rural, and in Indochina the proportion is greater. The chief exception is Japan, where only 50% of the people live rurally. At the same time there are cities and large towns in Monsoon Asia which have great importance because the concentration gives their authorities the function of mouthpieces for their countries, however small the town population be in proportion to the nation. In this region there are at least twentytwo cities containing a million or more people, the largest, Tokyo, containing over nine million; there are probably another fifteen towns each with over a half a million. Unlike the pattern in Europe and North America where many cities have inland locations, that of the Asian fringe is characteristically coastal and city size is largely consequent to function as points of overseas contact. Often such cities monopolise national trade (as Karachi does for West Pakistan and Rangoon for Burma).

RACE

Because this region contains nearly half the world's people, it includes several of the world's races or types of people. Discussion about racial types has been confused by attempts to rouse emotions about race for political purposes, particularly by those who have named the racial types after a country or language rather than from physique. The word "race" is best limited to mean a group of people approximating to an average combination of inheritable physical features, such as size and proportion of anatomical parts, colour of hair and skin or blood groups.

On the continental sector north and east of the Himalayan line are people who have the Mongolian or epicanthic eye—a slight overhang of skin on the upper and inner eyelid; such an eye is also common but not universal

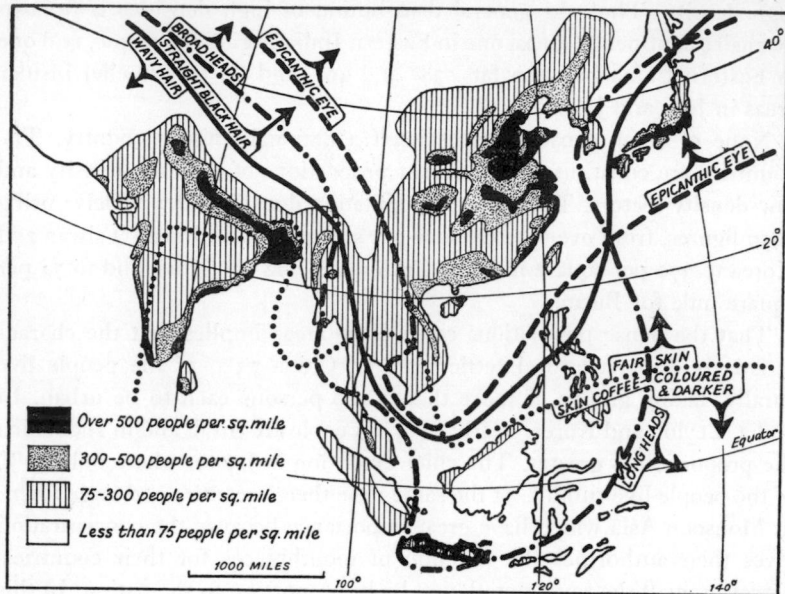

FIG. 7—Population densities and the limits of some racial physical features

in Japan. Within the same part of Monsoon Asia, but excluding Japan, hair is frequently straight, wiry and black. South and westward in Monsoon Asia, human hair is of cells so arranged as to form natural waves. Skins pigmented to appear coffee-coloured or darker are common on the Deccan and in Bengal, and from Lower Siam and the Mekong southwards; north and eastward, skins are less pigmented, becoming more fat-coloured towards Northwest India and towards Northeast China. South of the Yangtse and east of the Deccan, people average 2 or 3 inches shorter than those living farther north and west. Northeast and south of Eastern Tibet, but excepting Malaya and Sumatra, people's heads are broader in proportion than on the Indian subcontinent.

Thus a broad line from the Tibet Highland through Southeast Asia separates two racial types: the group living in Southeast India has dark skin, less height, long heads and wavy hair; the other in Eastern China has the epicanthic eye, broad head, straight, black hair and taller stature. In and adjoining the border between these two groups and among the Southeast Asia islands are people with varying combinations of these features; whether this third group is a separate race or the result of prolonged inter-breeding of the other two is not clear. While travellers are often confident about their ability to recognise races when they see them, the statistical basis is not easy to formulate, and much is hoped of other standards—such as blood counts, chromosomes and similar inheritable features removed from aesthetic prejudices. The threefold grouping outlined has been named in many ways: the southern race has been described as Australoid and Dravidian—it has no counterparts in Europe, but may be related to dark-skinned races in Africa. The eastern race is known as Mongoloid or Alpine, the last term arising from similarities with broad-headed peoples in Southeastern and Northern Europe. The third group of mixed characteristics is often called the "Mediterranean race" through having features resembling those of people living round the Mediterranean Sea. It is part of a group of people with similar racial and cultural features found through the Pacific Islands and in Southeast Asia, described by Huxley as "heliolithic" people, "small brown men living on sunlit shores and at home on tropical seas which they seem to have wandered restlessly for many millennia, but whose culture has left few long-lasting relics or writing such as are the basis of our knowledge of other ancient peoples". Racial differences among people with the same nationality have led in some Asian countries to internal tensions. For example, in Burma 9% of the population is described as Indian, 6% Chinese; in Sarawak, 27% Chinese, 17% Malay; in Ceylon, 23% Tamils (Dravidians).

POPULATION CHANGE

Population is always dynamic, changing in total according to the difference between birth and death rates. The cumulative effect leads to a change of density distributions and often to migrations. The distribution map is best thought of as a snapshot of population in a process of change.

In the postwar period, birth rates in the countries of the Monsoon Fringe have been between 20 and 31 per thousand people per annum as compared with between 16 and 30 in European countries. The Asian death rates in our times have been between 12 and 18 per thousand; those of European countries between 8 and 13·5 per thousand. Thus the natural population increases between 1932 and 1950 ranged from 17·5 to 26·5% for countries of Monsoon Asia, and from 1·5 to 24·5% in European countries. World population between 1932 and 1950, increased about 20%, that in Monsoon Asia by 17%. While the world's people multiplied 2·6 times from 1800 to 1950, the Asians multiplied about 2·1 times. In that 150 years, Europeans extended themselves by migration to empty parts of

North America, Australia and South America; the population increase (of 600 million) in Monsoon Asia has very largely been confined to the region so that there have been domestic intensifications and migrations within Asia to accommodate the additional people.

Between 1938 and 1958, India, Pakistan, Japan and Burma have each increased population by about 30%, the Philippines, Laos, Thailand and Northern Borneo by 50% and Malaya by over 70%.

This expansion of numbers has not been even; some localities have increased much faster than others not far away, inducing migration and urbanisation. The migration has been from the country to the cities; from districts of limited soil potential to those of greater—which has generally meant from the uplands to the lowlands; from the older agricultural areas to the newer ones where pioneering was possible and profitable; to the marginal areas; and from one Asian country to another. Though hindered by a tradition of equal inheritance which tended to tie all children to the parental farm, migration has been aided by improvements in communications and transport, particularly by sea, making it possible for people to move considerable distances at a time—in contrast to being limited to places near the home farm. Thus the population of Monsoon Asia has gravitated to the more fertile lowlands of the great river basins, pioneered on new delta lands of Southeast Asia, pressed out into the Manchurian Plain which is the most difficult of its kind in the Orient, and into the less benign climates of Western China and Hokkaido.

Apart from modifying the distribution, migrations have steadily mixed the racial types. The change has been so fast in some places that newcomers could not be absorbed by intermarriage so that plural societies have become a feature, sowing the seed for disputes internally.

Because the terrain north and west of Monsoon Asia combines the deterrents of height, aridity and short growing season, the chief direction of expansion for Asian populations has been towards the wet, equatorial southeast. That has been the sector of greatest change and of greatest pioneering by Asian people over the last 150 years, during which Java and the Philippines have each multiplied their people about ten times, Burma nearly six times and Malaya probably more than ten times. Into the southeast have also moved from overseas Indians and Chinese in such numbers that they are not yet fully absorbed locally. Some Indonesians have also moved to other islands of Indonesia. The colonisation of Southeast Asia by other Asians has been as striking and as long lasting in its effects as the coming of western colonial administrators. The Japanese expansions in that direction were political and military expressions of the

54

same tendency. The drift of Mongoloids towards the southeast has been massive in scale, now possibly totalling 15 million immediate descendants of Chinese parents now in Southeast Asian countries.

The continuing movement of people within the region in modern times has thrust some local communities into the background. At many places in Monsoon Asia will be found small tribes of people living in isolation, often primitive in their way of life by comparison with their neighbours and not related physically to them. Such vestigial groups shelter on the Deccan, in South China and in the forests and islands of Southeast Asia.

The expansion has also led to migration to places outside Monsoon Asia albeit in smaller numbers. Chinese and Japanese have travelled into the Pacific islands and to North and South America. Chinese also settled in Australia and New Zealand. Indians are established widely along East Africa, extending well inland and into South Africa; they have gone to the West Indies and Fiji by their association with the British Commonwealth, so that by now four million Indians are living outside India. These external movements overseas have significantly been greater than any overland into continental Asia.

A further internal consequence of expanding population has been the increasing proportion of farmers who became landless by subdivision of farms into uneconomic parcels. Thus in India about 55% of country people are landless, in Kwangtung about 50%, in Burma 40% and in Ceylon 44%. This dispossessed group is the most fluid one, drifting wherever opportunity offers and forming a source of social friction.

At the same time, some races foreign to the region have immigrated to Asia: Arabs may be found everywhere round the Indian Ocean, Europeans visiting for considerable periods have given rise to Eurasian stock of which the largest groups are in the Philippines and Java, the only parts where Europeans settled down in considerable numbers, modern European colonisation having been chiefly of transient managerial personnel rather than settlers.

CULTURAL ASPECTS

People acquire some characteristics by practice and by learning. These cultural features may be passed from parents to children, from teachers to taught, from conquerors to the conquered and between indigenes and migrants. It is possible to impose religion and language by force; it is possible to drop one's old way of living when arriving at a new place, or to continue it whether suitable or not. Cultural traits are often the subject of sentiment and emotion because they often form the means by which groups cohere; but they need not do so—economic and social considerations may cause people with the same religion or the same language to be divided; though both are Buddhist, Siam and Burma have been military or economic rivals for centuries.

There are many language groups in Monsoon Asia. Tonal languages are used from Tibet through Burma and Indochina and everywhere northward of these countries, while non-tonal, polysyllabic languages prevail elsewhere. Within these two major categories considerable differences exist so that in China alone about four very different, mutually unintelligible variations of tonal languages are spoken. In Malaya and Indonesia related "Malay" languages are used with several variations in written and spoken forms. In Peninsular India is a group of distinct Dravidian languages, and in the Indo-Gangetic Plain are languages related to the Mediterranean tongues. The language consideration has had less meaning as a bond owing to the low literacy rates of Asian countries; they add to local difficulties in plural societies, but their significance is further weakened by long use of colonial languages for administration. English is widespread as the international language of Asia, and even as the lingua franca among different peoples of the same country, a continuing relic of Western traders and colonial administrators. In China the linguistic differences are partly overcome by a writing whose "characters" can be pronounced many ways, as one picture of a table might be called "mesa" by a Spaniard, "tafel" by a German and "tavolo" by an Italian. China's literary tradition thus became strong, and the Mandarin civil service exercised a major influence in controlling the large mixed communities of that huge territory.

Islam spread by land into Monsoon Asia from Arabia through dry Central Asia into Northwest India and Western China. It was also waterborne by Arab traders to the Malabar Coast, East Pakistan, Malaya and Indonesia. The Hindu religion is a feature of India, where the sects are complex and numerous. It was transmitted by sea traders as far as Bali and Cambodia. Buddhism, which originated at Gaya near Benares, has been largely transferred to Ceylon, Burma, Siam, Japan and parts of China, carried eastwards overland through the Himalayas and by sea across the Bay of Bengal. Family cults are strong in China; animistic faiths extend everywhere in Monsoon Asia, influenced by an isolated country life in which people are struggling alone with nature for long periods and where nature has a peculiarly intense vitality. After so much population shift and

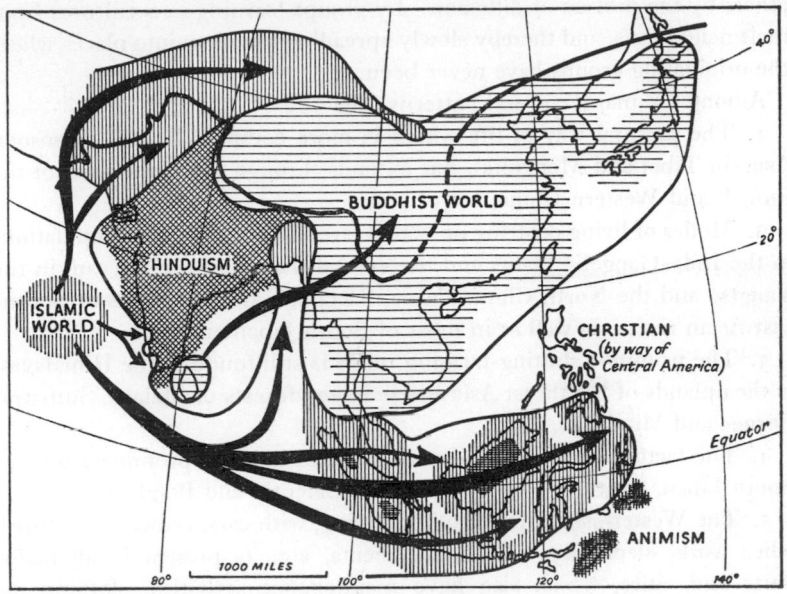

FIG. 8—Distribution of religions in Monsoon Asia, showing how
they have been transferred

the diffusion of ideas, the Oriental religions and languages have become
very intermixed.

More difficult to analyse is the distribution of people with similar ways
of doing things—the forms and methods of buildings, weaving, weapons,
utensils and clothing. These techniques range widely from "primitive" to
"advanced"; from those recalling the most ancient Britons to those of
twentieth-century industrial life. It is doubtful whether any communities,
however isolated, are really untouched by modernity; sometimes the
modernisation has been no older than World War II which, by being
fought with modern methods in the forests of Southeast Asia and among
the lesser islands of the volcanic arc, had a powerful contact influence.
Often a cultural innovation seems incongruous—as when villages use
bicycle wheels as spinning-wheels or old tin cans for lamps of coconut oil.
There has been no clearing away of any one mode of living, so that many
styles continue among relictual groups isolated by distance, by relief or by
poverty, making Monsoon Asia a museum of almost every stage of development and every mode of living that has ever existed. Cultural complexes
have arisen from migrating people carrying their ways into new territory;

others by the process of diffusion—by groups learning new cultures from their neighbours, and thereby slowly spreading the ideas into places where the originating groups have never been.

Among the major cultural patterns are:

1. The pastoral way of life which is more common beyond Monsoon Asia (in Tibet and Mongolia), but extends through the dryer parts of the Punjab and Western China.

2. Modes of living centring on cereal farming occupy dense populations in the Indo-Gangetic Plains and the coastal fringes of the Deccan, in the Yangtse and the North China Plains, Szechuan and the deltas of Southeast Asian rivers, as well as in most of South Japan and Java.

3. The primitive shifting-farming mode is still found in the Himalayas, in the uplands of Southeast Asia and in inland forests of Malaya, Sumatra, Borneo and Mindanao.

4. The factory and heavy industry mode of living is prominent only in South Japan, South Manchuria and near Calcutta and Bombay.

5. The Westernised urban mode of living, with cars, cement structures, office work, electricity, mass amusements, etc., is present in all major ports and cities, which also have maintenance activities, clothing industries and the mechanisms of commerce.

CHAPTER SIX

Rural Land Use

PASTORALISM

BECAUSE THE vegetation round the China Sea is dominated by evergreen forest, animal farming is small both on the adjoining mainland and on the islands. Even in the northeast where a little steppe extends from the interior as far as Peking, the interest in sheep and cattle is slight compared with that in cereals. On the other hand, the vegetation from Indonesia to West Pakistan is a transition from evergreen forest into savannah and thence into steppe, the latter lending themselves readily to pastoralism.

Thus the meat animal round the China Sea is the *pig*, of forest origin, now domesticated on smallholdings, living on wastes and kept on the basis of a pair of pigs per family. Chinese have carried the pig with them into Southeast Asia, but the animal disappears west and south of the Kra Isthmus, limited by the Islamic tradition. Probably one-third of the world's pigs are in Eastern Asia. Pork forms the leading animal protein food among the Mongoloids, but East Asia counts for nothing in the international pork trade.

Cattle are the chief animals round the Indian Ocean. In India the cattle population is startlingly high despite the Hindu objection to beef eating; it contains more cattle than any single country in the world, and far more than in all Europe. The Southeast Asian countries alone (Burma, Siam, Indochina, Malaya and Indonesia) support more cattle than Australia. Zebu or humped cattle are the type commonest in India and, while milk is to some extent produced and consumed, they are for draught, the meat being negligible in commercial value though a trade in hides goes on. In this sense the numbers of cattle in South Asia are of small commercial significance, and rarely denser than one or two per farmer. Their distribution correlates with cultivated land, being used for every kind of rural work and cereal farming. This applies to the many cattle kept in China, more especially towards its south where, despite no interest in milk and precarious dependence on weed-grasses round fields or on the "straw" of cereals, there are more than in Australia. Outside the Hindu region, beef will occasionally be eaten, though the quantity is negligible in relation to

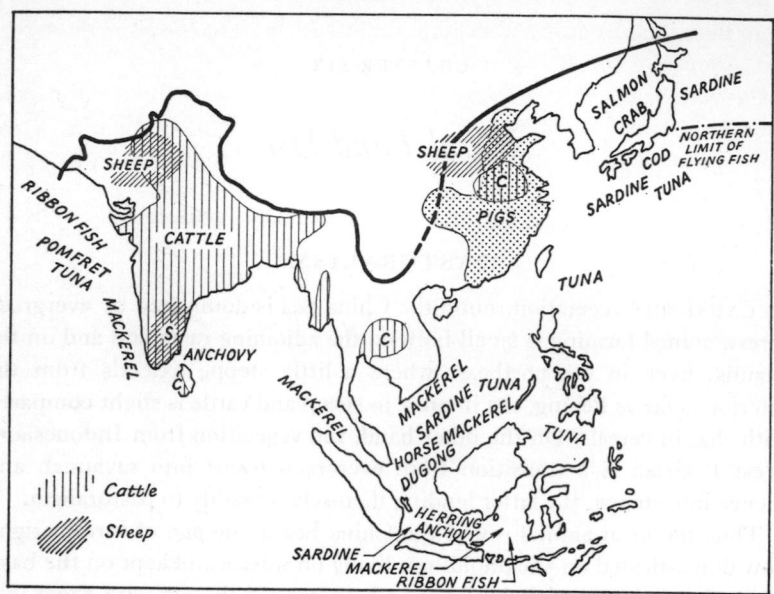

FIG. 9—Distribution of economic animals and fish

the population and comes from cattle too old for fieldwork. The proportion of cattle to people in Monsoon Asia equals the world average.

Sheep are more numerous in India and West Pakistan, most of those commonly recorded for China being outside or marginal to Monsoon Asia. Their number in the Southern Subcontinent is doubtful because the sheep are a small-scale, marginal venture rather than a continuous commercial production in large flocks. Yet Pak–Ind ranks fourth largest of the sheep-rearing regions, being exceeded only by Australia, Russia and Argentina. Sheep, now associated with the economy of the poorer, less-developed or pioneering areas, are present in the economy of long-settled and over-farmed India. While distributed more in the steppes and mountains round the Punjab and Thar, a substantial concentration of sheep occurs on the Deccan, being surprisingly dense in Mysore and Madras. Their wool-clip averages only about 1 lb. per animal a year as compared with the Australian average of about 10 lb. Used chiefly for meat, the Indian out-turn of mutton frequently exceeds that of any other country. Mutton is a major food in Muslim zones.

Related in distribution and usage is the *goat*, of which India supports more than the rest of the world together. Goats live largely by scavenging, and seriously deter the regrowth of scrub and bush.

Horses are associated with the military in Pakistan and India and played a classic role in the military history of North China, but they are exotic to most of the tropics and little used for fieldwork, their function being to carry persons.

AGRICULTURE

By far the largest area used for any one crop in Monsoon Asia is that sown with rice. Over 95% of the world's rice acreage lies within this region, so that rice is a characteristic Asian product and staple. Today it is being spread into regions outside Monsoon Asia, where it originated. But rice is not and cannot be grown *everywhere* in Monsoon Asia. On the Deccan and northwestwards it ceases to be prominent, and it is difficult to grow on the Yellow Plain. Rice occupies only a quarter of the arable land in both India and China; only in Taiwan and Indochina does rice occupy over two-thirds of the arable land. Of farmed land in China, wheat occupies only an eighth less than rice.

Rice

Rice has reached a peak in cultivation through a technique by which the fields of "wet padi" are covered with water for the growing period. Types cultivable without standing water are "dry" or "upland" padi, yielding about one-third the quantity obtainable from "wet padi", much more precarious and hence less in use. Greatest interest in dry padi is in Java where about 10% of fields carry it.[1]

The standing water gives unique character to the padi-growing landscape and sets the chief ecological limit of farming. For water to remain on a field requires that the ground be levelled and have low porosity, and the water supply to be large to offset seeping and evaporation. A dry, sunny spell must follow the wet stage to ensure ripening.

These conditions can be met in several ways. The levelling involves reshaping the landscape into step form, small in localities of changing or steep slope, and edged with shallow ridges or bunds to hinder run-off. To prevent water seeping underground, fields are located where the water-table is close to the surface or where a clay layer is not far underground, or where men understand the tilthing technique. Such requirements encourage rice farmers to gravitate to swamp terrains, to the heavier and

[1] Padi is the unhusked grain and rice the cleaned, milled grain; the latter is about two-thirds the weight of the former and more directly indicative of food value.

more finely divided alluvial materials of valley bottoms. The water needed can be obtained where rain comes in downpours heavy enough to offset run-off and evaporation, where streams overflow or where water can be lifted or led into the fields. The plant tolerates conditions of very little oxygen at its roots, and responds more to ammonium than to nitrates. The summer temperature requirement of the padi plant is not significantly limiting, but it germinates only above 52° F., and while growing needs at least three months exceeding 68° F.—both conditions being common from Karachi to Korea.

Only the lesser part of rice-land is irrigated by canalising water to the fields. In the Bengal area, less than 15% of padi-fields are artificially watered; the proportion is much less in Burma and Southern India, but higher in South China and Japan, where water-lifting devices are used. Thus padi growing depends mainly upon natural water supplies by rainfall and to a lesser extent by natural flood. Heavy, hot-season rains are of a paramount importance for optimum development of padi.

Hence wet padi has been most cultivated on coasts of seasonally heavy rain and in flood-plains and delta locations. In the coastal plains of Peninsular India and South China, in the deltas and lowlands of the Ganges, Irrawaddy, Chao Praya, Mekong, Red and Yangtse Rivers rice has responded well and now occupies large, continuous areas. Outside these zones padi is more discontinuous, frequently arranged in narrow belts beside water-courses, but nearly everywhere identified with the lowest level of the landscape. Where practised on terraces in hilly or mountain districts, the levelling problems become acute though partly offset by the ease of piping the water from mountain streams to the terraces, as in Java, Japan and Luzon.

That the crop does well in low-lying clay land means that it concentrates in places inimical to most other crops, so that a rice-field tends to be used for that purpose alone. Double cropping of rice, a possibility related to continuous growing-temperatures, necessitates a considerable control of water and less dependence on local rains; it is more common in the eastern part of Monsoon Asia, under those conditions which give rise to evergreen forest, than in India, much of whose setting is identified with savannah. That the padi plant tolerates an alternation of flooded and dry field means that the water-level may be manipulated in such a way as to destroy weeds of wet and dry types alternately. Because it is difficult to gauge accurately when the intense rain will occur, the seed-bed system has been evolved; the whole crop is first sown in a small, handwatered patch, where the seedlings germinate under virtually garden conditions. Mean-

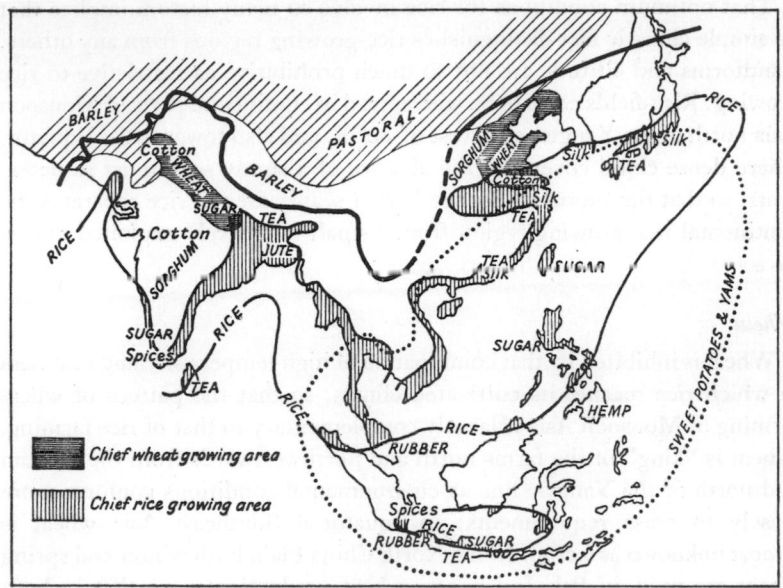

FIG. 10—Distribution of agricultural plants. The map shows the cultivation of rice to be peripheral and indicates a separate rice-growing area round the Java sea

while the fields are prepared, levelled and tilled until the rains come, when the seedlings are transplanted. This "horticultural" method serves as a major insurance against rainfall variations. Related to this manual process, to the dense population of the rice-growing areas and to generations of sub-division by inheritance, is the smallness of the average padi holding. In Java and South China, padi farms average less than two acres; in Eastern India, East Pakistan and Japan about three acres. Only in those ricelands opened recently are holdings much greater in size than these, yet even in such parts of Burma and Siam they average only ten acres. From these farms whole families must be supported. Limits of workable size are set by the tools and manual methods in use; the hoe is the only soil-working tool upon many millions of acres.

Only to a limited extent can the yield per acre be taken as summarising natural conditions; yield includes a factor of intensity related to local population and to alternative work. The 1956 average national yield in Japan was about 3,710 lb. cleaned rice per cultivated acre, in China 1,660 lb., in Java 1,480 lb., in Burma 1,485 lb. and in India 1,170 lb. (U.S.A. yield is about 3,000 lb.).

That optimum conditions for rice involve so many factors implies that no simple climatic fact distinguishes rice-growing regions from any others. Landforms and altitude are not so much prohibitive as restrictive to rice growing. Rice-fields cease to be widespread in continental parts of Monsoon Asia north of the Yangtse and west of 80° E. and also towards the Equator, where dense cloud cover and the absence of a sunny season act as deterrents, so that the Sumatra–Borneo belt of scanty area in rice separates the continental rice-growing region from a small intensively exploited one in Java.

Wheat

Wheat is inhibited by that combination of high temperature and raininess in which rice reaches its cultivated climax, so that the pattern of wheat farming in Monsoon Asia is largely complementary to that of rice farming. Wheat is "king" of the farms north and northwestwards from the Deccan and north of the Yangtse line as environmental conditions conform more closely to grass requirements: in equatorial Southeast Asia wheat is almost unknown as a crop. In the North China Plain both winter and spring wheat are used, in Pak–Ind winter wheat predominates, so that in both it is the gentler rains of winter cyclones which exercise greatest influence. While the complementary location of wheat to rice is evident in the regional land use, it is true also in detail. There are considerable areas in India and China where rice and wheat at different times in one year occupy the same fields, and where adjoining fields may contain the one and the other, corresponding to slight differences in level or porosity. Thus wheat grows for part of the year as far east as the Bengal delta and south into Mysore, well south of the Yangtse and in South Japan. Almost a third of Eastern China's arable land is used for wheat at some time, Pakistan and Japan using over 10% for the same crop.

Although the wheat ecology differs so much from that of rice, the size of Asian wheat farms is not materially different from the padi holdings. Small-scale, manual operations predominate, and wheat yields are low by world standards, in pounds per acre for 1957 being 1,830 in Japan, 700 in China, 650 in Pakistan and 620 in India. Irrigation is more common for wheat than for rice in the Subcontinent and North China. Cattle are everywhere the draught animals employed. On landscapes more exclusively for wheat, trees are less evident and the fields less levelled than where rice dominates.

The attraction of rice as compared with wheat is apparent by comparing the Asian yields of the one with the other. The yield of cleaned rice (i.e.

64

ready for cooking) grown by the wet method is greater than that for wheat, so that in localities marginal to both rice takes first place. In Sind rice displaced wheat when irrigation became available.

To keep a sense of proportion we must note that in 1957 China had under wheat 20% more acreage than U.S.A. and India farmed four times as much wheatland as Australia.

Sorghum and Millet

Peculiar to Monsoon Asia is the prominence of the coarse cereals—sorghum, millet and the Chinese kaoliang. Over two-thirds of world sorghum acreage is in Asia, where its area equals that of wheat. Over half the Asian sorghum is in India and related to savannah conditions in the Deccan. Sorghum, kaoliang and millet are more reliable than wheat under high summer temperatures and low or erratic rainfalls. It is the summer crop of places on the dry margins of rice-growing regions. "Tall grass" in form and requirements, these coarse cereals are intended for human consumption after boiling.

Other Food Crops

Monsoon Asia has less land under *maize* than might be expected, since this is a grain of the "tall grass" regions. Part of the explanation is that maize was introduced by Europeans. Though now a familiar human food in Asia, it is never grown for animals. It has greatest local importance in Java and Central Philippines where Western influence has been long-standing, but it also occupies substantial areas on the North China Plain and in the middle Ganges Plain. Its place in Asian farming is supplementary, rotational or marginal, and its yields well below world average.

In Northern India and Northern China *barley* is much cultivated as a staple food crop by reason of its tolerance of high relief and uncertain rainfalls.

A specialist crop of Monsoon Asia is the *soya bean*, a legume with a short growing period but needing the long days of northerly locations. It is in use as a rotation crop and of major importance as a protein food and vegetable oil. Confined largely to localities from the Yangtse northward, it is most extensively grown in the short summer and long days of the Manchurian Plain which carries nearly two-thirds of the total world acreage.

Hundreds of lesser plants are cropped in Monsoon Asia, many of them little known elsewhere, the variety being a consequence of (*a*) the varied environmental conditions which aid plant evolution, (*b*) a dense population intensely exploring the plant world for food and (*c*) long settlement.

Most vegetable foods are annuals, but there are also many perennials, of special interest being those whose reproduction is vegetative, i.e. by runners, rhizomes or cuttings—a feature of plant growth towards the Equator. The yam, sweet potato, sago palm, banana and similar plants are reproduced in this way, which prevents rapid evolution because each plant becomes virtually everlasting—being extended and duplicated rather than bred. Bamboo and sugar-cane are reproduced by forms of runners. The transplanting technique in rice is curiously parallel to the tropical method of reproducing by cuttings from a parent plant. Although yam, banana and tapioca may have been Man's first cultivated plants, their potentialities have proved more limited than the annuals. It is a comment on the horticultural technique they involve that South China has almost half the world's reported acreage in sweet potato and yams; Java leads the world in acreage under tapioca, introduced from Tropical America.

Subsistence Farming

Much of Monsoon Asia's agriculture is organised primarily for subsistence on a self-contained basis. The peasant aims to grow his family's food and his family looks only to their own field for their needs. It is to be contrasted with commercial agriculture now more common in Europe and America where the objective is to sell almost everything produced and to purchase the supplies for the farmer's family and workers. The subsistance system limits the farmer's outlook, almost eliminates cash income and eliminates or restricts his purchasing power; it confines his helpers to his own family or to others who will accept payment in kind, and it produces a static economy. What is produced never leaves the farm, reducing the needs for transport and obliging every farmer to produce much the same range of crops as his neighbour. The system makes for a high degree of rural independence, is much influenced by the "horticulture" or gardening tradition, and leads to exchange by barter or payment in kind. It is facilitated by and itself facilitates isolation. It is buffered from the effects of world prices whether favourable or unfavourable. Its greatest difficulties arise when population is increasing, directly converting that increase into "pressure on the land". The subsistance system suits pioneering conditions, and is partly responsible for poor statistics from places where it operates.

Commercial Farming

Commercial agriculture was one of the technical innovations following the development of bulk trade when Westerners reached Monsoon Asia by

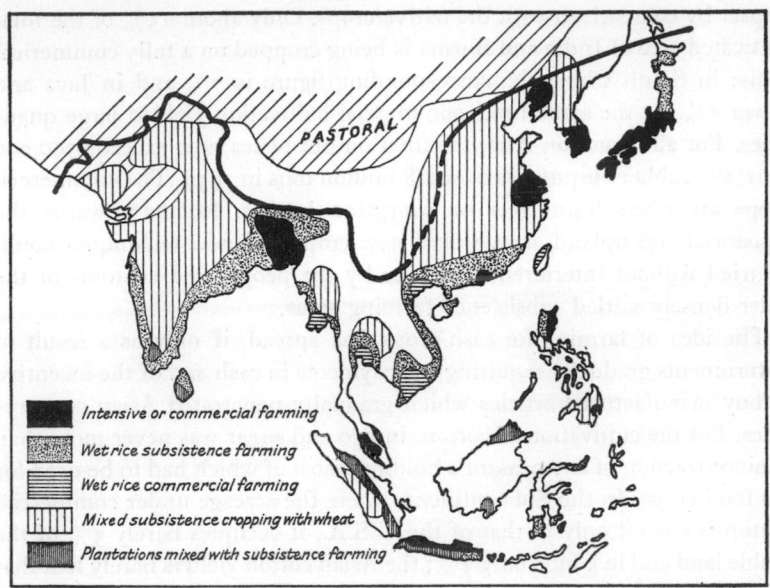

FIG. 11—Types of farming in Monsoon Asia. The scheme is highly generalised and ignores much variation and transition in detail

sea. Previously farmers had been forced by their system to grow a little of everything and avoided producing any one commodity in quantity. Their subsistance system resisted specialisation, and Westerners were obliged to set up their own estates or plantations to meet their needs for bulk production of Asian commodities. This was only possible in new areas and not in densely peopled localities so that the commercial crops of Monsoon Asia were largely pioneering efforts by farmers, who faced labour difficulties when opening up the unpeopled terrains. Great wealth came from commercial farming, yet the total acreage it occupied has at no time approximated to that of the staple foods cultivated by Asians. It characteristically produced crops able to withstand the distance to industrial markets. Thus Asian commercial agriculture has for a long time been largely complementary in location to Asian subsistence agriculture, and mostly has gone on without displacing other crops, drawing away only a small population to the new cultivated areas, and rarely bringing to native agriculture any change of method, reinvigoration of style or regrouping of property.

Thus the consequence of commercialised tea, pepper, sugar, rubber, manila hemp and similar products has been small in area and limited in impact by comparison with the native crops. Only about 15% of the total cultivated area of India and Burma is being cropped on a fully commerical basis: in South China the corresponding figure is 7% and in Java and Japan 5%. At the same time, commercial cultivation yielded large quantities. For all Monsoon Asia, the total output of tea now exceeds 790,000 tons; the rubber output was over 1.8 million tons in 1957. The commercial crops are often from trees or evergreen bushes, located towards the equatorial and upland areas where new crops and new techniques could be tried without interference with or by the people and customs of the older densely settled subsistence farming areas.

The idea of farming for cash crops has spread, if only as a result of governments gradually requiring tax payments in cash and of the incentive to buy manufactured articles which gradually penetrated Asian countrysides. But the cultivation of cotton, indigo and sugar was never more than a minor fraction of any peasant's holding, most of which had to be used for his food crops. In the Subcontinent, where the acreage under commercial cotton is second only to that of the U.S.A., it occupies barely 5% of the arable land and in China only 3%; the Asian cotton yield is barely half that of fields in the U.S.A. and the production *per capita* everywhere less than one-eighth that in the U.S.A. While India has over half the sugar-cane acreage of Monsoon Asia, less than 1% of its cultivated land is so used.

The difficulties of procuring a steady trade in agricultural commodities in face of traditional methods were always present, slowing the growth of processing industries and mechanised farming. Asian food-crops entering international trade were derived from very small units of production—the fraction of any farm's produce moving into trade being never more than half, often derived from rents or similar payment in kind, and therefore not directly sold by the farmer. It was first channelised towards the local towns and later into international trade, the surplus being stimulated by modern irrigation canals in the Punjab and the opening of new rice areas in Burma, Siam and Indochina. The Indian wheat surplus was eliminated by local population increase, and a reduction of Southeast Asian rice surplus due to increased population is now apparent.

The importance of payments in kind goes deep. Little money passes into the hands of subsistence farmers, even though their production be good and their family feeding well. Those who take rents in kind are few compared with the total rural population because the percentage of owner-farmers is high. The landowner is frequently himself only a small-property owner, and his concern to be paid in kind partly reflects his need to feed directly from the produce of his property. Those localities where landowners are common are areas of long history, where the process of sub-division by inheritance has gone on for generations and regrouping of lots by purchase has taken place, more especially by those who have savings after working for a time in the towns and cities. Some long-settled areas (as in India and Pakistan) also have remnants of feudal property systems.

Thus the physical, biotic and human association with agriculture in Monsoon Asia is complex. Over-use and over-extension into marginal localities are general, and the low yields are symptomatic of prolonged and frequently intensive farming, a condition encouraged by the dense rural population but concealed by the small quantities passing into trade. Changes of crop or system are difficult to introduce and it is even more difficult to estimate the possible ecological consequences. Continued pressure into marginal lands has had the effect of exposing some farming people to climatic vagaries and to famine. Catastrophic famines common in India and China are less due to exceptionally difficult natural conditions and more frequently to an extreme over-populated condition, leading to a precariously narrow gap between average production and normal need.

CHAPTER SEVEN

Mining, Industry and Transport

MINING AND industry make little mark on the Asian landscape. This is the great contrast between the landscapes round the North Atlantic Seaboard and those round Asia. It is at once evidence of the predominance of Asian farming, sign of a different stage of development and cause of the complementary trade pattern between Asia and the West.

MINING

Whereas in agriculture Asians have pressed heavily upon the vegetation potential of their soil and climate, exercised ingenuity in plant breeding to produce a wide range of crops, and evolved complex techniques of water use within limits of small capital investment, they did no similar ferreting at their mineral resources. Over considerable areas dense natural vegetation and thick lateritic and alluvial soils have impeded the discovery, exploration and exploitation of Asia's minerals, and at the same time key minerals are apparently less common and less well located in relation to one another in the Asian Fringe. Monsoon Asia's known resources of coal and iron are less than elsewhere, area for area, which has major consequence because these two minerals are the foundations of heavy industry and the origin of that power and capital equipment which make possible modern productivity. China has less proved coal resources than Germany and India less than Poland; Monsoon Asia appears to contain scarcely 7% of the world's exploitable coal. India has less proved iron ore than France and China less than Britain; the whole region containing only about 15% of the world's known iron ore. In view of the historic role of copper and bronze in the region, it is remarkable that even its copper resources are poor—less than 1·5% of the world's reserves and largely in South China. In bauxite, the ore of aluminium chiefly evolved under laterisation, Monsoon Asia has huge supplies, equal to the known bauxite reserves in North and South America combined. Minerals in Monsoon Asia are not as mutually accessible as, say, the Ruhr coal to the Loraine iron ore, or Pennsylvania coal to Lakeside ore, so that Asian use is far less than known reserves. Reducing all the kinds of coal to one standard, in 1957 Monsoon Asia produced only about 230 million tons, which was about equal to United Kingdom production. Even Japan, which has good seaboard coals developed intensively, produces less *per capita* than the world average. Mining for iron is even less: in 1957 Monsoon Asia produced less than 20 million tons, which is roughly that of France alone and less than one-third of U.S.A. Of petroleum, Southeast Asia has 1·5% of the world reserves, worked chiefly in Northern Borneo and Sumatra.

Metallic mineralisation is great in the igneous Deccan, which also has workable coal flanking it to the northeast. The Himalyan–Island Arc, for all its great length, has very limited exposures of minerals; where they occur they relate to old block structures involved in the folding process (i.e. Luzon's gold and the coal of Southwest Japan). Among Eastern China's complex block forms are the chief exploited coal resources of Monsoon Asia, the structure being sufficiently intact to preserve economic strata from excessive erosion, while at the same time broken enough to make them accessible from the surface. Southeast Asia is rich in tin, found from Yunnan through to Sumatra where contact metamorphosis has taken place.

While the picture of mining is of scanty resources widely scattered and little developed, it has occasioned some local developments, attracting much capital investment and changes of far-reaching significance. In unmanufactured form they have been for many Asian countries the chief items of external trade and the means of inducing close relation with industrial regions overseas.

Japan's coal gave it the power for an industrialisation unique in the region, the relative scarcity of other minerals stimulating the kind of expansionist economic policy which culminated in World War II. Gold in Luzon, tin in Malaya, lead and oil in Burma and oil in Sumatra and Borneo drew foreign companies and foreign personnel at both managerial and labour levels into places previously thinly populated, and led to supplementary economic transformations. The pioneering miner has "skimmed the cream". His success here and there cannot be taken to indicate average potentialities. Bonanza economy brings changes at a pace rendering them almost unabsorbable, and often works contrary to conserving resources for the steadiest return over the longest period. In lesser minerals Monsoon Asia is more productive. China and India rank after the U.S.A. and U.K. as leading salt producers, for human consumption rather than for chemical industries. Japan is a major sulphur producer due to its volcanic geomorphology, for export as well as for its own chemical works. Asbestos is mined on a substantial scale in Japan, and India is the world's second largest mica producer.

HYDRO-ELECTRIC POWER

Those substantial rainfalls which characterise parts of Monsoon Asia and help to sustain a forest cover represent great water-power potential in the conveniently accidented terrains of the Himalayan–Island Arc and in Southeast Asia. There is less potential where there are monsoonal seasonal extremes of aridity and rain. On the other hand, the prolonged agricultural exploitation has caused population to gravitate to the alluvial plains away from the localities of water-power potential. The low commercialisation of the agriculture limits the capital available for hydro-electric schemes, and reduces the incentive to use it, more especially as irrigation has so far assumed priority over the power need. The administrative situation has commonly been one of weakness, of expediency, of discontinuity or of small units, hindering the development of regional schemes embracing transport, power and irrigation water as exemplified by the Tennessee Valley Authority. Even simpler devices such as watermills are not in the Oriental tradition either for milling cereals or for weaving and spinning.

Monsoon Asia is estimated to have a hydro-electric potential equivalent to about 600,000 million kilowatts per hour of which a large part is in the Himalayas, the Western Ghats, South China, Burma and Japan. Scarcely 5% is exploited, and of the hydro-electricity now being produced Japan is responsible for about four-fifths. Many schemes for further development of water-power have been put forward and encouraged by international organisations for technical and economic aid, so that the pattern of hydro-electric production may soon change.

INDUSTRY

Because Monsoon Asia exploits so little of its fuel resources, industrial development is slight. In only five sectors does mechanised industry occur: (a) near Bombay, (b) in the Damodar Valley near Calcutta, (c) along the Yangtse in Shanghai and the Wu-Han cities, (d) in South Japan, (e) in South Manchuria. The coastal location of these localities marks their external associations. Concentration on textiles is a feature, but heavy iron and steel and chemical industries are present in the Damodar, Manchuria and Japan.

Japanese industry is far more developed in range and in intensity than any others in the Oriental World, now turning out about 12 million tons of steel annually, while India is producing annually about $1\frac{3}{4}$ million tons and China 11 million (1957). Japan has about $3\frac{1}{2}$ million persons engaged in factories, India about $1\frac{3}{4}$ million and China possibly 2 million. The interest in textile industries reflects the basic need of Asians for cotton cloth. Although Japan is known for its textile exports, its production of cloth is less than that of either India or China. India processes 0.75 million tons and Japan about 0.32 million tons of crude cotton a year. Japan surpasses the others in artificial silk and woollen textiles. The Bombay and Shanghai regions concentrate on textiles. Japan's silk industry, related to small-scale agriculture both for its raw material and for its cheap, frequently part-time labour, has resumed production after wartime occlusion. The output of silk yarn is now about a third of the prewar and of silk cloth about half. Regarded in the West as a luxury, natural silk is diminishing in world trade. The Chinese silk trade shows little sign of rehabilitation.

Monsoon Asia has little industrial preparation of its foods. Rice needs little processing. In India where half the people eat wheat, only about half a million tons of wheat, 6% of production, is milled into flour each year.

That so much of Asia's population is rural has led to that form of industry known as the crafts, where work is done part-time, in small units and semi-domestically as contrasted with the industry of mechanised factories. The tradition of cottage weaving persists, though it has suffered from factory competition. Hand-made leather work, shoes, pottery, furniture, clothing and ploughs are still the usual rather than the exception throughout rural Asia. The pool of manual skill is far higher than might be expected, though it may not be easily available in towns. It accounts for the dispersed small-scale units which were the first steps of industrialisation in the Monsoon Fringe, and also for the frequent use of part-time workers. The kind of village industrialisation which went on in Alsace, Switzerland and Czechoslovakia has been repeated in the Far East. Small spinning industries in cottages or small village buildings are widespread on the Deccan behind Bombay and in the Lower Yangtse. Similar small units of domestic or village silk weaving and embroidery are common in South China and Japan. Because this has been done in conjunction with subsistence farming, it follows that the costs of production have seemed low by world standards. The system has considerable flexibility and permitted a wide range of products with a trend towards articles involving more manual skill than material content. Grouping and concentration into larger, heavily capitalised units went on for a time, stimulated by foreign capital and foreign competition.

Japan industralised on the basis of good local coal, some waterpower, plentiful population and powerful governmental protection but in face of

73

scarce materials, this last factor having had much to do with the extension of Japanese industrialists into Manchuria and Central China where materials were more plentiful and large markets accessible. While its heavy industry concentrated in Bengal, Bihar and Orissa, where large deposits of iron ore and coal are close together, most Indian manufacturing is also dispersed; the textile mills round Bombay, where lives about half the Indian industrial population, are about 800 miles from the coal and industries of Bihar, inducing the exploitation of hydro-electricity in the Western Ghats. Other cotton processing is scattered round Cawnpore and through the Punjab. The average Indian cotton mill employs on an average only a thousand persons and uses about 1,500 tons of cotton per annum. Indian industrialisation is both recent and mainly private, protected by a tariff against foreign steels and similar goods which are more cheaply made outside India. Chinese heavy industry has concentrated at places in Manchuria, in Eastern Shantung and in the Yangtse and Canton Deltas, a sign of foreign contacts. Cotton textiles have been a feature of Chinese industry, but chemicals, cement, iron and steel are also produced. The whole position of Chinese industry is confused by the events of the last fifteen years or so, during which there was a mass withdrawal of industrial installations into the interior away from the Japanese, and a postwar flight of entrepreneurs. Re-equipping and re-establishing the industries has been hindered since 1948 by the "Bamboo Curtain" and restriction on contacts overseas.

From the general scarcity of metals, it follows that while small metal-working units for making and repairing tools and equipment are fairly common in Asia's small towns, high-grade modern machinery is not produced on a significant scale, except in Japan where the interest is in ship-building and in making such things as sewing-machines, electrical machines and mechanical tools suiting the domestic and scattered character of Asian industry. The expansion of industry is exceeding the prewar rate under the impetus of foreign aid. Light-machine production has appeared in India only since World War II; the out-turn of diesel engines, small ships, electrical equipment and transport machinery is increasing rapidly, having benefited by India's isolation during the war. Related to the steady expansion of building for domestic and capital installations, cement output has steadily increased everywhere in Monsoon Asia, marking a trend away from wooden buildings. Japan's output in 1957 was 13 million tons, India's 6 million and China's about 7 million tons. Bengal, identified with both jute production and the manufacture of gunny cloth, hessian or sacking, has seen a substantial change since East Pakistan separated. Previously most jute was marketed and manufactured near Calcutta, drawing the raw material from the entire Ganges Delta. Today jute growing on the Indian side of the delta exceeds that in East Pakistan, which has built new jute-mills to compete with the Indian.

Wood-pulp, needing timber, water and power, is manufactured in Japan to a total of about $2\frac{1}{4}$ million tons annually (about $4\frac{1}{2}\%$ of world production). India manufactures about half this quantity, but is expanding. The potentialities of the equatorial forest for wood-pulp are considerable though not yet exploited.

TRANSPORT

In Monsoon Asia because mining is a lesser development and agriculture so self-contained, there is only limited modern transport. Over large areas cattle carts are still much used because of the need for transport cheap to establish and able to handle bulky, low-grade freight. Because population is at its densest near the coasts, shipping plays a major role in servicing it. Rivers have small native craft which, while adequate for the sprawling, agricultural population, have rarely grown to importance. The Yangtse and the Irrawaddy, upon which regular modern river steamers ply far inland, are the exception; each functions for its territory as the Rhine does for Europe, permitting bulk movements between the interior and seaboard. Other Oriental rivers are casually and irregularly used in their deltas; many of them fluctuate widely or have long periods of low water, and in many cases that flooding which attracts wet agriculture has deterred town building at riverside locations. Thus the Ganges, Brahmaputra, Mekong and Hwang carry little traffic outside their delta zones.

Large-scale transport canals have not been built in Asia, a consequence of limited technical facilities. The Grand Canal from Peking across the North China Plains to the Yangtse begun in the third century is unique in Asia and a comment on the importance of inland grain transport in earlier times when Central and South China were colonies of North China.

How important shipping is can be estimated by the fact that most of Asia's major cities are seaports. Yet the total Asian merchant marine is merely 8% of world tonnage, significant at once of limited local capital, the preference for small junks or sailing ships for coastwise movement, and of Western dominance of steamer facilities in Asian waters. Only Japan has a major merchant marine (5.2 million tons registered in 1957); China and the Indian Union, so much larger in area and population, respectively have 0·6 and 0·5 million tons registered shipping, thus continuing that disinterest in the sea which was their characteristic before Westerners reached their shores.

The pattern of land transport is to link hinterlands to seaports rather than to provide an even regional network. Everywhere roads and railways from Asia's coastal cities fade out towards the interiors, and the Tibetan Highlands stand as a transport blank, few lines even reaching its margins. Little transport crosses the landward boundaries and international over-land transport is almost non-existant, the great exception being between India and Pakistan whose common boundaries cross continuous belts of well-peopled land. No road or railway links India overland to Burma or Burma to Siam or Indochina to South China. Only rough tracks from Pakistan run northward or westward through the mountainous limits of Monsoon Asia at its borders, and from Northern China into Central Asia. Railways in Asia mostly have single lines and lack that pattern of branches normal in Europe, functioning as single arteries rather than as regional networks. Often the road is discontinuous because designed as "feeder" to the railway in an attempt to secure local traffic. The bulk involved between intermediate points on a line is usually small and seasonal, so that few railways outside Japan are economic propositions or comparable in com-plexity of organisation and commodity flow with those of Europe. Large areas remain unserved by railways: over 85% of Indochina and of China are more than 10 miles from the railway. Java and Japan are exceptional in the closeness of their railway and road coverage. The railway layout is fre-quently intended to unify the countries by securing greater internal asso-ciations and offsetting the centrifugal effects of seaborne transport. Thus the railway links across the Deccan have aided the unification of India as well as enabling the bulky cotton of Bombay Presidency and of the Middle Ganges area to be brought out. The Saigon–Hanoi railway likewise was aimed to secure a political association between what are now North Viet-nam and South Vietnam.

Outside the major city areas metalled roads are few, but the modern tendency is to build roads rather than railways. China possesses less miles of motorable road per thousand square miles of its area than any other nation: half China is more than 10 miles from a road. Japan again is exceptional, reflecting its greater urban and industrial development; it has as much mileage of road per unit area as Switzerland. India has a far greater mileage of railways than of motorable roads, its long distance road traffic being small; trunk roads link Calcutta to the Punjab and to Madras and run from Bombay to Delhi and Madras. Malaya's rubber and tin chiefly move to seaboard by road, but in Monsoon Asia the seasonally torrential rain operates to interrupt road movement, and the poor, scattered farmers live in localities which, while suiting "wet" agriculture, make bridges and road foundations costly. The great deltas are obstructions to land transport.

The transport systems of many of these countries were seriously disrupted by wartime denial actions. In 1945 transport was less adequate and worse organised than in 1905. Postwar uncertainties have precluded large-scale rehabilitation. Transport in China and Indochina was worse in 1954 than at other times this century. Several wartime attempts to open new transport lines indicated possibilities for future development, but the Ledo Road from Assam into Central Burma, the Burma Road into Yunnan and the Burma–Siam Railway have already fallen into disuse because they reflected no continuing need.

That the key areas in Monsoon Asia are separated by large spaces of low traffic potential suggests that air services might solve transport difficulties. The newly independent countries have set up national air services. In general, Asian airlines have operated more internationally than domestically, seeking prestige rather than serving a need, and finding in practice that the local demand is small. Few of them are self-supporting or work towards unification in the way railways did, last century. Added to them are the long-distance international airlines which traverse Monsoon Asia from across the Pacific and along the route between Europe and Australia. So far the orientation of China towards Soviet Russia seems not to have induced any comparably large-scale trans-continental air traffic. Even for this, the most modern method of movement, the mountains and wastes of the continental border to Monsoon Asia still act as barriers.

CHAPTER EIGHT

Historical Development

EARLY CONDITIONS in Asia are concealed by two facts: economic change was taking place there as far back as 2500 B.C., and has been accumulating ever since; damp, heat, insects and war have destroyed most evidence recorded on wood, fibre and skin.

So long has the historic process operated on the enormous Asian stage, and so many peoples have been involved that the following brief review of Asia's historical geography inevitably omits far more than it includes and dangerously foreshortens the perspective of events.

EARLY INDIANS AND CHINESE

Two areas in China and India have had critical significance during the evolution of these now densely peopled zones. The nursery area for Chins (sometimes called Ts'ins), who founded China, was round the Hwang and Wei confluence, near Anyang and Sian. That locality resembled Tennessee in climate, vegetation and continental position, though by now over-cultivation and erosion have made its landscape bare and desiccated. It adjoins the Kansu corridor through the Wei Valley to the Central Asian plains (recalling the Hudson–Mohawk gap). The nursery for Indian people was the Punjab, where piedmont plains have a climate and fertility resembling that of the fertile crescent from Babylonia to Palestine, near routes through the Himalayas and Pamirs to Central Asia. Continental access to the Punjab and Hwang accounts for recurring Central Asian pressures in the development of both China and India.

The Hwang nursery consisted of fertile, wooded "cantons" of millet and wheat farmers with some sheep. The valleys converge and facilitated confederation, leading to higher social organisation. To their early rounded economy, limitations were set by the surrounding hills and valley-bottom marshes. In tackling those small marshes, ancestors of the North Chinese learned methods which proved more useful as they spread from the cantons downstream to the North China Plain (the Yellow Plain), then a swampy terrain by reason of the wide fluctuations of the Hwang distributaries across their great alluvial deposits. Once control of water and drainage was achieved on that plain, it yielded good wheat crops and provided the economic and technical superiority upon which Chinese first rose to significance, using their simple resources to resist pressure from restless nomads on their northwest. Thus the North China Plain became the "core area" of Chinese, whose mixed farming was the basis of their economic resource and whose adjustment to varying water on the land and to continuing pressure from overland was the chief purpose of organising themselves and the incentive to their expansion.

In Northwest India the belt of fertile and well-watered piedmont fans was where wheat- and cattle-farming communities (called Aryans, Indo-Aryans or Caucasians) settled, the climate being better than that of the middle Hwang, but the layout less helpful to consolidation. The mixed farmers were always exposed to threat from nomads and hill tribes. Extension from these alluvial fans was first south, out into the middle Punjab where dryness deterred farming until streamside irrigation was invented. Later, under continuing pressure from horsemen from the northwest, they extended eastward to adjoining fans, gravitating away from the Indus. Moving along the Himalayan piedmont north of the Ganges, the groups came to countrysides more productive because better watered. Dividing up, dispersion and moving eastwards and southwards made the early history of the Indo-Gangetic Plain and echoed through the centuries. The Plain is less uniformly settled and less unifying than at first appears, the water availability differing widely.

While these lines of evolution were being worked out in India and China during the third millennium B.C., what was taking place in the forests of South India and Southeast Asia is not clear. The forest people seem to have been dark-skinned and lived much as Melanesians do today, differing radically from the Aryans and Chins in techniques and economy.

EXPANSIONS IN INDIA AND CHINA

Each extension of Aryan groups along the Ganges increased the agricultural resource. Extension south of the Ganges was mostly limited by the increasing aridity and hilliness of the Deccan, which became the base of militant groups periodically raiding from that side the producers on the Plain. Continuing pressures led to chain reactions of shift and disruption throughout the Ganges Plain. As farming moved southeastwards, it went to places where wheat and millet were less and less suited to the seasonally sodden terrain and monsoon rains. The potential of the eastern Plain was exploitable only after the invention of wet farming for rice, which seems to have had its origin here. The economic strength then released as the swampy terrains towards Bengal were harnessed for rice growing appear to have been the basis of the vigorous Mauryan Empire (322–185 B.C.). The additional food thus available made possible thrusts back into the Punjab to resist pressures from across the Himalayas and thrusts south into the Deccan. Plentiful resources never led the Indian armies as far back into the continent as the Chinese went, though Persian and Greek armies came well into the Punjab, far from their own core areas. From India overland, however, there passed trade into the Mediterranean world, fine cotton cloth and other processed goods technically more advanced than those of Europe at that time . . . and for which it is thought that the gold of the Roman Empire mostly gravitated into the Indo-Gangetic Plain.

The Southern Subcontinent was never unified by any one Indian potentate, as the whole of China was by its emperors. Periodical attack by North Indians southwards upon the dark Dravidians of the Deccan never conquered them all. Under pressure, the Dravidians intensified their agriculture, causing widespread destruction of southern vegetation and soil, and moved overseas in early times to Ceylon, Kra and Southeast Asia.

That command over water achieved round the middle Hwang enable the Chins to extend from the North China Plain to the wet terrains round the lower Hwai, thence to the Yangtse lake plains and finally to the Sikiang delta. At each advance southward they faced more swamps and danker vegetation which, when under control gave greater returns of food per unit of ground because of better climate and a longer growing season. Every expansion southwards involved a phase of pioneering, then of prolific production per person and finally a full-up phase as population expanded. The prolific phase was always an invitation to attack by less-endowed groups in the western mountains and to immigration from the denser-peopled North China. People pressed into the new areas militarily or peacefully according to circumstances, but the new wealth of food also made possible defensive thrusts back by the lowlanders, military expeditions through the western mountains and the transfer as trade or tribute of southern surplus. Thus the agriculturist in China extended slowly southwards, the merchant transmitted northwards and soldiers fought northwards and westwards. In the Han period (roughly the Roman era), the Yangtse was newly under occupation, enabling large armies to be supported with food whose surplus was the greater by the revolutionary switch to wet rice farming which yielded higher returns than at any other place or with any other crop farther north. The wet-farming method is thought to have

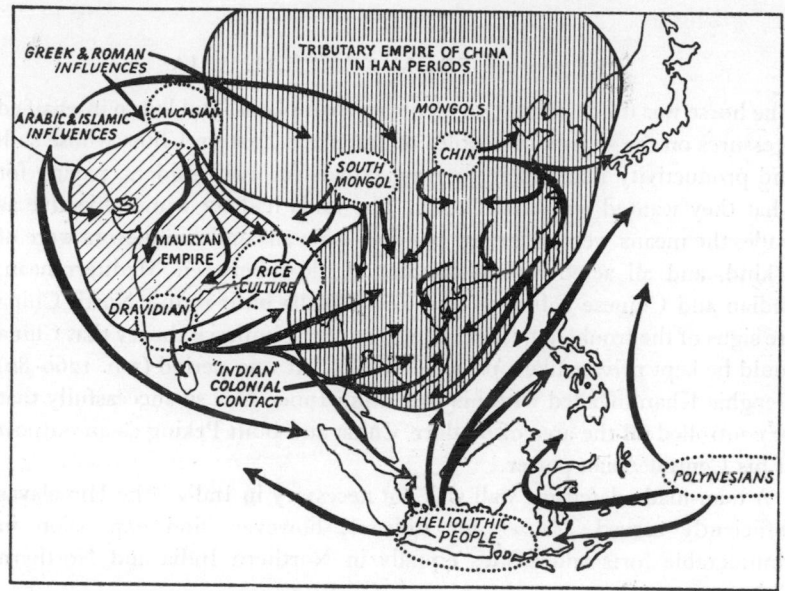

FIG. 12—Historical centres of national growth, and the lines of cultural
and political transmission

been transmitted overland from India. Han armies were supported by the
extension of Chinese economy in the south, but were engaged chiefly along
the trade route through the Tarim Basin where great caravans carried silk,
then unique in Eastern China, to the west (to India and the Levant), and
to the east gold and copper, of which China had poor supplies. As the
Yangtse Plains filled and surplus lessened, economic capacity to maintain
armies and long lines of communications diminished; Chinese inland
influence weakened and pressure came again from Mongolia into the
eastern plains. The last phase of agricultural expansion in China was during
the Tang Dynasty (A.D. 618–906), during which South China was pioneered,
producing much surplus in Canton and a basis for another thrust inland
along the Silk Road, when armies reached as far as the Caspian. Though
the sailing people of Fukien were then absorbed into China, inland waterways remained the characteristic of Eastern China, perpetuated by the
Imperial Canal linking North China to the south and by the maze of
waterways along the Yangtse. A little seagoing transport developed round
the Shantung and Fukien coasts, but the trade and the defence were almost
always directed towards the west and north, not overseas.

PRESSURE FROM CENTRAL ASIA

The horse was domesticated on Central Asian plains, and led to intensified pressures on the sedentary peoples of India and Eastern China whose skill and productivity made them inviting targets for swift raiders, paying for what they wanted only with blows. The raids had the same objective as trade, the means were different. Bandits, caravans and conquerors were of a kind, and all acted as transmitters of ideas between Mediterranean, Indian and Chinese cultures. The Great Walls built round North China are signs of the troubled border, as well as of the imperial theory that China could be kept private like a palace demesne. At one period (A.D. 1260–80) Genghis Khan invaded with his men from Inner Asia so successfully that he controlled all the area of modern China and built Peking as an outpost of his Central Asian power.

A man-made defensive wall was not necessary in India—the Himalayas sufficiently served. Causes for defence, however, find expression in innumerable forts and castles equally in Northern India and Northern China.

Thus over two and a half millennia the two civilisations were increasing and extending farther into the hot, wet tropics, increasing their food resources at every step. While it is doubtful whether the pioneer groups received much technique from the peoples already in the tropical forest, much of the myth in what is now Hinduism may have spread back from the Dravidians. The culture of Southeast Asia today is mostly a much later transfer from India and China or East Tibet.

Agricultural Civilisations

The civilisations of India and China, developed apart in space and only tenuously linked across Central Asia, had features in common. They were agricultural, and their populations were tied to their fields, glorifying in their religions the self-contained, subsistence way of life. Cities were few and small in both places, more like castles or forts than cities of the Greek and Roman type. Local self-containment went with rural autonomy in the feudal manner, and the city state conception did not arise. Merchants were few and their influence limited by barter and other inelastic monetary methods and by transport difficulties. Artisans were for many centuries countrymen with time to spare, and the crafts evolved widely scattered on the self-contained farms. Political authority sat lightly on the stable, slow-moving rural society. Power in India was with those militant horsemen who linked space by speed and the sword, and in China with the mandarins who linked space by a common written language. Both civilisations tied people by economic dependence on direct food production, and through common practices in a religion such as Hinduism or in a code of manners like Confucianism. These circumstances explain the continuity among peoples in India and China despite the vagaries of princes and generals. They had civilisations with a rigidity stemming from manual agricultures based on rice, wheat and millet.

CONTACTS WITH GREEKS, ARABS AND ROMANS

India has been more directly in contact externally; for several centuries after Alexander's expedition in 326 B.C. Greek influence was strong in the northwest, where large parts were later subjugated by Muslims. For several centuries Arabs transferred ideas by sea and land between the Mediterranean and India. They were the chief navigators of the Indian Ocean even before the time of Mohamet (7th century A.D.). They used the monsoon winds for return voyages and regular schedules. They dominated the coastwise and transoceanic movement from Arabia round India to Malaya, Java and Mindanao, proselytising as they went and leaving the present distribution of Islam in Monsoon Asia as a relic of their trade routes.

China was further removed from the Mediterranean and out of direct touch with it until late in history, despite the Silk Road across Asia by which non-Chinese linked the Roman and Han Empires. China's prime cultural contacts were with India by way of Central Asia, partly through third parties, often directly through Buddhist missionaries.

WESTERN NAVIGATORS DISCOVER ASIA

Direct contact between Asia and W. Europe dates only from the fifteenth century, when the European need for Asian goods was great enough to drive European vessels into the Indian Ocean by an entirely new route round Africa, consequent to a breakdown of exchange through Arabia. This discovery completely transformed the trade pattern. The Arabian routes collapsed for several centuries until Suez was opened. Soon Western Europe, South Africa, India, the Malacca Strait, the China coast, California and the Cape of Good Hope became parts of the vastest trading circuit ever known, involving a round-the-world journey. It brought massive cultural contacts, and gradually transformed the orientation of Asians from landward to seaward.

The European sea route followed some patterns already established over small distances by Arabic, Indian and Chinese seamen. It continued for a long time to be limited to coastal contact, not greatly changing the closely knit modes of Asian life. At the Renaissance period, Western traders had greater need for Asian produce, cottons, silk and spices, than Asians had for theirs. In many respects the economic and technical levels in India and China were then higher than those in Western Europe, and the chief superiority of the European was his gun. In quantity and quality Asian textiles were superior to the European, until the Industrial Revolution transformed the productive capacity of the West by engines multiplying the power at men's disposal. Thereafter trade turned increasingly on bulk production, bulk transport and bulk food supplies. This new basis stimulated coastal urbanisation to handle it, induced large outflows of wheat, other foods and raw cotton from India and China, and soon injected into Asia mass-produced textiles. Domestic weaving lost its place in Asian rural life as textiles from Europe proved easier and cheaper to get.

THE INDUSTRIAL REVOLUTION

The Industrial Revolution in Europe thus caused the subsistence mode to begin breaking down. Money became the basis of economic activity instead of barter. Possibly the old systems of India and China had been collapsing under the weight of a great increase of people without a corresponding increase of farmland or productive power, but the undercutting by European merchants completed the collapse and reversed the old balance; whereas Asia had traditionally absorbed gold from the West, Europe began to draw wealth out of Asia. Instead of contacts coming to Asia from landward, they came from seaward, the Europeans reaching India and China from the south. Seaboard sites became the frontiers of innovation and development. Routes internally became oriented to seaboard instead of to riverine or landward foci. Change came fast and massively, increasing as mechanical power introduced steamers and railways handling huge quantities of raw materials and inducing the greatest change in farming since wet farming was invented. Delhi, Peking and Mandalay, the old inland foci, lost significance to seaboard cities like Calcutta, Shanghai and Rangoon. The reorientation, soon underscored by roads and rails, turn Asian countries inside out. The new cities created new outlets for farmstuffs and commerce in Asian foods. Mechanical power helped to reshape the landscape with large-scale irrigation for new farming, and extended the usable land, at first for growing industrial raw materials like

84

cotton and sugar, then for other foods. The stimulus to food production led to opening up the Irrawaddy, Chao Praya and Mekong deltas previously almost empty. There large surpluses of rice were produced by old methods, but the new commerce and new transport enabled the rice to reach distant Asian populations.

Yet until 1914 Asian countries were sources chiefly of raw materials for industrialised Europe and markets for processed goods from Europe. Raw cotton for example, was exported from the Deccan to Britain for manu-facturing cloth, some of which then returned to Asian markets. Europe began to export its capital equipment and machinery, beginning with transport and power equipment, then factory equipment, spinning and weaving machinery. Manufacturing began to take place closer to the raw materials in Asia, at which stage Asia could produce goods cheaper than Europe though made with European methods, thus undercutting twentieth-century Western products as these had previously undercut Asia's craft products. Textile industries became established in Bombay, Calcutta, Shanghai and Osaka, in locations very different from those where Asian weaving had existed earlier; weaving returned to factories in towns and not to cottages in villages. Heavy industries became slowly established by similar processes, and the Industrial Revolution in Asia was well advanced by 1930.

JAPAN, THE PHILIPPINES AND JAVA

Japan exemplifies the change brought by the varying contacts. Off the track of events in Asia, it had been settled by refugees from the mainland and seaborne wanderers from West Pacific islands. In that isolation these continental and island stocks mixed to form a distinctive community operating a farming system learned from the mainland but more complexly developed owing to the limited land available in Japan. Position and form provided for Japanese maritime experience, and when the Industrial Revolution emphasised seaborne association, they were at an advantage, especially later when Japan's coal resources, its accessible and productive coast, its crossroads position between China and North America and its large pool of domestic skill, came into play. Its assets were realised later than elsewhere because Japan for a time shut itself off from outside developments. When that self-imposed policy changed industrialisation took place swiftly, even though the islands were short of most raw materials for industry.

The contrast in other Asian islands is also illuminating. The Philippines, while farther off the main track of Asian events, was squarely athwart the Trade Winds coming from across the Pacific. Its external influences have largely come from that direction. When it was a Spanish colony, it linked as much to Mexico as to Madrid, by sailing routes through the Pacific. In this century the Philippines was a U.S.A. colony, perpetuating the trans-Pacific contact. Local fuel resource being negligible, the American link induced no significant industrialisation but stimulated Filipino sugar and coconut products for export.

Java, on the southern edge of that "green desert" of densely forested equatorial islands, was at one end of a circuit of winds prevailing in the South Indian Ocean. The Trade Winds could carry large European sailing vessels from Java to Africa. Such vessels could use the westerlies to cross the South Indian Ocean from South Africa, and then the off-shore winds from Australia to bear northwards to Java. This circular sailing route in the South Indian Ocean helps to account for the presence of Malay people in Ceylon, Cape Town and Madagascar, and was the pattern of pre-Suez Dutch trade overseas. The Indonesian population is related racially to the Pacific because their islands lie west of the Pacific Trade Wind belt so that island-hopping people have continually reached them from the Central Pacific, the similarity between Indonesians and Pacific Islanders being striking even though now overlaid by cultural traits derived long ago from Indian colonists moving through the Malacca Strait. South Indians introduced rice to Indonesia in historic times, Indonesians having previously been sweet-potato and yam farmers like Pacific islanders.

MIGRATION INTO SOUTHEAST ASIA

In continental Southeast Asia, migration and development were slowed by the terrain. From overland there is the obstacle of broken relief and thick forest so that entry from the north has been limited to hill clans drifting south and slowing down in the difficult terrains. Whatever these people had in common to start with, they became increasingly different by evolving in separate diverging valleys. Differentiation was complex: some remained valley-bottom clans and others hilltop clans. They have features in common racially and linguistically with Mongoloid people, but lack the uniformity reached by China's Mongoloids during millennia of a unifying society. They are known as South Mongoloids, most prominent being the clan of Tais (or Thais), most numerous in Siam and Burma. Their names, languages and beliefs vary within short distances, and they mixed with more primitive peoples already living in the south. Towards the seaward

86

fringe of continental Southeast Asia, the South Mongoloids came into touch with seaborne colonists from South India, who transmitted rice growing and religious ideas to the South Mongoloids whose chief centres of interest remained inland and upstream until last century.

Overland movement into Southeast Asia was easiest to the east, where Tonkin was frequently incorporated in the Chinese Empire. On the western side, the Brahmaputra, Khasi Hills and Arakan Yoma were forbidding obstacles, dividing the South Mongoloid stream rather than facilitating movements from India into Burma.

ADMINISTRATIVE COLONIES

The later phase of European association with Asia was the acquisition of colonies, not for settlement but for administration. The fringe of Asia was thus divided into units tied to different states in Europe so that some of the divergences peculiar to Europe were added to the differences and divergences which had already evolved from local Asian conditions. Indonesia was linked to the Netherlands, the Indochinese countries to France, India, Burma, Ceylon and Malaya to Britain, Macao and Timor to Portugal and the Philippines to Spain and later U.S.A. China as a whole was a colony only to the medieval empire of the Khans in Central Asia; parts of its coast were administered by Westerners as treaty ports. The administrative colonies often originated as warehouses or "factories" for trading interests. The colonial approach from the coasts dominated Asia in the late nineteenth century, introducing technical changes enabling a quicker rate of development than was possible by local organisation. Through the colonial association, Asian countries have evolved to their place in the modern world.

THE TWENTIETH CENTURY

Seaborne trade became so great that at the turn of this century the going and coming of ships along the Asian seaboard was probably greater than along any other sea lane of the world. Japan developed a mercantile marine to rival that of Europe, which once monopolised the Asian seas. Seaborne Japanese products and power quickly came into conflict with those of other seaborne powers, climaxing in World War II. The militarist form of industrial and maritime strength in Japan was occluded in 1945 by seaborne military strength based on the greater economic and industrial power of U.S.A. across the Pacific. At that stage the European resource was so preoccupied in the West that it could not be mounted against Japan in the

Indian Ocean before the trans-Pacific thrust had proved fatal. China's contribution to the war was negligible, the country had disintegrated so much that neither supplies nor organisation were available.

In the second half of the twentieth century, old patterns are reappearing in Asia. Central Asia resumes its old relation in new terms. The Chinese extension back through Tibet as far as the border of Kashmir revives the imperial pattern of Han times. Modern China's "bamboo curtain" repeats the isolation of its past. India resumes its place as a textile producer on a large scale, now in factory instead of cottage. The Western colonies have evolved into independent states, often called "succession states", and some older local political units have revived—as in Cambodia.

The present economic and political development in Asia is more fully reviewed in Part V.

CHAPTER NINE

Regions of Monsoon Asia

GROUPING MONSOON ASIA into regions in which the relation between peoples and places is distinctive is made difficult by the great size and long history of the area. Three major realms may first be distinguished, each being part of Asia's continental fringe and adjoining the cold, high and bare plateau of Tibet. The realms are: *Southern Asia*, lying south of the Tibetan mass, *Eastern Asia* sprawling east of it and *Southeast Asia* which fans southward from a narrow mountainous neck in Eastern Tibet.

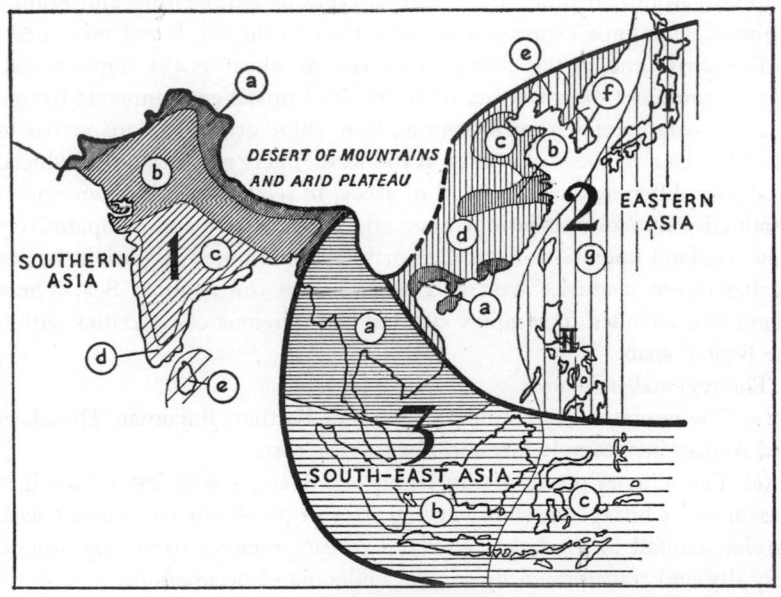

FIG. 13—Regions of Monsoon Asia. The numbers and letters are those used in the text

1. *Southern Asia* is a subcontinent, everywhere distinguishable from its surroundings by the circumstance that the arcuate Indus–Ganges–Brahmaputra Plain adjoins the steep, high mountains of the Himalayas and its

offshoots, so that physical change is evident at once both to people looking from the subcontinent towards Tibet and to those approaching it from Tibet. Its inland boundary is a high mountainous watershed.

The geographical relation of Southern Asia turns upon life in its huge sweep of low-lying alluvial plains and on its lightly etched plateaux of great antiquity. Trapezoidal and compact in form, the realm lies roughly symmetrical to the Tropic, warm throughout the year and subject to an annual interplay of two air streams, from the Continent and from the Indian Ocean respectively. In adjustment to the hot-season rains, vegetation is deciduous, and the streams which originate within this realm fluctuate widely. So prolonged and intensive has been the use of its surface by a dense population of small-scale cereal farmers using cattle as their source of power, that little of its landscape is in a natural state.

The regions constituting this realm are distinguished by different combinations of the dominants. From south to north they develop changes of emphasis from maritime to continental types of temperature and rainfall régimes. This finds expression in more trees to the south and more grass to the north, and in the change from rice to wheat as the staple cereal. Ceylon combines most features of an insular tropical environment; Bengal is a wet, continental tropical region; from these are transitions across to the Thar Desert, focus of aridity in the west. There are variations induced locally by differences of relief and of aspect in relation to wind movement. Distinctive human associations have arisen by massive and comparatively slow overland migrations from the northwest, and quick migrations by sea during recent centuries west and south across the Arabian Sea. These migrations have led to complex cultural and religious complexities within the limited space.

The regional units are:

(a) The mountainous boundary ranges of Kirthar, Sulaiman, Himalaya and Arakan increasingly forested towards the east.

(b) The alluvial plains of the Indus and Ganges with extensions into Assam and Chittagong. Here varying sizes of piedmont fan interact with varying rainfall to produce a lowland culture ranging from very wet to very dry and transformed by several millennia of occupation.

(c) The uplands and plateaux of the Deccan have structural complexities accentuated by erosion. Dry and difficult to deal with, it has some riverine alluvials which are the foci of drier types of cultivation separated by eroded ridges and basaltic mesas. More negative in history and development than areas surrounding it, the Deccan has been a zone of economic transit and cultural transition between areas marginal to it.

(*d*) The coastal plains east and west of the Deccan are narrow, abundantly watered, intensively cultivated for rice, and identified with modes of living associated with both land and sea which here, unique in South Asia, are closely related, greatly affecting the development and contacts of local people. To the south, the eastern and western coastal plains are the nursery of Dravidian peoples.

(*e*) Ceylon, the one major island outlier, is by its position and form distinctive in equability, uniformity and extensive forested cover, but is otherwise an extension of conditions and developments in Southern India.

2. The limits of *Eastern Asia* are not sharply distinguishable on the continental side. The Tibetan Highlands gradually merge into the ranges and plateaux of the Great Snowy Mountains and the Tsin Ling. The arid basins of Ninghsia and Gobi similarly merge into the dry landscapes of Northwestern China; the frozen mountains of Kinghan merge with the great blocks of Eastern Siberia. The Toyen Shan is little different from both the South China Upland and the Annam Highland. The inner boundary thus lies athwart the lines of structure and of rivers broken, and quite different in kind from the Himalayan boundary to Southern Asia. The core areas of Eastern Asia in population, history and development are the easternmost plains—the North China Plain, the Yangtse Lowlands and the Canton Delta. Each plain is different from the others as well as differing from the uplands round it. Off shore lies a huge belt of islands of which Japan, Taiwan and the Philippines are the main groups.

This realm lies mostly north of the Tropic, which implies greater seasonal variations of insolation. Temperature varies also with increasing distance from the coast inland, but is most equable through the year on the islands. Because this is a broken terrain stretching into latitudes where winter cold becomes significant, variations are great within short distances, accentuating or neutralising the seasonal interplay between a westerly air stream of continental origin and a southerly one of maritime origin. Natural vegetation, by now extensively eliminated after prolonged exploitation by people, changes from tropical evergreen in the south and upon the islands, to deciduous forest in the north and to annual grasses in the west. Activity and population gravitates to the plains everywhere, yet only to a limited extent are they maritime, so that landward associations are nearly everywhere greater than seaward. The drainage pattern is one of west to east lines and dominates the lines of movement.

Here has evolved an intensive agriculture based on rice in the south and east and on wheat and kaoliang to the north and west; but a feature everywhere is mixed farming. Human associations of Eastern Asia have for many centuries been by way of the northwest, with some along the valleys from Eastern Tibet. In the insular section, migration has been from the mainland and from the southern islands. For millennia slow movements of people occurred from the continent into the plains. More recently there have been swift, massive movements of people and ideas by sea, with greatest effects on the islands and at the coasts.

The Eastern Asia regions are:

(a) The small, coastal alluvial plains of Canton and Vietnam have the South China Upland to surround and isolate them. A definitely tropical and evergreen region, it is more intimately related to sea-going than anywhere else in the continental part of the realm. Less homogeneous than the Deccan, the South China Upland has functioned like it in several respects, but is more compacted and continental, with pockets of coastal plain in contrast to the ribbons each side of the Deccan.

(b) The plains along the Yangtse differ in structure and size from those south or north of them. Densely peopled, they form a region with an agriculture of unique intensity. The perennial Yangtse has acted as a transport link between the plains, the interior and the coast. The most productive region of China, it combines everything characteristic of China.

(c) The plain of North China is comparable to the Indo-Gangetic Plain in extent, and in function as the nursery of Chinese tradition and economy. Flat and alluvial by origin, it is everywhere much farther north than its Indian counterpart, but resembles it in variations from wet tropical farming in the south, transitional northwestwards into arid environments. While the uplands rise distinctively from it, the plain has extensions through them, so that the Tsin Ling–Shansi–Kinghan Mountains by no means function as continuous barriers on the continental side. Intense cold in winter, increasing aridity and overland accessibility are factors to the north, yet the plain has supported an exceptionally dense population. To some extent neutralised by the deep penetrations of the Gulf of Chihli and the Yellow Sea, the latitude combines with proximity to Central Asia to subject this region to continental extremes of climate and to continental cultural links. The plain almost surrounds the block uplands of Shantung.

(d) The Western Mountains, a complex "block and basin" country, is more continental than maritime, suffering extremes of temperature and aridity. Marginal to Monsoon Asia, it has become associated with it more by migration from the eastern plains than by similarities of environment.

(e) The plains of Manchuria form a region which, by northern latitude, by its surround of pine-covered mountains and by isolation from most streams of development in Eastern Asia, remained little developed until this century. Flanked by cold highlands, its general environment, climatic cycle and agricultural development resemble that of the Middle West of the U.S.A. more than other parts of Monsoon Asia.

(*f*) Korea is an anomaly in Eastern Asia, a highland peninsula subject to hard winters and virtually isolated from the mainland by difficult terrain, yet with small plains sufficiently sheltered along its southwestern coasts to permit an agriculture based on rice despite a short growing season. Developed by migrants from the North China Plain and more recently by colonisation from Japan across the narrow Japan Sea, it forms a region transitional between Siberia and Japan.

(*g*) Japan and the islands southwards to the Philippines, Taiwan and the Moluccas form an insular region where distance from the mainland, volcanoes and small maritime lowlands form a combination of characteristics different from those of continental China. More equable than the continent itself, latitude for latitude, and permitting tropical plants to extend through them well to the north, the islands differ between themselves by their varying extent, position and exposure to the continental winter climate. Historically the association of this "palisade" of islands has been with the continent, but pressure towards them from the continent was never strong. An old racial association with Indonesians and Polynesians can be traced. In modern times maritime traders from the west came to the islands both from the south (through the China Sea) and from across the Pacific Ocean. The region continues southwards in the Celebes and Lesser Sunda Groups, where, however, the influence of the Asian mainland is negligible and the climate equatorial. Within the "island palisade" it is possible to distinguish the following subdivisions:

I. *Japan*, which by latitude is temperate in location and climate though tropical in its form of agricultural development.

II. *Taiwan* and the *Philippines* are tropical by location and climate, with much forest and wet-farming.

3. *Southeast Asia* is in contact with the Tibetan Highlands only in a difficult mountainous terrain, which is repeated to a lesser degree through the Arakan–Yoma and the Annam Highlands, the continental limits of this unit. Its feature is a series of peninsulas and islands thrust well out from "the heart of Asia". Through them have slowly moved people from Eastern Tibet and from the Central Pacific Islands. It has been influenced by Asia through seaborne contacts with people passing between Eastern and Southern Asia through the peninsulas and islands. The roughly north–south pattern of the landforms occurs in conjunction with a roughly fan-wise pattern of shallow seas. The major units off shore are islands on a

93

continental shelf whose water-level has varied so that several times there has been a continuous land connection with the mainland and consequent link in flora and fauna. Symmetrical roughly to Lat. 5° N. the realm is exclusively within the tropics, and much is covered by equatorial evergreen forest which has presented difficulties of clearing. Across the realm play the Trade Winds which, despite their seasonal changes of direction, produce similar conditions over large parts of the realm. Seasonal variations in rainfall are related largely to relief, and most emphatic on the continental side. Agriculture here is a mixture of tropical and equatorial types. Southeast Asia is in general more thinly peopled, less elaborately exploited and more recently developed than either of the two other realms, differing from them by the pioneering in modern times on the basis of Indian and Chinese migrants and commercial agriculture for European markets.

The realm divides into three parts:

(a) Its continental portion stretches as far south as 6° N., where the Kra Isthmus is so long, narrow and thinly peopled that it functions to isolate rather than to link. Here the longitudinal patterns of forested mountains and valleys, and the seasonal alternation of winds blowing athwart them, have led to distinct wet and dry seasons in the intermontane plains. Here the human stock is strongly influenced by Mongoloid strains derived from ancient migration overland.

(b) Its insular portion includes Malaya and the "continental shelf" islands of Sumatra, Java and Borneo. Here an equatorial uniformity of climate and forest cover is the dominant note. The indigenes are more Polynesian than Mongoloid, and strongly influenced by recent seaborne contacts from South India, Arabia and Europe.

(c) To the east is the island group, from Mindanao to the Lesser Sundas, which includes a string of equatorial islands, warm and wet throughout the year. Their landscape is dominated by evergreen forest upon young volcanic mountains, and by a mode of living and human stock more Polynesian than Asian. Marginal to the Southeast Asian realm, these islands are transitional between Japan and India on the one side and the mid-Pacific islands on the other.

Part II

Eastern Asia

CHAPTER TEN

Landscape Types and Coastal Plains

LANDSCAPE TYPES

IN EASTERN ASIA human activity concentrates on alluvial plains. The North China Plain, the Lake Plains of the Yangtse, the inland Plain of Chengtu and the deltaic plains of Kwangtung and Tonkin support two out of three Chinese, whose culture now is identified with broad, flat terrains. Mountains have functioned for them as nurseries for invaders, bandits and calamities, and as refuge from the plain's monotonous toil.

These plains can be exemplified in maps of two parts of the largest— that of North China which is nearly 600 miles from north to south and extends inland for about 300 miles without rising above 40 feet, and with only gentle slopes except for man-made dykes, walls and mounds. It ranges over the latitudes from Istanbul to Cairo and across an area one and a half times that of Great Britain.

The landscape in Fig. 14, a sample of the northern half of the North China Plain, is 50 miles north of the Hwang,[1] where the level varies a foot or so either side of 30 feet though the sea is 55 miles away. Local relief is dominated by man-made embankments (bunds) to confine the fluctuating streams, which have built beds higher than the general level with the heavy load they bring from the yellow loess country to the west. So dry does this landscape become (note the scarcity of feeder streams) that for several summer months the bunds flank dry beds; rain here averages less than 20 inches annually, coming in spring and late summer, but offset by a very porous soil and by steady, desiccating, dusty westerlies.

The Grand Canal, here an old Hwang distributary remodelled, is for grain transport to Peking, a function duplicated on this map by the more modern Tientsin–Pukow Railway. Its water is erratic and the Canal may be empty for months. Ineffective for years, the Canal is a slighter mark on the landscape than its history might suggest. Many embankments are broken, indicating how calamitous some seasonal spates have been, setting people the problem not merely of repair but also of getting water back to the

[1] Hw is often written Hu so that the Hwang and Hwai may be spelt Huang and Huai.

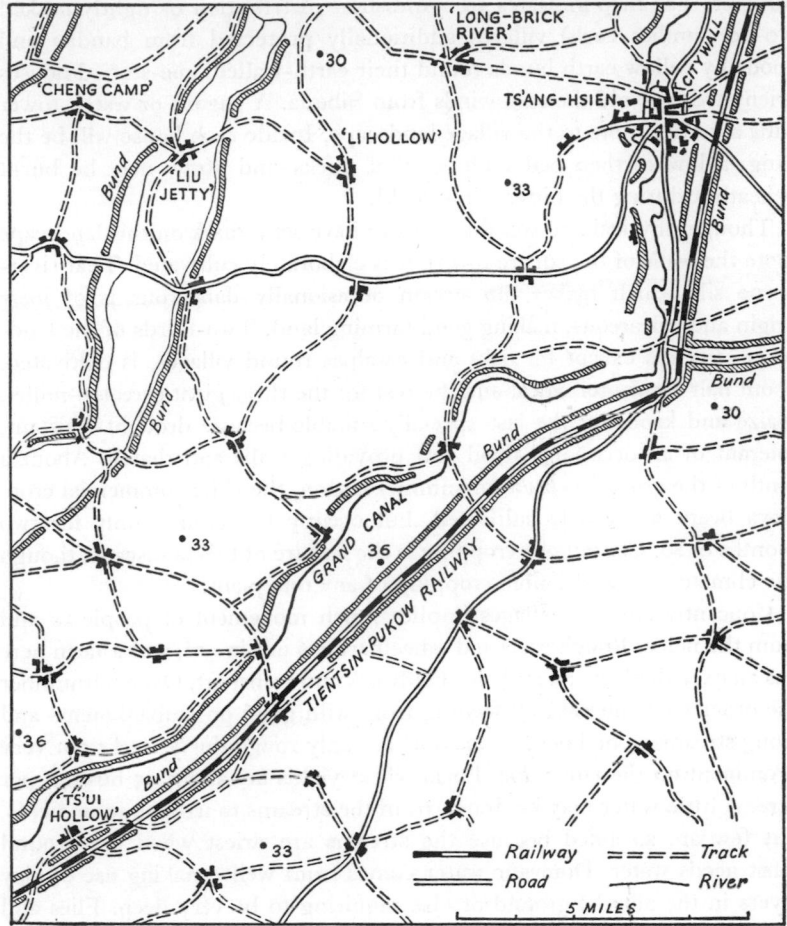

FIG. 14—Yellow Plain landscape from a topographic map centring on
38° 13′ N., 116° 46′ E.

original channel from slightly lower surroundings. Some of these depressions are left water-logged and stagnant until naturally evaporated. They may be left to reeds for years, or used for winter wheat crops harvested before the water reappears. Other floods leave patches of sterile gravels. The struggle with local floods, broken embankments and irregular distributaries is added to the struggle to produce crops from a dry terrain, gripped by hard frosts in winter and afflicted by hot, dusty winds in summer. The map indicates an equidistant distribution of tightly packed (50–60 families each) villages additionally protected from bandits and floods by yellow earth bunds round their earth-walled, one-storied houses orientated to avoid the cold winds from Siberia. A pagoda or watch-tower adds a vertical note to the village landscape. Inside each house will be the kang, a low earthen bed built so that sticks and straw may be burnt beneath it during the bitter winter cold.

Though physical and social insecurity have set a mark on this landscape (note the walls of the square town), it is elaborately cultivated. That river-borne silt which makes the stream occasionally dangerous is of loess origin and calcareous, making good farming land. Two-thirds of the landscape, treeless except for oaks and catalpas round villages, is cultivated, about half for winter wheat and the rest for the three giant cereals—millet, maize and kaoliang; the last specially suitable because drought-resistant, tolerant of an occasional flood and providing walls and thatch. About a tenth of the ground is used for summer cotton, the chief commercial crop. Soya beans are widely cultivated, but occupy the ground only for two months or so. Continuous cropping is the feature of this landscape, though the climate prevents double cropping of any one plant.

Concentration into villages implies much movement of people to and from the fields. Rough carts and wheelbarrows are in use, and a farm here has an ox, a donkey or a mule for fieldwork and transport. Oxen outnumber the other farm animals, all feeding from wild grass on embankments and along streams. The lines of transport are only rough dusty tracks not very prominent on the landscape. Local wheat yields are about 15 bushels per acre. A little water may be drawn from the streams to irrigate some fields, but few are so aided because the streams are driest when the ground most needs water. Domestic water comes from wells, making use of clay layers in the alluvial ground or else requiring to be very deep. Flies and insects add to the health risks during the dry, hot summer. The chief pest is the locust which periodically devastates the millet and kaoliang.

Fig. 15 shows a landscape far south on the North China Plain at a point 50 miles north of the Yangtse. It includes another part of the Grand Canal which is flanked by one embankment and an earth road. Dykes are numerous everywhere in this landscape, whose levels vary only a foot or two from 25 feet above sea-level. Large areas are poldered to keep out the flood water from local streams and lakes. It is an "amphibious" landscape where local rains and overflows from the Yangtse combine with sheet floods from the Hwai to the northwest, so that the cultivator struggles always against excess water. Many straight "streams" are man-dug drains.

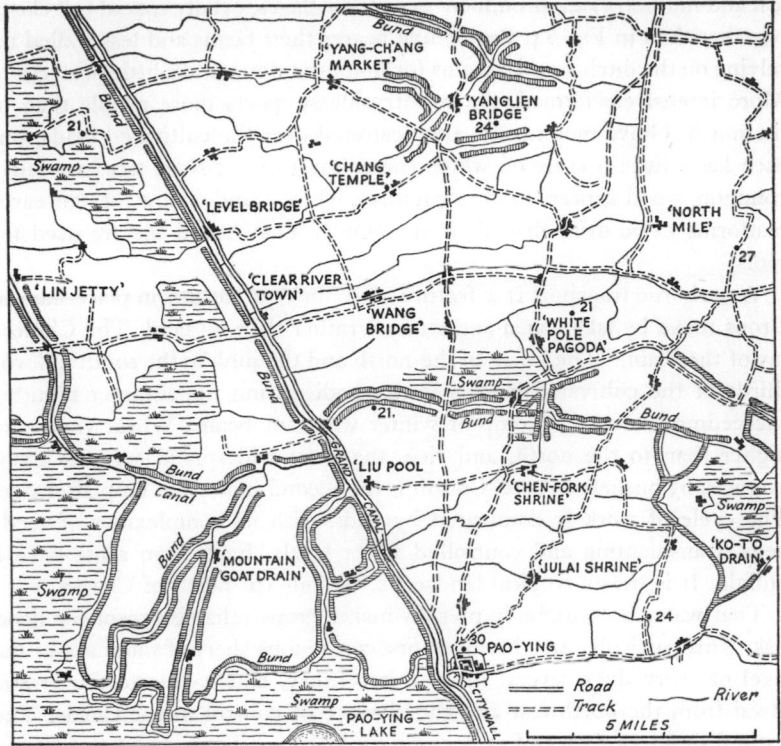

FIG. 15—The southern part of the North China Plain from a topographic
map centring on 33° 20′ N., 119° 20′ E.

The farms and fields are surrounded with dead-end arms and ditches of
water whose form while roughly square has a wavy outline due to being
unsurveyed and cut by hand with a large hoe which suits the soft soil. Here
is the water-logged landscape in which Chinese wet-farming techniques
evolved, reclaiming from swamps and lakes and manipulating water levels
to produce high yields. The map shows the reticulated outlines of reclamation, and also how the embankment of the Grand Canal protects from flood
large areas east of it.

Wet-farming here goes hand in hand with year-round cultivation. The
Janurary mean is well above freezing-point and any snow is short-lived.
Summers are hot and enervating. The alluvium here is darkish red or
blackened by humus content; a different origin and high temperature
make it non-calcareous. Evergreen broad-leaved trees (willows, rosewood,

99

ash and mulberry) are prominent near the villages, evenly spread but closer together than in Fig. 14. People live nearer their farms and less walled in, relying on the ditches and streams for domestic water and a little protection. More intensively farmed, the countryside supports more people than to the north. Grave mounds are also scattered over the cultivated fields, but each has a little pasture on which the animals graze; since trees are fairly common, wood appears in the structures, which stand on low, beaten-earth platforms to be drier than their surrounds. Thatch and tile are used for roofs.

Waterborne transport is a feature, and "bridge" recurs in place-names. Crops move by lake, canal and stream, rather than on land. The Chinese say of the Plain, "The horse to the north and the junk to the south". Two-thirds of the cultivated land is under padi during the summer months, succeeding a secondary crop of winter wheat or beans. Wheat yields are higher than to the north, and rice, the most widespread summer crop, averages 63 bushels an acre. Cotton is the second important crop after rice. The cycle of work is dominated by padi, with its complexities of seed-beds, transplanting and controlled water levels. Each farm must have a buffalo. It is thus a tropical landscape, though 10° north of Cancer.

That water is continually present makes crops reliable except for flood risk. This particular area has been one continuous sheet of water above the level of every dyke several times this century, chiefly due to the erratic Hwai from the northwest and the absence of control in the canals. The natural drainage pattern has become confused, particularly by the Grand Canal embankment which renders the Hwai without natural outlet to the sea. Hwai water normally ends in "lake country", but in spate the distinction between it, the lakes, the fields and the Yangtse is lost.

Hills and coasts are prominent in Eastern Asia, and Fig. 16 exemplifies them together east of Kobe, on Japan's Inland Sea. The Tarumi coast between two stretches of hills has been smoothed by reclamation, by long-shore drift and by protective sea-walls. Hills are left in woodland (evergreen firs and conifers) or badly eroded into rock exposures where the natural timber has been too intensively cut for fuel or buildings. Settlement is "foot of hill" in location, and productive land-use concentrates on valley bottom. Tarumi town is sited on the coast in "foot of hill" position, pre-serving a maximum of alluvial plain for farming.

Here are elaborate water-control arrangements. The valley bottom is dominated by wet-farming, with rice as the key cereal cropped twice a year because over 220 days are frost-free. At "foot of hill" location and in side valleys are artificial lakes serving to safeguard the valley from "flash spates" during heavy showers on the steep landforms, and to conserve run-off for irrigation. Ponds of this type occur from Japan to the Canton Delta. By thus conserving run-off, the river is reduced to little more than a drainage canal, except during storms when it quickly rises over the banks built to offset this risk as well as to hold water on the fields. Conservation is vital in such a hilly landscape and reflects not low rainfall (on the area shown the rainfall is about 70 inches per annum), but the need for water control when cultivating year-round in a region of seasonal rains. The ponds

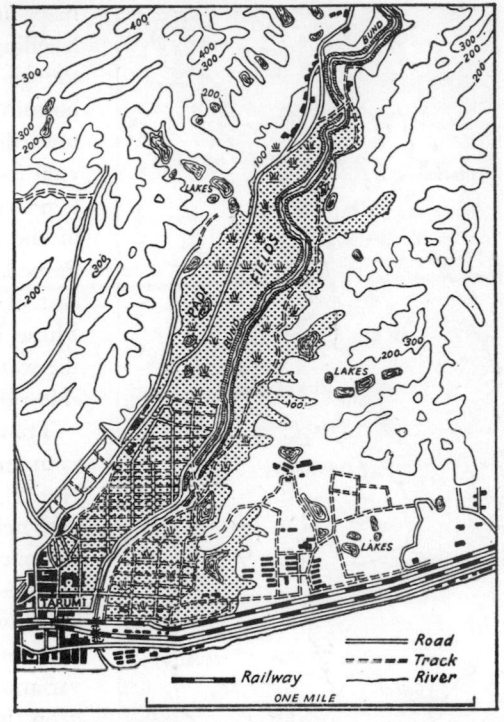

FIG. 16—Japanese coastal landscape, from a topographic map centring on 34° 39′ N., 135° 4′ E.

and lakes on this map are primarily for farming, but may be used for fish culture also.

The squared pattern of fields, paths and canals in the lower valley relates to the high water-table at a position where swamp is the natural condition, and the need for subsurface drainage as well as irrigation presents complex problems only adequately solved by a modern "engineered" landscape. In the lowest levels of this valley, two crops of rice and short-term vegetables are grown. Inland where the valley bottom is 10 feet or so higher and subsurface drainage is greater, summer rice and winter wheat are cropped.

The one-storied houses are mostly of timber even in the towns. Farm-houses are withdrawn from the fields to lines near the hills, for shelter from wind and for springs for domestic water. Fruit-trees and bamboos stand close to the houses. Earth or bamboo walls and moats may remain. Terracing is not a widespread feature and registers poorly on topographic

FIG. 17—Eastern Asia and its
sea approaches

maps in any case. Bunding and levelling are characteristic even on the gentle inclines of the valley bottom, but are more frequent towards the sides. The terrace, vital for wet agriculture on slopes, is restricted to low levels because of the difficulty of raising water. Some high-level padi is to be seen east of the middle of the valley, where irrigating is possible using the water of high-level ponds in a side valley.

Transport inland is limited, and even tracks peter out in the hills. Here the associations of people are with neighbouring valleys on either side along the coast so that movement is by the coast, particularly by railway (here a multiple track between Kobe and Osaka). Many variations of these forms occur, deep indentations being equally common and serving to provide shelter for boats. This example indicates no sea-going interests, but the light fishing vessels customary in Eastern Asia will be drawn up on the beach.

Critical facts for farming under the climates operating over Eastern Asia's countrysides are exemplified in Table 1, which permits estimating the proportion of rain falling in the period June–September from place to place. It will be noted that each month with a temperature above the lower limit for padi is almost everywhere rainy and therefore satisfies another condition for padi growing. The table should be compared with that for Southern Asia, where the concept of a "wet monsoon" rainfall régime originated.

TABLE I

EASTERN ASIA'S RAINFALLS AND PADI-GROWING TEMPERATURES

	J.	F.	M.	Ap.	My.	Ju.	Jy.	Ag.	S.	O.	N.	D.	Months with Means over 50 F.[1]	Mid-year Daylight Hours[2]
Continental:														
Harbin . .	0·2	0·2	0·4	0·9	1·7	4·1	5·8	4·2	2·2	1·2	0·4	0·2	My.–Sept.	15·5
Seoul . .	1·1	0·9	1·5	2·9	3·7	4·3	15·1	10·1	4·2	1·6	1·8	1·0	My.–Oct.	14·6
Peking .	0·1	0·2	0·3	0·6	1·3	3·3	9·8	5·7	2·3	0·7	0·3	0·1	Ap.–Oct.	14·8
Sian . .	0·1	0·1	0·7	1·6	2·3	2·5	2·9	4·0	3·5	2·0	0·3	0·1	My.–Oct.	14·2
Shanghai .	1·9	2·3	3·3	3·7	3·7	7·1	5·8	5·6	5·1	2·8	2·0	1·4	Ap.–Nov.	14·0
Hankow .	1·8	1·9	3·6	5·8	7·0	9·0	7·0	4·1	3·0	3·1	1·9	1·2	My.–Nov.	14·0
Chungking .	0·7	0·8	1·5	3·9	5·7	7·2	5·5	5·0	5·8	4·3	1·9	0·8	My.–Dec.	13·8
Hong Kong .	1·1	1·5	3·0	5·2	11·6	15·6	15·4	14·5	11·5	5·0	1·5	1·1	All	13·5
Kunming .	0·5	0·4	0·4	0·7	3·6	6·2	9·9	9·2	5·2	3·8	2·0	0·6	Feb.–Nov.	13·6
Hanoi .	1·0	1·3	1·9	3·6	8·4	10·4	11·1	13·9	10·5	4·3	2·0	1·2	All	13·3
Insular:														
Sapporo .	3·5	2·6	2·4	2·2	2·7	2·8	3·3	3·7	5·0	4·6	4·4	3·9	My.–Sept.	15·2
Tokyo .	2·0	2·6	4·3	5·3	5·9	6·3	5·6	4·6	7·5	7·2	4·3	2·3	Ap.–Nov.	14·5
Taipeh .	3·5	5·5	7·2	6·6	8·9	12·0	8·9	11·5	8·8	4·4	2·4	2·8	All	13·5
Manila .	0·8	0·6	0·6	1·5	7·5	10·1	21·5	19·0	15·5	8·9	7·4	3·7	All	12·8
Zamboanga .	2·1	2·2	1·5	2·0	3·5	4·2	4·9	4·0	4·7	5·7	4·2	3·4	All	12·5

[1] Months listed inclusively.   [2] Summer solstice

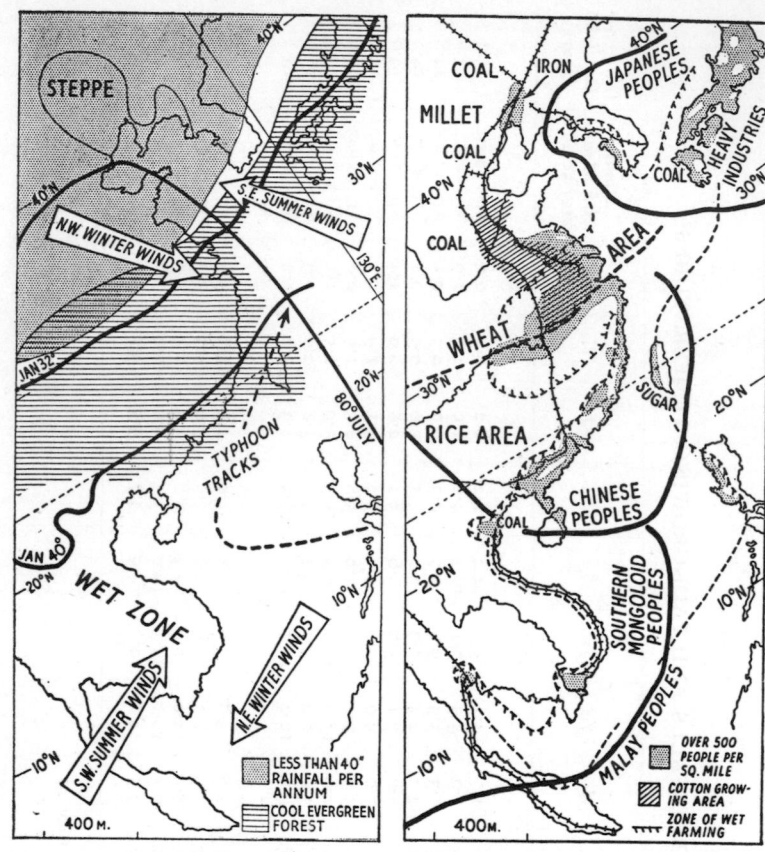

FIG. 18—Eastern Asia:
Physical Features

FIG. 19—Eastern Asia: Population,
Economy and Race

THE COASTAL PLAINS OF EASTERN CHINA

The North China Plain

Of China's plains, that in the north is the largest as well as the longest occupied. Today the North China Plain supports more than the entire population of North America. One of the world's major alluvial features, it is
constituted by a thickness of at least 300 feet of riverborne materials, chiefly
from the Hwang, Hwai and the Yangtse, which are still extending its surface seaward and building up its level.

Water Régimes on the Plain

The problem of dealing with its surface for securing crops and assuring settlement still turns upon the deltaic régimes and silting processes of the rivers crossing North China. (*a*) The Yangtse, drawing its waters from so vast a basin and from so many varied, well-watered sources, flows regularly in its deltaic section, and its load is the less troublesome because its Lake Plains inland serve to equalise both the flow of water and its silt content. Inland at Hankow and Kiukang the seasonal difference of level in the Yangtse averages about 35 feet, while at Chinkiang towards the mouth it is only 12 feet. (*b*) In the Hwai, due in part to the debris thrust from the north across its outlet by the migrating Hwang, and in part to the Grand Canal whose main bund lies athwart the direction of discharge, the river has no well-defined mouth. Complicating its régime is the east-facing and much deforested catchment basin, in which spates develop quickly during the on-shore, rain-bearing winds of summer. The river being short, a spate from upstream reaches the coastal plain immediately after it has already been soaked by rains of the same storm. (*c*) In the case of the Hwang, the regulating effect of great length is largely offset because the river passes through great areas of arid climate whence it receives few tributaries. Its silt load is unusual because the river carries a high content of finely divided loess material, which settles only in the long stretches across the plain, where the water impetus is very low, rainfall light, tributaries few and evaporation high. The Wei, much shorter and therefore more erratic, is effectively responsible for most fluctuations in the lower Hwang water-levels. Floods, however, are less due to rise of water and more to the river drifting sideways, corroding its sides and moving from a heavily silted bed to the lower levels either side of its levees. (*d*) The plain round Peking and Tientsin is dominated by the many short, mountain streams which contribute to form the Hai. Their steep, intermittent flow from the largely deforested Shansi Mountains implies well-marked seasonal variations of volume so that silting takes place as fairly steep piedmont fans complicated farther out on the Yellow Plain by the barrier of old Hwang levees and the Grand Canal running across the lie of the land, preventing streams taking the shortest course to the sea.

The Grand Canal almost everywhere has complicated the problem of drainage on the North China Plain, and has itself gradually built up the level of its original bed by prolonged silting. It therefore subjects the near-by areas to the same risks of overflow as the Hwang, which for a long time before 1938 tended to run along the Canal itself and abandon its

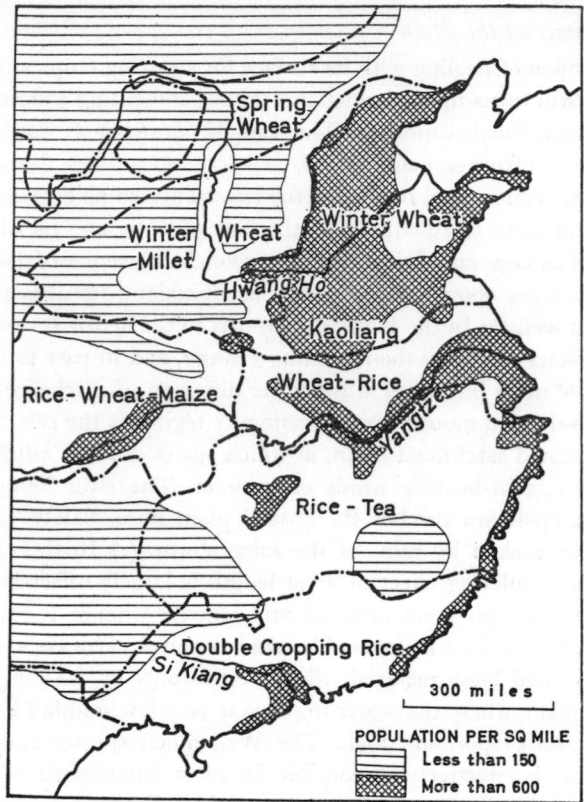

FIG. 20—The coastal plains of China: Population and
Crops

distributaries to the north. The Canal, remarkable feature as it was in its
time, was never "locked", and it has become in places (Fig. 15) a series of
ribbonlike, fluctuating lakes west of the original bund, now acting like a vast
earthen dam. Much of the drainage difficulty on the Plain is thus man-
made. For twenty centuries dykes have been built by slow, manual methods
in an attempt to bring the discharge (of the Hwang in particular) under
control, but the scale has never so far been adequate for long at a time
and the maintenance of dykes and bunds has often been interrupted. The
Plain thus inherits centuries of technical inadequacy for the volumes of
water and silt involved. The uplands of Shantung directly in line with the
valley where the Hwang discharges from Shansi and Honan Mountains,

form a natural impediment conducive to dramatic changes like the shift of the Hwang outlet hundreds of miles at a time. It has been claimed that human occupation of the Plain has taken place too early in geographical time, before its mature consolidation and grading.

The Yellow Plain

In that northern portion known as "the Yellow Plain", dominated by the Hwang and the Hai, the building up by sedimentation conflicts with agricultural land use. Embankments intended to prevent natural floods have confined silting to the river-

FIG. 21—Physical features of the North China Plain

bed, gradually raising it and leading to calamity when an embankment breaks and the discharge moves to the lower level of the surrounding countryside to assume a new course. The Hwang, whose load is heavy, has repeatedly changed course (hence its nickname "China's Sorrow"), and at one time or another has entered the sea at points varying from well north of Tientsin to as far south as the Yangtse whose waters it has sometimes joined. In 1938 the Hwang was for strategic reasons diverted from a course north of Shantung to an old southerly course south of it, where the river then merged with the Hwai, the intention being by this means to flood great areas of the Yellow Plain and impede military movements into North China. The long-term effect was to add more silts to the already confused drainage pattern and water-logged landscape of the lower Hwai and round the southern sector of the Grand Canal. That it should be possible to divert the Hwang outlet several hundreds of miles indicates the low level of the plain, its irregular surface and the ease with which devastating floods and gigantic changes can here be caused by slight changes in the levees or dykes.

The Hwang is the master river of the Plain. It discharges from a narrow valley near Honanfu, rapidly loses impetus and begins to drop its load.

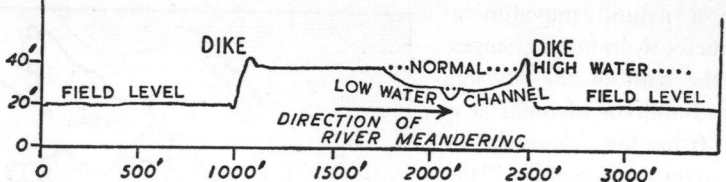

FIG. 22—A section across the Hwang-Ho on the North China Plain

No tributary joins the Hwang on the Plain—a sign both of local dryness and how its bed is built up above the general level. The irregular rivers from the Shansi mountains drain northwestward separately to join the meandering Hai (on which Tientsin stands), whose course across the Plain is probably an old Hwang distributary. The Yellow Plain is everywhere dry (mostly less than 25 inches of rain per annum), almost treeless and subject to seasonal temperature extremes from 110° in summer to a winter cold able regularly to freeze the Hai to its mouth. Bitter, dry, anti-cyclonic winds blow across it from the north and west during winter, bringing great clouds of dust from the continental deserts of the Siberian interior. In summer a train of cyclones crosses the Plain from the south and east, but the air-streams involved quickly gain temperature over the bare countryside and dry out. Most rains occur in late spring. These continental extremes cause farming to turn upon spring-sown wheat in the colder north and west, and upon winter wheat (autumn-sown) towards the milder south and east. While wheat dominates farming interest, the hardier and coarser cereals—millet and kaoliang—are widely grown for food. Maize and cotton crops are grown towards the milder south and east. Salty soils, always the mark of prolonged desiccation, impede land-use not only towards the drier northwest but also towards the coast where salty marshes are extensive. Crops are erratic from year to year, partly arising from the short growing periods, the irregularity of showers, the violence of floods, the intensity of wind erosion on top soils, and partly from swarms of locusts blown eastwards from Central Asia.

This natural precariousness of farming is aggravated by a rural population so dense that farms average only 3·5 acres each and by the use of equipment and methods scarcely more advanced than those of Elizabethan England. One ox or a mule is often the sole draught animal on a farm, and the level of production is low. Millions of people live in a self-contained economy scarcely above subsistence. Natural increase of population is no longer absorbable in the country, so there is movement to the cities where large "proletariats" are the basis for industrialisation.

Worsening the natural limitations has been the long history of insecurity. For centuries marauding nomads scourged the Yellow Plain, which seemed a "land of milk and honey" for tribesmen from the deserts and mountains farther to the west. They swarmed periodically through the valleys from Kalgan and along the Hwang and Wei, which were also caravan routes between the Plain and Central Asia. Peking itself, still with walls and moats, has throughout its history been a military centre for defending the Plain, and the danger from the north and west is indicated by the Great Wall

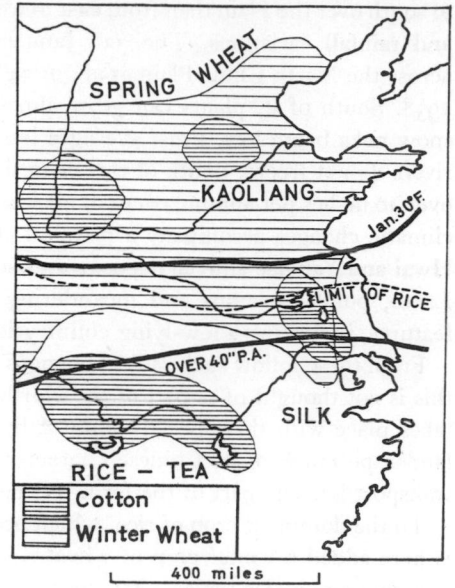

FIG. 23—Critical limits and crops in North China

running for hundreds of miles across country and by the walls that still surround settlements on the Plain. The huge scale of landscape engineering in the Great Wall and the Grand Canal is the sign not merely of constructional skill but of the great material surpluses once at the disposition of the Chinese.

The Yellow Plain, nursery of Imperial China, is now a region of low standards of living, though carefully worked to the limit of local skills. Its way of life and farming is different from what the Western world imagines to be "Chinese"; flour is a local staple food whether derived from wheat, millet or kaoliang, which may be eaten as steamed bread or boiled in forms of porridge. Furs and woollen or padded clothes are customary for winter dress. Houses with thick earthen walls, often windowless, are structural signs of the long, harsh winter and the torrid summers.

Southern Part of the Plain

The uniformity of relief implies that there is only gradual change of climate from point to point over the North China Plain. Variations due to distance from the sea are only slight, and the more noticeable landscape changes relate to change of latitude. There are more changes from north to south over the Plain than from east to west, and turn on both temperature and rainfall variations. The 32° January mean isotherm runs roughly across the North China Plain at about 34° N., where the Hwang was after 1938. South of it, plants can grow almost the year round, the frost and snow risks being low. Frost averages less than sixty days a year, but the rivers do not freeze. South of this critical isotherm reliable rains, totalling over 40 inches per annum, occur at all seasons. Summer lasts longer. These climatic changes accompany a physical change: the landscape is built of Hwai and Yangtse alluvial deposits and subject to their different régimes. Lakes, ponds, swamps and meandering distributaries become common features, indicating a low-lying countryside with a high water-table.

From these follow such radical changes of land-use that quite commonly this is not thought of as part of the North China Plain. Here rice-growing takes place with that special mode of living which it implies, giving the landscape much of its Chinese character. Water manipulation and water transport become part of the farm technique.

To the dominant crop of rice, which occupies the fields during summer, is here added a winter crop of wheat. Cotton becomes a significant commerical crop, maize replaces kaoliang as a subsidiary cereal and the buffalo replaces the ox and mule for draught. Sugar-cane and citrus can be grown. Tea appears on slight rises above the general level, and its evergreen bush is a sign of the long growing period of these parts. More trees appear round villages and fields, and wood has general use in domestic structures. Tiles and bricks are common for roofs and walls. The wet environment provides many varieties of reed, used for mats and baskets of many kinds. Down by the sea are salt-pans depending on natural evaporation.

The Hwai has always been a harass to Chinese people, 60 million of whom live in its flat basin, due to the disasters its vast, erratic and unforeseeable floods have caused on at least a thousand recorded occasions since the fourteenth century. Five million people drowned there between 1938 and 1950 in the confusion of waters caused partly by the Hwai itself and partly by the diverted Hwang waters and the heavy silting it induced on the lower Hwai plain. So far attempts to control the Hwai have been limited by manual methods and piecemeal planning insignificant in scale to the areas and volumes involved. Inland many large "ponds" have been constructed behind low dams in the foothills to restrain run-off. Thousands of miles of dykes are always being constructed and reconstructed lower down, as well as much dredging attempted, notwithstanding the scarcity of the most modern types of dredge. At Junghochi, roughly at mid-course, a long, low, modern concrete barrage has recently been completed, able to halve the discharge if need be, and also serving to irrigate 8 million acres—because the disasters arise not only from flood but also from drought at higher levels in this region near the limit of rice growing. It follows that the Hwai landscape is a complex of residual lakes or sumps inland and large irregular lakes remaining from floods and obstructive silting across earlier channels (Fig. 24).

Farther south on the plain calamities are, as a whole, less frequent, the Yangtse being more even in its flow and water not usually exceeding what can be harnessed in the wet-farming system. A few locusts may occasionally fly in from their breeding zones to the northwest, but southern crops maintain a higher, more regular level than farther north.

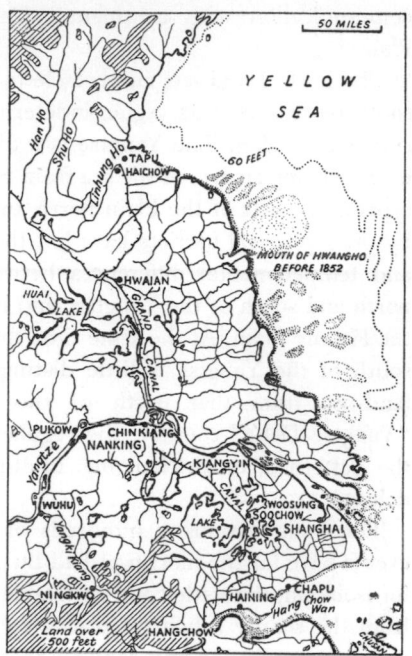

FIG. 24—The southern part of the North China Plain, showing the confusion of lakes on the Hwai flood plain and the Yangtse Delta

Movement, however, is hindered by stagnant waters, which combine with distance to render the area safer from attack from the northwest. Local banditry, a feature everywhere in China for the last few centuries, has led to the little country towns being protected by moats. Water movement along the many thousand miles of navigable waterway on the Plain has permitted trade in the bulky local crops so that some goes into commerce, supplying food for the townsmen and cotton for the factories which have grown up along the Yangtse this century. It has remained a region isolated from the north by tradition and differing in farm techniques and productivity. The Grand Canal linking Peking to the Yangtse dates from sixteen centuries ago, when this was a rich pioneering zone whose function was to supply food and cloth to the older Chinese communities living to the north on the Yellow Plain. More important still for contact, the great Yangtse has afforded an easier and freer movement between this wet plain and the interior so that in many ways the deltaic plain has had easier communication with continental China than it has with the Yellow Plain.

The lower Hwai sets an obstacle to land movement between north and south by reason of its vague, indeterminate drainage patterns of swamps, sumps and lakes. The Yangtse is a distinctive broad barrier of water, its estuary being an arm of the sea from 2 to 25 miles in width, very definitely separating parts of the Plain north and south of it. Centuries of isolation by these physical barriers have left their mark in the provincial, linguistic and temperamental differences between the people living immediately north and south of the Yangtse, and between those of the Hwai Plain and the Hwang Plain. At the same time the lake-studded country immediately south of the Yangtse is little distinguishable in landscape, landform or land-use from that north of the river. While undoubtedly this is "Yangtse Delta" country, the regularity of the main river has obviated the pattern of quick-changing, multiple distributaries common to many deltas.

The Plain has many hundreds of miles of coast, yet its people and events have for the most part had little to do with the sea. Its coast makes for isolation, the settled and cultivable areas of the interior being separated from the sea by a belt (at places 10 miles broad) of saline muds, reed-swamps, mudbanks and shallow shores which cause it to be difficult to approach from both sea and land. Fishing and sea-going are not part of the tradition among the plainsmen of North China. Apart from the Yangtse which is a river more of the Asian continent than of the North China Plain, local rivers provide no deep channel across the Plain. Tientsin and Shanghai are modern cities; older settlements are away from the coast; and the Grand Canal underlines the historic preference for going from north to south by inland route rather than by sea.

Cities of the Plain

The total area of the North China Plain is about 170,000 square miles and contains a population of at least 160 million. This is as though the present population of U.S.A. were compressed into somewhat less than the area of France. While its low *per capita* economic development has been based on small farming families spread densely over it, the Plain has a large urban population. Within the lowlands between Chekiang and Jehol are eight cities of over 100,000 each and seventeen more of over 50,000 each, so that about one in seven of the region's people live in large towns, about twenty of these being in the Yangtse Delta. Peking and Tientsin, each over 3 million people, are in the less-urbanised northern section of the Plain.

I. The Hwang-Ho frequently overflows, and here Chinese farmers have come from miles around to construct a new embankment. They work in large gangs and are equipped only with shovels and baskets. It will be seen, too, that their clothing in the cool season must be heavy and that they may even wear fur hats.

II. In a Peking street may often appear a donkey cart carrying sacks of wheat-flour to market and led by a peak-capped carter in padded cotton clothes . . . indicating the "continental" winter of Northern China.

III. Shanghai—the greatest seaport of China and gateway to the Yangtse Lake Plains. The Whampoa Creek is to the left, a distributary of the Yangtse Delta where ocean-going steamers can berth. Through the city runs another creek affording a shallow way to Soochow across the delta and usually crowded with the junks of an amphibious population trading anywhere from here to the Wu-Han cities hundreds of miles inland.

IV. The South Coast of China (Kwangtung) is an alternation of small "dead-end" bays and rocky promontories, intensively cultivated in the lowlands and much deforested on the hills. The sea offers easier transport than any overland route.

That there is so much urbanisation in this agricultural lowland cannot be too strongly emphasised; the type of art and culture Western people associate with China is essentially urban though not industrial.

Peking, the capital of ancient China and now restored to that function, is set in a landscape of "imperial grandeur decayed", with many cultural and architectural relics of other eras epitomised by the division of Peking into four cities separated by walls. Such walls recur in the urban pattern on the Plain, except for Shanghai which grew up in the last century. The town wall reflects the prolonged instability of China and of the fact that, though its mandarinate is the oldest type of civil service, administration in the last century had broken down. The provincial war-lord with his private army and gangs of bandits have obliged every community to defend itself and maintain walls long after anywhere else in Monsoon Asia, in Europe or America. The present administration is attempting to make Peking a modern industrial city by establishing blast-furnaces, machine-shops and textile mills. It has recently reached a population of nearly 6 million people. Peking continues as eccentric to the pattern of modern China at it always was to Imperial China, more continuously interested in Inner Asia than with Monsoon Asia as whole.

Tientsin is technically the port of the Yellow Plain, but it lies 50 miles inland along the meanders of the Hai, which requires continuous dredging to maintain a deep channel. It has more limited access for shipping than some of the Yangtse ports hundreds of miles inland. Tangke is its outport developed to avoid these awkwardnesses, which are less now due to the virtual cessation of overseas trade. Tientsin itself retains a curious mixture of cluttered, narrow streets of small, brick-built shop houses or walled Oriental residential areas and of modern sections built during the period of "concessions" to Western nations which made this the focus of trade contacts with the Plain. It is now described as "the chief port of modern China", indicating the political isolation of Shanghai from Peking and of the intensified interest between the Yellow Plain and the Manchurian Plain. Tientsin's population has become over 3 million and much industrialised. Coal for its factories comes by rail from the Kailan coalfield to the northeast.

Peking and Tientsin together have a latitude and a position in the Asian continent comparable to that of New York in relation to North America. The sites in each case relate to corridors between the coast and the interior. That there should be so great a contrast between the developments at New York and Peking–Tientsin may turn upon the fact that New York has functioned as a point of entry to the interior from overseas, whereas

Peking has functioned defensively—to prevent movements from the interior to the coastal plain.

Shanghai. Along or immediately adjoining the whole Yangtse stands 25 cities each of about 100,000 people or more, and altogether constituting an urban population of at least 12 million people. Of these, Shanghai is the biggest (7·1 million in 1957), but Nanking exceeds a million and Hanchow and Soochow are each over half a million.

Shanghai combines something of the size and international significance of New York with a position on a continental arterial river comparable to New Orleans; yet it is little more than a century old having been a fishing village in 1843, when it became a "treaty port" or "concession" for foreign traders. It grew from separate concessions developed by nationals of European and American countries who by trade and by manufacturing industries turned this into the greatest single city in Eastern Asia, and an example of what modern organisation can do on the basis of China's production and markets. To this foreign port where Western conceptions of law and administration prevailed in the form of extra-territorial rights, flocked millions of Chinese, learning by this means the Western methods of which they have become adept and which in turn they used to establish their own factories and industries until by the beginning of the Second World War the extra-territorial conception was abandoned and Shanghai became a Chinese-administered city, though international in racial composition, function and outlook. As a port, Shanghai has limits: the Yangtse estuary is too open and the shore too shallow for safe anchorages and the city stands beside the sheltered Whangpoo Creek which, 50 miles from the open sea, has required dredging to keep it adequate for ocean-going traffic. The restricted space of the original concession led to building upwards. Every extra storey involved ever-deeper piling in soft and yielding alluvium. For the multi-storied modern blocks of concrete buildings now characteristic of the waterfront, great lengths of underpinning were necessary. A large movement in and out by water takes place, now mostly along the Yangtse, once in an entrepôt trade all round the China Sea, and in long-distance trade with Europe and North America. Cotton and raw silk from the near-by countryside comes for manufacture to huge textile factories driven by fuels which also have to be imported with other raw materials from the hinterland, which formed a great pool of labour as well as a source of cheap food. For most practical purposes, Shanghai is served by water routes, its rail and road contacts being poor and all involve some ferrying across the wide reaches of rivers. A large population live in junks, plying through the delta's creeks and channels.

The present isolation policy in China has paralysed Shanghai's commerce, and the volume and structure of its trade over recent years is unknown.

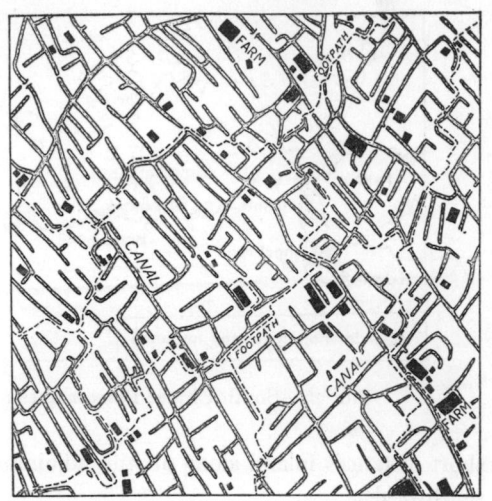

FIG. 25—A map of a one mile square showing isolated farms on the wet, padi-growing landscape inland from Shanghai

The Kwangtung Plain

South of Canton spreads another alluvial plain still being built seaward by river-borne silts, and occupying half of a structural gulf of 7,000 square miles. At least 12 million people live on the Kwangtung deltaic lowland, through which rise island-like rocky knobs of much the same materials as the steep edges of the uplands around the gulf (Fig. 29).

Three main rivers have built the plain with their alluvials, the Si-kiang, the Pei-kiang and Tung-kiang, which enter the region from west, north and east, as their names imply. The plain is thus a "compound" delta formed by three streams. The water-channels across it are mostly tidal, even as far within the bay as Canton City where the tidal range is about 6 feet. The surface is, like that of all deltas, a complex of elongated alluvial belts, sand patches, meanders, abandoned channels and braided distributaries dividing the area into separate strips and low-lying islands. The main plain (about 60 miles by 20 miles) lies between the channel of the Si-kiang (which the earth's rotation has deflected well to the west), and that of the Chu-kiang, broadening into Canton Bay, the wedge-shaped arm of the sea to the east.

The deltas of the Pei-kiang and the Tung-kiang are continuous with the mainland, and in consequence more continental in character than the half of the plain physically isolated by broad channels useful for water transport. The Tung-kiang, a short river, adds another deltaic fan to the southwest, thrust well out from the mainland to form a partially isolated lobe of the plain, south of Kongmoon and east of Sunming. Finger-like extensions of the Kwangtung Plain extend for

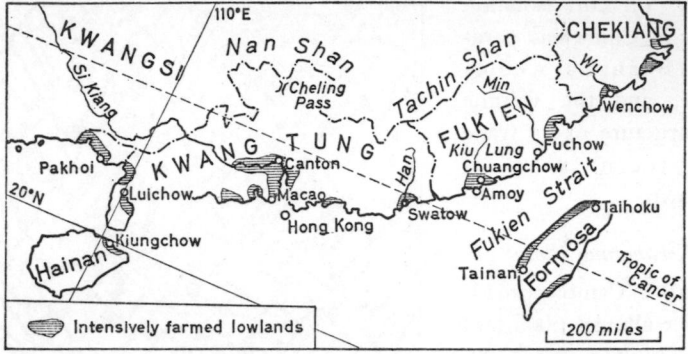

Fig. 26—South China: Place-names and Lowland farming

short distances inland along all the adjoining valleys and along the coast southwards.

The delta surface is so modified by man-made canals, drains and the polders of reclamation at the seaward fringes that little of it retains its natural profile. Each dyke is emphasised by trees (the mulberry and tropical fruits) and carries the house clusters through which thread footpaths. Periodical floods are common. The Si-kiang, whose catchment basin extends west into the continent, fluctuates widely because there are few basins in its course through steep mountainous terrains to act as sumps, so that the effects of spate are concentrated upon its deltaic fan. At Samshui, head of the delta, fluctuations of 30 feet in the river level are fairly common, so that low-lying delta surface is regularly inundated over large areas. Successful settlement here necessitates protection from this occasional excess of surface water by sites on dykes, mounds or the low rocky islands.

The Kwangtung Plain differs from other Chinese lowlands by being within the tropics. Canton City has a latitude of 23° N. and, always frost-free, the countryside has a year-round growing season. No season is rainless though the cool quarter (December–February) receives only a tenth and the warm season (March–September) two-thirds of the annual fall of 70 inches.

A dense, dispersed population is spread thickly on the lowlands with densities exceeding 2,500 per square mile over its greater part. Water movements are a feature of the farming life and people's houses are withdrawn outside the padi-fields. Commonly their houses have earthen floors raised slightly above ground-level. In detail the ditches and canals

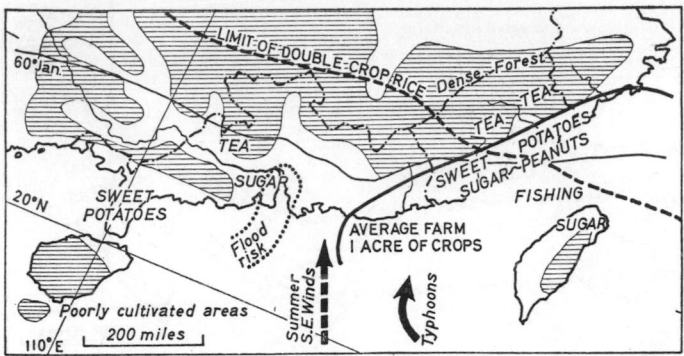

FIG. 27—South China: Agricultural features

are not engineered but hand-cut, and their forms on the map are plastic and irregular as in the Yangtse Delta.

The combination of alluvial soil and continuous growing season has made it possible for the plain to be one of the most intensively cultivated in the world. Padi and mulberry dominate its farming, the former lying upon the lower level of the landscape, the latter upon the higher and more inland parts. From each field two crops of rice and one other short-term crop (vegetables, etc.) are common, often interplanted so that the plant cycles overlap and produce an extra crop. Water is carefully controlled within the limit of manual operation, and no landscape engineering has been done. The intensive farming is maintained by continuous fertilisation, using nightsoil, pig-manure, green mulches and the application of mud collected from the bottoms of water channels. Ducks, chickens and fish ponds are an integral part of farming, for their by-products and for their wastes as manure. Rice is the climax of food-growing and cottage silk-spinning of the commercial farming. Bananas, pineapples and sub-tropical vegetables (sweet potatoes), together with sugar-cane, ginger and tobacco, are also grown for urban markets.

The delta has many large towns and, though distinctively a farming country, much commercial activity takes place in it, concentrating at the inner riverport of Canton which contains nearly 2 million people, and in the outer seaports of Macao and Hong Kong on the seaward fringe, where rocky outcrops provide easy deep-water approaches for ocean-going ships. Whampoa is an outport for Canton downstream on the Chiu-kiang, where deep-draught shipping can handle freight for Canton whose silting presents a continuing problem. A substantial population lives on boats

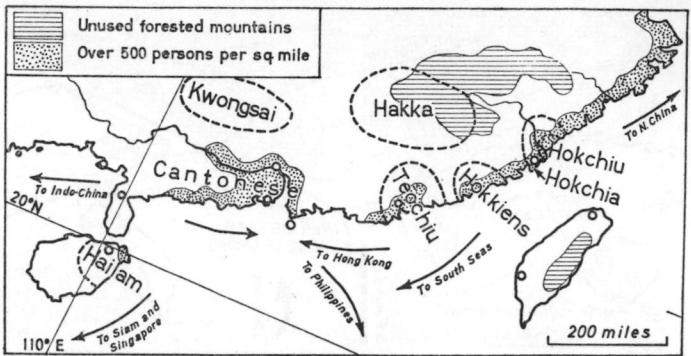

FIG. 28—South China: Clans, population and lines of contact

called junks which move through the water-courses and along the rivers, some to the interior, others along the coast. About a fifth of people in Canton City live thus on the river. Their water-borne life has extended to sea-going, causing Cantonese to differ from most other Chinese by having had prolonged overseas exchanges to goods and people and a highly commercialised agriculture. This lush region has, by its accessibility and overseas connections, played a big part in establishing that picture of China commonest in foreign minds. It is, however, isolated from the interior by steep hills and from adjoining regions to the north, so that it has preserved languages and traditions unlike those of the North China Plain.

Three major cities, Canton, Macao and Hong Kong—lie at three corners of the Kwangtung Delta. *Canton*, still a walled Chinese city now nine centuries old, is isolated far within the great deltaic gulf, for whose 12 million farming people it is the provincial capital. Its own population lives in a mixture of congested, irregular streets with one-storey buildings of traditional Chinese form, and of broad roads with tall, modern concrete buildings, in the "concessions" district. Canton has had long connections with the Western world for the original trade in tea and silk. From it millions of Chinese emigrated overseas. Its vigorous modernity and revolutionary political opinion (the Chinese say everything new originates in Canton) were due to the overseas association, particularly to the influence of wealthy repatriates who brought back invigorating ideas as well as some fortunes. From Canton's waterfront is usually exported tung oil, Turkey rhubarb (for purgative pills) and raw silk. Silk and cotton are both spun and woven in small factories round the city. Though there is a railway leading north from it, Canton's overland connections are slight even today, re-

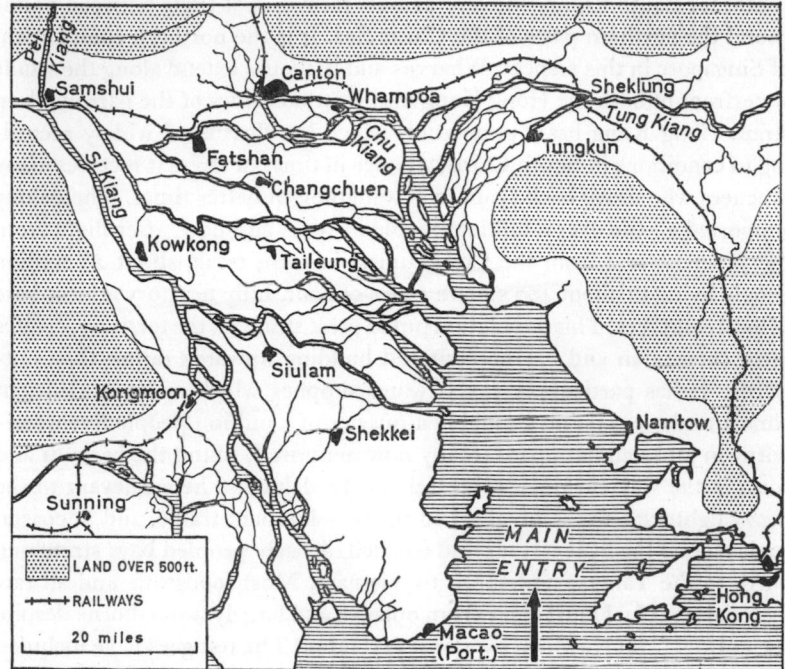

FIG. 29—Kwangtung Coastal Plain, the deltas, Hong Kong and Macao

minding us of the long isolation of this region from the North China Plain.

Either side of the main arm of the sea penetrating the gulf to its east are the colonial cities of Macao and Hong Kong, which occupy mere toe-holds of land and are the last of many foreign trading stations which grew up last century on the China coast. *Macao*, the Portuguese port, dates from 1557 and is on a hilly knob at the southwestern extremity of the main delta and has a shallow harbour which contributed to its historic significance. The port is physically and politically isolated from Kwangtung, and serves little function today except as tourist centre; hardly any international shipping uses it now.

Hong Kong, the British trading port, dates from 1841, and is a rocky island surrounded by deep water. It includes a small peninsula of the main land (Kowloon) since 1898, when that addition was taken on lease. Its spectacular development has probably surprised everyone concerned, the British no less than the Chinese, though it now suffers from the restriction of space its rocky site implies. The port acts as a major trading and banking centre for South China, and also as base for entrepôt trade between points round the northern parts of the China Sea. It is the northern complement of Singapore in this respect. Wharves and harbours extend along the whole waterfront of both the Hong Kong and Kowloon sides of the narrow, deep strait. Hong Kong has a population which has fluctuated widely according to conditions in South China, whence in times of stress it receives many evacuees who move back again to Kwangtung in better times. The colony supported a little over a million people in 1941, and now, after flight from the Japanese and from the Communists in turn, totals about $2\frac{1}{2}$ million people living in about 400 square miles of poor, hilly territory almost bare of local resources. This population puts a great strain on the territory, creates great congestion and has necessitated building upwards rather than outwards. It has particularly taxed water supplies which are now deficient almost to danger-point. Probably a quarter of a million people live waterborne in junks and sampans (many now motorised) round the harbour and coast in the way customary throughout the delta and here relevant to the heavy lighterage traffic involved in the transhipment traffic, and in coastal trade among the little islands and isolated, densely peopled bays stretching north to the Yangtse and south to Vietnam. Most foodstuffs and all raw materials and fuel must come from outside, and largely water-borne despite the railway from Kowloon overland to Canton. The refugees have included wealthy people and intellectuals as well as displaced farmers and workers, and they have brought to Hong Kong the assets of plentiful capital and labour on the basis of which a vigorous industrialisation, now occupying nearly a third of the population, has gone on processing some of the raw materials involved in the entrepôt trade. Industry includes shipbuilding, cement making, rope making (with Manila hemp), sugar refining (using Taiwan and Philippines cane), knitting (a mechanised cottage industry using Australian wool), cotton weaving (using both American and Indian cotton), domestic metal articles such as pots and pans, rubber goods (using Borneo rubber), vacuum flasks, electric torches and plastics—all intended for overseas export as well as serving the Kwangtung Plain. Definitely within the tropics, Hong Kong has a warm climate in which heavy clothing is unnecessary even during winter, but the rocky setting precludes significant agricultural land-use to exploit the climate. The harbour, carefully protected from the effects of typhoons and tropical cyclones which are a major risk to the lighter and junk traffic for the months from July to October, was used by about 8,500 ocean-going vessels, totalling nearly 15 million net registered tons, and 22,000 small craft in 1957. In recent years, Hong Kong has become a major airport despite the difficulty of establishing a suitably long runway in a terrain so restricted and rocky. The airport, "Kai Tak", is on the Kowloon peninsula and hemmed by steep hills, but reclamation from the sea is extending the runway in view of the increasing traffic by no less than fifteen airlines.

Liuchow and Hainan Plains

The Liuchow Plain forms a square-cut peninsula stretching south of the Kwangtung coast, and is unusual in being a peneplain of igneous and crystalline rocks eroded and weathered to a low-average level of smooth rounded forms. It is much fractured and the Hainan Strait takes form and direction from faults. Across

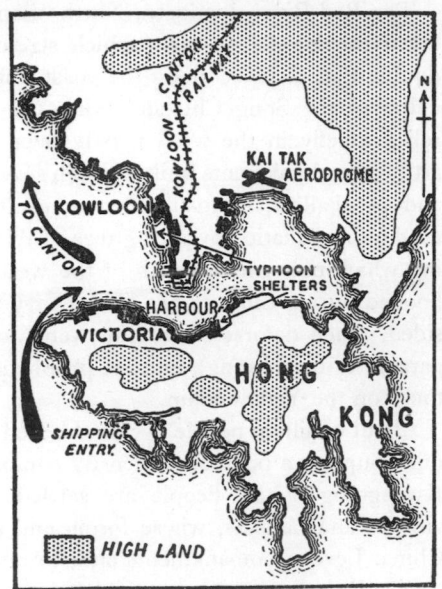

Fig. 30—Hong Kong and Kowloon. (The map represents an area of 18 × 13 miles)

the strait lies the lowland of Hainan Island with similar structure. These two plains have weathered, lateritic soils of low agricultural potential, very different from the plains of sedimentations, a contrast which explains why its farming is low-grade, the population scanty and the level of development low. From both Liuchow and Hainan whose combined populations are probably about 4 million, there has been steady migration overseas, and the maritime contact was, until the Second World War, underlined by the small French colony of Kwangchowan on the east of Liuchow.

The North Vietnam Plain

Now that a new boundary has been drawn conventionally at 17° N. in Indochina, the delta country of Tonkin, core area of the Communist state of North Vietnam, resumes its place as a coastal plain associated with China. Hemmed in, like the Kwangtung Plain, by rugged uplands, the plain is built by the merging of serval deltas and subject to tropical conditions. It is more readily accessible along the coast to the Kwangtung Plain than Kwangtung is to the Yangtse Plain.

The Red River dominates North Vietnam, and been chiefly responsible for triangular deltaic plain which stretches 150 miles inland and about double that distance along the coast, taking into account the contiguous deltas of the Song Chu and Song Ca. It has only minor variations in relief, chiefly in the west, mostly been produced by natural levees and artificial embankments built through several centuries to control the rivers, and by shallow, basin-like forms resulting from the polder techniques used for reclamation by padi-growers. Without the elaborate river engineering which now exists, much of the western delta would be continuously flooded during the summer. The heavy river loads coming from a steep-sided, much deforested interior, tend to produce high river-beds (comparable to the Hwang), and set problems of level and of flood similar to those on the Yellow Plain.

About 9 million people live on the Red River Delta, and its 6,000 square miles support a population density comparable to that of the Yangtse and Kwangtung deltas. People are settled evenly in small, closely spaced villages and hamlets, whose forms and sites are like those of the South China. Levees, embankments and, towards the sea, old sandspits are the usual places for settlement, which is withdrawn from every square foot of lowland which permits padi to be grown. Scarcely 5% of Tonkin's people live in towns, which are themselves little more than large villages acting as marketing centres for an otherwise scattered farming community. *Hanoi*, the chief town, is located well inland close to the main focus of distributaries. Movement by water and living on the water is not so prominently a feature of life in this delta by contrast with the Lower Si-kiang and Yangtse.

Lying farther inside the tropic than Kwangtung, North Vietnam has an intensive agriculture, based on wet rice of 6–7 months' term and all-the-year-round farming. Hundreds of varieties of padi have been evolved to make the best of those many local variations of soil and water usual on the delta. Pig, fish and buffalo manure are heavily used, and water is elaborately controlled by manual methods to make production continuous and double crops of rice usual. Yields are high and necessary to support the dense population, where the average farming family of four must keep itself from the produce of about 4 acres. Besides padi, maize, sweet potatoes, tobacco and vegetables are grown. Too far north for the coconut, North Vietnam uses ground-nuts and sesame as source of edible oils in its self-contained economy. Buffaloes and oxen are the draught animals. The delta carries much mulberry, the basis of a cottage silk-spinning industry which was once the source of peasant cash incomes, but which in the last decade has declined in the face of competition from Chinese and Japanese silks and artificial fibres.

The alluviated coastal plains of Eastern China, extending through more than 20° of latitude, show substantial variations of crop types from north to south, the critical line being the January 32° F. isotherm. To the north of it are plains experiencing extremes of temperature and low rainfalls, to the south are plains of plentiful tropical rains, warmth and equability. A critical factor for double rice-cropping is the number of months averaging above 50°. Upon the plains live some of the world's densest concentrations of agricultural people engaged in activity involving high production per acre on the basis of a largely self-contained economy, manual methods and home-made tools. Only the Kwangtung Plain and the Red Delta have had long overseas associations.

CHAPTER ELEVEN

Continental Plains and Basins of China

THE CHINESE have, after centuries of colonisation, transferred modes of living they evolved on their coastal plains to large inland plains—the Lake Plains of the Yangtse, the Red Basin of Szechuan, the Kunming Plain, the Loess Plateaux (of Shansi, Shensi, Kansu), and the Manchurian Plain.

THE LAKE PLAINS OF THE YANGTSE

The Yangtse Delta ends at the hills near Anking, to which the river moves across a lake-studded plain which extends 600 miles deep into the continent landscapes of gentle slopes, fine soils and slow waters. Two basins are recognisable, one to the west round Tungting Lake, the other round Poyang Lake. Hundreds of lakes sprawl across the vast riverine plain in many stages of infilling and remodelling. Deltaic fans of many shapes complicate the landscape, which is traversed also by natural levees and by meandering or braided streams. Many types of river terrace show. The detail changes season by season because huge volumes of water are discharged across it from lengthy tributaries. The interplay of régimes and the impediment of previous silt deposits produced great variations of water-shapes on the plains, where slight rises of water-level cause great extensions. Some lakes may shrink to beds of reeds during the dry season, and in the wet cover hundreds of miles. Near Hankow the Yangtse seasonally varies from ¾ mile to 5 miles across. Few other parts of the world have such gigantic "flood" plains. The Chinese harness this superabundance of water to their farming, here largely of wet type.

These lake-plains lie on the warmer side of the 32° January isotherm, but just outside the tropics. Even Hankow, so deep into the continent, averages 40° F. in January, permitting plant growth continuously. Frost may occur briefly. Rainfalls exceed 50 inches a year, but it is the river-water which makes wet-farming possible, so that the kind of agriculture developed on the Yangtse Delta continues for hundreds of miles into the continent. Warm-season rice and cool-season wheat, with much maize and tobacco, are the keynotes. Continuous cropping is widespread, though rice cannot normally be cultivated twice a year. Water control, poldering and drainage are

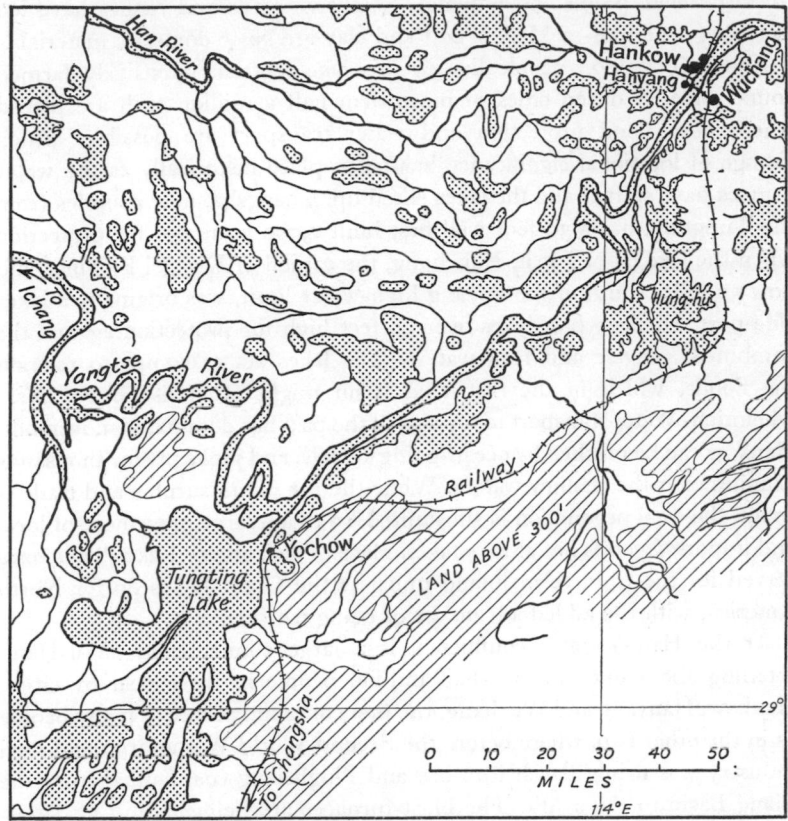

FIG. 31—The Yangtse Lake plain. While the lakes vary in extent from season to season, here is an example of the complex lake and stream pattern on the Yangtse Plain. The Han breaks up into many small "distributaries" near the Wa-Han cities. The Yangtse pours large "distributaries" into the Tungting which acts as a sump for its seasonal spate. At Yochow the flow changes direction according to the height of the main Yangtse channel. Only the railway is shown here but nowhere west of the line on this map is there a single metalled road

present everywhere, and all water channels are used by junks which provide cheap but slow links through to the riverine towns and the seaports. Cotton and mulberries (for silk) are cultivated on the drier soils. The river terraces and marginal hills are used for tea bushes, here grown by small-holders. The original evergreen broad-leaved forests have now practically disappeared. Villages and farms still nestle among trees (of holly, mulberry, pistachio and rosewood trees) or clumps of bamboo and fruit trees (peaches, plums and loquats). Extensive reeds and rushes have led to basket- and mat-making. Wood and clay are basic domestic materials.

About 60 million people live in this lake-spotted, intensively farmed countryside. A dozen cities of more than half a million each are placed where both flood protection and water transport are possible. Much change of locational significance has taken place historically as the water courses have shifted and the lakes silted up. Changsha, now 50 miles from the Tungting, has a 30-foot wall first built 2,000 years ago for protection when the lake lapped at it. Nanchang, the capital of Kiangsi Province and now 50 miles south of the Poyang high-water limit, was originally a lake-side port. Hankow has dykes over 90 feet high for protection against the combined Yangtse and Han waters. The lakes act as sumps to restrain the floods, which in the restricted basin might otherwise prove over-whelming. Water transport today and in the past has dominated movement. Hankow can be reached by ocean-going vessels, and junks ply for thousands of miles over the shallow waters. While the *per capita* surplus and trade is small, the total production is substantial, so that a large movement of local and imported goods has always taken place. The Yangtse Lake Plains have served for the Chinese mainland much as the Great Lakes do for North America, with the added advantage of being ice-free.

At the Han–Yangtse confluence is a large conurbation, "Wu-Han" totalling about one and one-half million people in three near-by cities, Hankow, Hanyang and Wuchang, the first containing twice as many people as in the other two, where before the Second World War an iron and steel industry was using Tayeh iron ore and Pinghsiang coal hauled from the Siang Basin to the south. The blast-furnaces are being rebuilt at Tayeh about 60 miles downstream to lessen transport of the iron ore. Similar industries are under construction at Changsha and Hengyang, but cannot for some years change the overwhelmingly agricultural economy. Mills in Hankow now use locally grown cotton, which was once always shipped to Shanghai.

While the lakes and waterways provide transport, the Yangtse is broad enough to separate effectively the northern and southern plains. The Tungting and Poyang are large enough to isolate farmers living round them. Aggravating the physical separation, products everywhere are similar so there is little basis for local interchange. No railway parallels the river. From Hankow a line links northwards towards Peking, and from Wuchang another goes south to Canton; the first bridge has now been built across the Yangtse to connect these lines. From Kiukiang near the Poyang confluence a line passes south to Nanchang, where there are rail links to Pinghsiang and by a more roundabout route to Hangchow. In this watery region, movement by road is negligible.

THE HAN LOWLANDS

The Han River has built a separate inland deltaic fan which resembles and merges with the Yangtse Plain to the west of Hankow.

Farther north and west of its "deltaic fan", the Han is passing through a maturely farmed, largely self-contained plain covering hundreds of square miles of low-lying and nearly level country, roughly diamond-shaped and between the foothills of the Fu Niu Shan and Ting Peh ranges. This lesser-known Han lowland has a series of tributaries converging on Siangyang, where the river follows a more restricted valley leading south to Anlu and Hankow. Its variations of water-level are less, floods less common, lakes fewer and drainage more mature than towards Hankow. The plain is traversed by old north–south overland routes between the Yangtse and the Wei, but new motorable roads have made Kiangyang the junction for three major routes—south along the Han, northwest through the historic Tsin Ling Pass to the Wei–Hwang confluence and northeast to Hsuchow and Kaifeng.

THE SZECHUAN BASIN

Set within a diamond-shaped surround of snowy mountains and equal in area to Great Britain, the Szechuan Basin is a high-level plain on fairly horizontal sandstones which have been incised by tributaries to the Yangtse running close to the southern edges. While large areas are gently sloping plains covered with high-grade forest soils, there are considerable breaks of slope. The Yangtse links this unit through the Ichang Gorge to the plains farther east, but physical features of the Lake Plains are not present in Szechuan. Old intermontane lake-beds, now unfilled, are common and intensely cultivated.

A thousand miles as the crow flies from the Yangtse mouth and 600 miles from the nearest sea (the Gulf of Tonkin), the Szechuan plains are deep in the continent, yet the region has an anomalously mild climate, thought to derive from föhn winds and air descending into it from the Tibetan Plateau. Most of the basin is almost frostless and the January mean is about 45° F. The rainfall, from reliable and effective cyclonic showers, averages 38 inches annually. Climatically the Szechuan Plains are perhaps comparable more to the Kwangtung Plain than to the Yangtse Lake

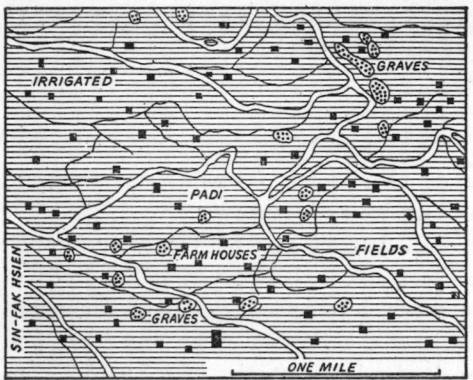

FIG. 32—Detail from a topographic map showing irregular canals near Chengtu leading water from the Min to scattered farmsteads. Also shown are the mounds which carry local graves and waste good land

Plains. The descending air of winter leads to prolonged fogs by reason of the inversions which occur, hence a local saying— "Szechuan dogs bark with fright when they see the sun".

Here the soil has a purple tone (hence the name "Red Basin of Szechuan"), derived from the weathered red sandstone and from the humus which remains after the forest has been cleared. Four major rivers (Min, Liu, Suining and Kiuling) have built alluvial fans of mixed soils and high fertility. The Chengtu Plain, laid down by the Min in the west, is the largest, most fertile and best developed.

Irrigation serves half the cultivated land and is necessary to make "wet-farming" possible despite interrupted levels and moderate rainfalls. Terracing extends farming up the slopes between the different plains. Rice occupies less than half the total cultivated area, but maize is cropped more extensively than in any other Chinese region. Farming turns on summer crops of rice and winter crops of wheat, oilseed, rape or sesame. Rice is often in rotation with sweet potatoes, maize, soya and sugar. Tree crops include peaches, apricots, oranges and persimmons. The indigenous tung and "varnish" trees are tapped commercially. The ox is the usual farm animal, and pigs are widely kept. Szechuan extends the style and productivity of land use in the Yangtse Lake Plains, and its broken, hemmed-in and lakeless landscape appears more different than the economy is. Its fertility, variety and reliability have given it a Chinese reputation as "the earthly paradise". Its plains are, however, more isolated than those so far considered; though the Yangtse and parts of its tributaries are used by junks, and small steamers can reach as far as the Min confluence, the Ichang gorge separates the basin from Eastern China. Overland transport is poorly developed. No railway existed until 1952 when a line was completed to link Chengtu with Chungking and so to arterial water movement on the Yangtse.

While three-quarters of Szechuan households are farming, pressure on

V. Lanchow in Kansu, once a great caravan focus and still a walled city, is taking on new importance as a "land port" for overland exchange between China and the U.S.S.R. It is the terminus of a new Chinese railway from the North China Plain and much road traffic now meets there.

VI. At Fushan in Manchuria coalmining is a longstanding development and basis of a rapidly expanding heavy industry. Lack of equipment means that crude manual methods have continued in use. Here is a pit-head scene where baskets and shovels are being brought back at the end of a shift.

VII. An airphoto of the South Korea coast on which are repeated features apparent on the South Japan coast. The hills are bare and gullied, the settlements withdrawn out of the fertile lowlands to foot-of-hill sites.

land is less than in other Chinese regions because, though now mature, this was a colonial development. About one-fifth of the 60 million population is urban. Chengtu had historic importance as an outpost of China's administration. Chungking on the Yangtse is the regional capital, and was the national capital from 1937 to 1946, while the Japanese occupied the eastern lowlands. Between the lower Min and the Liu brine wells have been exploited for centuries, and salt has been one of the traditional products of Szechuan which was traded far to the west and south. Petroleum has been found and a refinery is being built at Nanchung. Not far east from Chungking are coal seams of substantial potential.

The Chengtu alluvial fan is renowned for its agricultural productivity, made possible by elaborate and long-standing control of the Min by barrages and in canals. Besides irrigation, the distributaries drive small flour and vegetable-oil mills and paper factories. Prosperous farms and villages cover the Chengtu Plain, which alone supports 5 million people living in cedar, cypress and mimosa groves above which rise pagodas accentuating the flatness of the plain itself, although in the distance broken relief and mountains are always in sight.

THE KUNMING PLAIN

Inland from the Kwangtung and North Vietnam coastal plains, yet isolated from them by several hundred miles of difficult terrain, is the small Kunming Plain, the choicest farm area upon the Yunnan Plateau and supporting some 8 million people. The plain lies on the tropic and has the landforms and soils of partially infilled lakes. It stands about 4,000 feet above sea-level, and is cooler than the location close to the tropic suggests. Its hot-season rains and well-marked seasons of wind from opposite directions give it a monsoon régime and a climate comparable to Himalayan foothills.

Rice occupies only a quarter of Kunming farmland, but winter wheat, barley and soya can generally be grown continuously. Tea is prominent on the landscape. A dense population is supported, although Kunming is one of the newer colonies—of settlers from Szechuan. Its population includes hill tribes of Lolos, Miaos and Thais and a large colony of Chinese Muslims.

A French-built railway links Kunming to Hanoi, accentuating the outlook away from China. The town, roughly at the middle of a group of lakebeds, was the terminus of a Second World War mountain road from Mandalay ("the Burma Road"), now regularly in use. Kunming acts as a local market for tin, tungsten and copper ores, primitively mined in several parts of Yunnan.

THE LOESS PLATEAUX

Inland from the Yellow Plain is the dry region (less than 15 inches per annum) of the Loess Plateaux, a continental extension of that plain to which it is linked by the Hwang Valley south of the Shansi Mountains.

Contained roughly within a rectangle formed by the Wei on the south, by the south-flowing reaches of the Hwang on the east, by the Liupan Shan and similar mountains of Kansu on the west and by the Great Wall separating it from the Ordos Desert on the north, this region has a surface of finely divided, windborne loess, known to the Chinese as "hwangtu" (yellow earth). The loess lies in thicknesses from 50 to 250 feet over the varying rocks of the substructure, forming almost horizontal areas separated from one another by "steps" of precipitous, crumbling slopes. These cliff-like forms may last for years, and then slump during an earthquake or a rainstorm. The unusual shapes of this countryside results from the lightly compacted, friable loess which cleaves vertically as may a sand-heap. A contributory factor in the absence of enough rain to produce the gentler, rounded slopes of water-graded landscapes.

Loess here extends over an area greater than elsewhere in the world for three main reasons: (a) Strong, steady winds blow from Central Asia during the cold season, which is exceptionally dry. (b) They come over the near-by arid steppes and deserts, where dust rises easily, leaving much of Gobi as bare rock or gravel. (c) Rainfalls average less than 12 inches per annum, so that the settling particles do not get washed away. The rain sinks into the porous particles, so there is little run-off.

The loess is thickest in Kansu and to the north within the Great Wall. It is more valuable agriculturally to the south and east, where it is mixed with riverborne materials in valley bottoms along the Wei and Fen.

These loess landscapes are plains only in the valleys and basins. Because loess is low in humus as well as porous, fallowing and water are vital for farming. Little natural vegetation exists owing to the dry climate, and where present is bunch-grass and scattered shrubs which only slowly replace organic material. Only about a fifth of the landscape is cultivated each year as a result of these environmental difficulties. About 10% of the farmland has irrigation, mostly along the Wei, but the deeply incised relief impedes canalisation. Although wells are of critical importance and control the village locations, they frequently fail; less than one in seven has permanent water. Fields are small and farms isolated on different levels. The nearness of this region to marauding nomads explains the earth-walled farms and villages.

Since the area suffers from low rainfall, long, dark, cold winters and very hot summers, farming concentrates upon winter wheat (on 40% of the farmed area), millet and kaoliang. Cotton is the cash-crop, though cultivable only in small areas along the Wei and Fen. Year-round cropping is impossible. Dry-farming techniques of tilthing are in general use to conserve soil moisture. Dependent on irregular summer showers, the region has few tree crops, but vegetables occupy a bigger proportion of ground here than elsewhere in China; they respond flexibly to brief rains. Oxen, mules and donkeys are the local animals, despite scarcity of fodders, providing manure and used for the caravans to Central Asia. The pressure of population on the small, low-grade farms is greater here than in the Yellow Plain, and yields are so small and unreliable that the nutrition density is less than in all China. "Cave-dwellings" are dug in the cliff-like walls of loess valleys, and earth-walled houses with roofs of sun-baked tile are common. The pattern of the Fen, Hwang, King and Wei rivers is such that the lines of movement and the disposition of population are fan-wise, centring where the Hwang turns to the east. In this zone the densest settlement and busiest commercial towns have grown up, the latter having historic connection with overland routes in and out of the North China Plain. Near the Hwang elbow is the Chiehchow basin, a small area of high fertility, and with classic interest as the "nursery" of the oldest Chinese culture. At Chiehchow evolved that style of intensive farming and water control which was later transmitted through all Eastern China. The valleys through this region have been lines of movement on foot or horseback for several thousand years. The Wei Valley was a major caravan route into Central Asia, converging on Sian, junction for an overland way south to Szechuan and north to Yulin, a main gate in the Great Wall, scene of a prolonged struggle between farmers and pastoralists. Today these ancient routes are followed by roads, and the Wei Valley contains a railway with connections northeast to Peking (through the Fen Valley) and southward to Hankow. This area has revived importance for overland links with Soviet Asia, special significance attaching to the entirely new railway virtually completed along the Wei Valley to Lanchow (for Urumchi), and northwest to Paotow across Mongolia to the Trans-Siberian Railway, shortening the Peking–Moscow journey by 700 miles. Airports are scattered along the same route, so that the Loess Plateaux are resuming their cross roads significance after a century of decline.

MANCHURIAN PLAIN

Though the Manchurian Plain reaches the coast, in outlook, position, climate and character it is continental. Comparatively close to the Yellow

Plain and Japan, it is more "northern" (Harbin is analogous to Belgrade or Ottawa), and has only this century become drawn into economic ties with Eastern Asia. The late development derives from its location off the routes between Central Asia and the Yellow Plain, from its long, harsh winter and from the accident that its main river (the broad and navigable Sungari) flows north and is frozen annually. Tsarist Russians and Japanese played a part in opening up the Plain, but its people are chiefly colonists from North China. Flanked by high mountains hindering the entry of maritime air, the Plain has a rolling surface of erosion. It thus contrasts with other Chinese plains, which are alluvial. The rolling landscape suffers a great variation of temperature between summer and winter and between night and day, and resembles the prairies in North America, a likeness the closer because recent pioneering, makeshift settlements and immigrant people are features of both. Only 160 days a year being frost-free, the cycle of life, whether vegetable, animal or human, is one of short, intense summer activity and long winter quiescence. Rain (about 25 inches per annum) comes largely in the brief summer, some as snows which accumulate to become available on melting in spring. It has a régime different from other Chinese plains and may be considered to lie outside Monsoon Asia. The Manchurian Plain was grass-covered and developed a humusrich, "black earth" soil suited for large-scale wheat farming. Where not under the plough, the grass provides large, natural grazing for herds of sheep, horses and cattle. To the west, where dry winds blow for long periods from the mountains, bringing warm, desiccating föhn winds, are salty or alkaline soils; there the grass diminishes to steppe-like scrub. Towards the rainier south and east stretches of broad-leaved deciduous forest remain, but needle-leaved evergreen coniferous forest covers the mountainous boundaries in the harsher north and west. "Log cabins" and horses are as much features of the Manchurian landscape as they were of Midwestern America and still are of Northwest Russia. Horse-borne nomadism was the indigenous way of life before colonisation led to the present settlement, Manchurian nomads having regularly attacked Northern China and even established dynasties there. The Chinese put this plain under the plough, and set out farms of a size which had not been possible on the North China Plain for millennia.

Russians and Japanese dominated in turn the administration of the Plain until after the Second World War. During their occupation, the Japanese introduced large numbers of artisans and technicians to start heavy industries towards the south and southeast. The Chinese population only penetrated deep into the Plain after about 1900. Besides the attraction of cheap land, yields for the pioneers were high because the black earth was virgin. Thus export of farm produce was possible from the beginning, making a great contrast to the North China Plain. Although the climate obliges farming to be extensive, an annual harvest of 25 million tons of grain is normally gathered. Wheat, maize, millet, kaoliang and soya beans are cropped once a year, with regular surpluses which now move to the Yellow Plain. One of the large-scale developments has been in soya bean, several million tons of which are traded each year owing to its value as a multiple food and source of vegetable oil. Mechanised cultivation of large farms and large fields was initiated by Japanese administrators following conquest in 1931, and have been continued by the Communists since the style suits collective farming in the Soviet pattern.

Pioneering proceeded rapidly after the First World War. Between 1915 and 1930 the farm acreage doubled, and since then doubled again. The Plain has filled so rapidly despite political changes that farmland averages now only an acre per person, which is still large compared with other parts of China but dangerously low for maintaining commercial agriculture in so restricted a climate. The struggle between China, Russia and Japan to control the Plain indicates the importance attached to its resources.

On the Plain are many new cities, such as Harbin, Mukden, Chinchao, Changchan (Hsinking), laid out in an open rectangular pattern common to quickly built, pioneer settlements and reflecting Japanese influence in city design. About 25 million people live here, mainly dispersed on the farms. The prolonged inactivity in winter means that farms can be left, enabling country people to move seasonally into factories.

As a response to its commercial agriculture, the Manchurian Plain has many railways—a third of all railway lines in China. The Chinese Eastern Railway to Dairen traverses the plain to provide a short route from the ice-free Gulf of Liaotung to the Trans-Siberian Railway, whose terminus at Vladivostok is ice-bound for several months a year. Other lines were originally foreign-managed and capitalised, criss-crossing the country and vital to moving its bulky farmstuffs. Roads are plentiful, and river transport has been substantial though hindered by long freezing and alignment towards the north. The southeastern sector, where the Plain contacts foothills to the Korean Highlands, is underlain by accessible coal, iron ore and other minerals, which have given rise to heavy industry established by the Japanese and scattered in grim, built-up areas from Mukden through Anshan to Antung and along the Yalu River.

CHAPTER TWELVE

Hill and Mountain Regions of Continental Eastern Asia

BECAUSE THE PLAINS and basins so far considered total barely a third of Eastern China but support two-thirds of its people, it follows that the hilly and mountainous remainder is thinly peopled; there are spots and ribbons of densely populated farming country amid large empty wastes. Mountains constitute the harsh terrain between the eastern lowlands and the cold deserts of Tibet; relief has hindered movement from China into Southeast Asia and into Manchuria. Relief barriers have not been complete, the gaps dominating routes through or round them. The bulwark of mountains is broken northwest of the Yellow Plain, where the Hwang Valley and the Kalgan Corridor round the Shansi Mountains provide passage to arid Gobi and the Ninghsia Basin. The Great Wall was intended to close this gap.

The hills and mountains within Eastern China functioned to separate groups of people and to develop among them the feeling of regional distinctiveness, sometimes called regionalism. Nothing could be more emphatic than the division of South from Central China by the mountains from Yunnan through the Nan Ling to the Fukien coast, separating peoples of a different speech, outlook and traditions. Similarly the Yangtse Lake Plains are separated from the north by the Tsin Ling Ranges, dividing the wheat-eaters from the rice-eaters. While these hill and mountain regions have low development now, their mineral potential, little explored so far, may give them different significance in the future.

CONTINENTAL HIGHLANDS

(a) The *Ala Shan* and *Nan Shan* separate the Loess Plateaux from the dry basins and desert plains of Central Asia. Block mountains between 10,000 and 20,000 feet high without notable passes across them, they are skirted by caravan routes, the most famous (through the Jade Gate of the Great Wall) running south of the Nan Shan and along the Wei Valley.

(b) Wild highlands between Eastern China and the Tibetan Plateau include the Szechuan Alps (towering over Chengtu Plain), the Great

Snowy Mountains (Tahsueh Shan), which have at least one peak over 25,000 feet high (Minya Gongkar), and the Upper Hwang Highlands. Vast in scale, isolated and little known, the region has great gorges, thick forests and many glaciers. Here non-Chinese tribes live like Tibetans, but colonies of Chinese are farming in small alluvial valleys. The Chinese administration was never well established in this "border", which few caravans traverse yet where the major rivers of China and continental Southeast Asia (including the Hwang, Yangtse, Si, Mekong and Irrawaddy) flow in gorges and canyons, impeding movement both across and along them.

(c) The Great Kinghan Mountains edge the Mongolian Continental Plains here, thrust up in contact with the disturbed blocks and massifs of Eastern Asia. They rise steeply into well-dissected forms when seen from the Manchurian Plain, but appear as gently rising hills when viewed from the continental side. They bound the Manchurian Plain and merge into the arid, much-eroded peneplain of Jehol, reaching the coast at the Gulf of Chihli and dividing Manchuria from the Yellow Plain. The Taching Mountains are short, serried ranges rising like a screen to the south between the Great Kinghan and the plateau of Shansi. The bare, steep and thinly peopled ranges between Taching and Jehol are often known as "the Western Hills" or the Peking Grid, a reference to the tightly packed N.E.–S.W. scarps reaching above 10,000 feet.

The intermontaine basins along the Kalgan Corridor between the Kinghan and Shansi Mountains are well settled. The defence of Peking has led to this mountain border being dotted with forts and castles at ancient strategic points. The Kalgan Corridor carries from Peking into Ordos a railway now being extended to strengthen the connection with Central Asia.

(d) A more isolated border to Eastern China, the East Manchurian Highlands, reach the sea as the Liaotung Peninsula, structurally extended beyond the strait into Shantung. Rising above 9,000 feet, the Highlands form the eastern limit to the Manchurian Plain, and have N.E.–S.W. fault-lines apparent on the coasts and in the river pattern. Great sheets of ancient lava cover are deeply incised by rivers in glaciated valleys. Subject to long, bitterly cold winters, it is wild and unpeopled except in foothills to the southwest, where iron ores and coal beds at Fushan are being exploited for heavy industrial plants established at Anshan by the Japanese. The Highlands remain thickly forested and provide much timber.

MOUNTAINS WITHIN CHINA

The *Southern Uplands* constitute the most extensive of the internal relief features. A complex hill-and-mountain terrain, they extend for about 1,500 miles from the Tibetan border to the rocky coasts of Fukien and Chekiang, and for 200 miles from north to south, many of the east to west ranges sustaining heights above 3,000 feet. Fractures and eroded valleys establish a relief alignment from northeast to southwest: a north–south trend is more emphatic in the far west, where glaciated valleys are common.

The distinctive sections of this important upland are:

(*a*) The Fukien–Chekiang Upland adjoins the coast from Hangchow Bay to the Kwangtung Delta. Its plateau-like, warm, wet landscape is still partially forested and isolated. Sharp breaks of slope occur round it, the steep inland scarps of Wuyi being as distinctive as the rocky, cliffed coast. Greatest development is marginally, where in separate, small valleys and ria-like bays dense populations farm rice and tea intensively despite strong leaching. The climate permits virtually continuous cropping. Even the Chinese techniques of double and treble cropping (of rice, maize, sweet potatoes and yams), of intercropping (of vegetables between tea and the cereals), manual irrigation, manuring and terracing, have proved inadequate for the dense population, enforcing an interest in the sea. This coast is the home of China's chief maritime and emigrating communities. Wenchow, Fuchow, Amoy and Swatow are large market towns and ports serving the digital bays, where movement is more commonly by water and isolation promotes clannishness and distinctive languages. No significant routes run across this upland, and its mineral potential is not fully known.

Abutting its northwestern part is the Hangchow Basin, a series of open valleys and coastal strips where the landscape repeats features of the Yangtse Delta. The scarps overlooking these lush lowlands are related geologically to the Ta Pieh Shan on the northern side of the Yangtse, here very broad and flowing parallel to the N.E.–S.W. fault-line.

The Southern Uplands obstruct overland movements out of the Yangtse Plains, whence people have however slowly colonised the southern valleys where wet-farming is feasible. The Tsientang River, with Hangchow at its mouth, has a broad valley which, paralleling the fault trend, is as well-peopled and intensively farmed as the Yangtse Delta. It provides an overland passage between Shanghai, the Poyang Lake and Canton. A little-used railway runs across its delta to Hangchow, and from there inland to Nanchang, junction for a line north to Kiukiang on the Yangtse and south to Canton. The Hangchow Basin has preserved some of its original sub-tropical forest (with magnolia and tung trees), serving to control the violent run-off and hillside erosion common in the Uplands. Here is one of the great tea-growing area of South China. Many specialised varieties have been developed to suit the variation of terrain.

(b) The Nan Ling Shan is a sinuous east–west belt of hill country which only occasionally rises above 3,000 feet, but is eroded into sharp relief, obstructing movement and impeding wet-farming. These features accentuate differences of relief, climate and latitude, and clearly delimit the sub-tropical Yangtse Lake Plains from tropical Kwangtung country to the south. Set well inland between the Fukien Uplands and East Tibet, the Nan Ling ranges include igneous rocks known to contain ores of tin, copper, zinc, antimony and wolfram not yet fully exploited. The Nan Ling Shan is forested, but large areas have been crudely cut in response to the great demand for timber in the adjoining plains; camphor, lacquer and tung trees are exploited commercially.

There are three old routes through the Nan Ling Shan by way of the Kweilin, Cheling and Meiling passes. Both ancient and modern armies have used these routes from north to south, which two railways now traverse to link Changsha with the eastern and middle Si-kiang Valley at Canton and Liuching.

On the northern and southern sides of Nan Ling are foothill regions transitional to the lowlands and carrying considerable tea. To the south high rainfall and temperature have led to poor lateritic soils so that only the valley bottoms can be farmed for padi.

(c) Inland from the Nan Ling the landscape rises abruptly to high plateaux buttressing the East Tibetan Highlands. These thinly peopled regions include:

(i) The Gorge Mountains, a great eroded anticline of limestone and granitic rocks divided by the canyon (near Ichang) of the Yangtse which runs 2,000 feet or so below the general level.

(ii) The Kweichow Plateau at about 4,000 feet above sea-level has a karst landscape of limestone, much dissected by streams which accentuate lines of old erosion by ice. Once thickly wooded with deciduous trees, the region is largely deforested following centuries of floating timber to the Tungting, and is now largely grass covered. It contains small, well-farmed, densely populated basins of dolina type (as in Yugoslavia), colonised by migrants from the Yangtse Plains. Outside such basins, a few scattered hill tribes continue a primitive subsistence farming. Igneous intrusions into the limestone include ores of tin, wolfram, molybdenum, zinc, lead, copper, antimony and mercury, only the last being mined north of Kweiyang. Coal strata occur, but are not worked.

(iii) The Yunnan Plateau farther to the south is still higher (above 6,000 feet except for the Kunming Plain). The Plateau, sometimes included with Kweichow under the name Yun-Kwei Plateau, is a country of rocky mountains broken by deep canyons, little known, difficult to reach and to cross and thinly peopled. Large areas remain forested because they are so remote from the timber-hungry populations farther east. Yun-Kwei Plateau has been a zone through which Tibetan and Mongolian peoples slowly seeped into Burma and Thailand to the south.

(iv) Between the Nan Ling and North Vietnam is an old, eroded upland (about 1,000 feet) traversed by the trench-like Si-kiang Valley and known as the *Kwangsi Tableland.* Here are the low watersheds between Si-kiang and Red River, and a few small lowlands colonised from the Kwangtung Plain by way of the coast or the Si-kiang, and used for continuous farming like that in the delta. Along the coast are little settlements like those in the rias of Fukien and Chekiang. The Kwangsi Tableland is of sandstone and limestone, weathered into a karst landscape of gorges and pinnacles. The Tableland has higher surroundings to the north and west, and within it converge a series of valleys—the Kwei, Hochih Lung, Hongshui, Siyang and Lung tributaries of the Si-kiang—which provide caravan routes to and from Yunnan. Only from Wuchow eastwards is the Si-kiang a good water-way, and other streams flow too swiftly in gorges to permit junk traffic.

Settlement is riverine, farming for rice, sugar-cane and similar tropical crops being confined to irregular narrow alluvial belts along valleys. Confluence sites are a feature of its market towns, where tung oil is traded. Overall population density is very low and local people have been obliged to look to trade for their livelihood. The coast has been notorious for piracy. Kwangsi dates its colonisation by Chinese only from the late imperial period, and two groups, one Mandarin-speaking from the Yangtse (now centring on Kweilin city) and the other Cantonese-speaking from the east (centring in Wuchow), having converged upon it, subjugating and displacing local hill tribes.

The Central China Mountains

The main ranges north of the Yangtse are the Tsin Ling whose rugged structure can be traced into the Fu Niu Shan and the Tapa Mountains which overlook the plains of the Han–Yangtse confluence. Together these ranges are wide and high enough to form a negative and deterrent region parallel to the Nanling, and combine the functions of protective barrier to the Yangtse Lake Plains, and of divide between dry, continental, wheat-growing environments to the north and the sub-tropical, warm, rice-growing lake plains to the south.

The Tsin Ling rises wall-like south of the Wei to heights exceeding 13,000 feet. Loess covers some lower levels round it and is cultivated, but the ranges are nearly bare. The northern foothills are dry and exposed; the southern well watered by in-blowing summer winds and wooded or farmed in the valleys.

The Tapa Shan is distinctive as a west–east feature which, apart from the Han Valley gap, continues high relief eastwards towards the Ta Pieh Shan. In its high west are large areas of limestone with karst landscapes divided by a gorge tributary to the Han. An historic imperial courier route crosses the high pass of Tiensha and connects Fengsiang in the Wei Valley with Chengtu—a route now perpetuated by a road and a proposed railway. The broad trough between Tsin Ling and Tapa ranges contains the Han, whose course is divided by several gorges. The Upper Han Valley is fertile, intensively cultivated and densely peopled, and often described as a miniature Szechuan Basin. The centre of its self-contained population is *Hanchung*.

The North China Mountains

On either side of the Yellow Plain are two mountain masses prominent in Chinese history. The plainsmen call them Shansi (Mountains of the West) and Shantung (Mountains of the East).

(*a*) Shansi is an immense rocky plateau roughly the area of Britain, lying between the Loess Plateaux and the Yellow Plain. Rising over 6,000 feet, it includes several blocks shattered by N.–S. faults. Fault-scarps set the pattern of its ranges and its major rivers (Fen and Sangko). The Fen drains a series of long basins such as those round Taiyuan and Linfen, whose fertility derives from water-sorted, wind-blown soils which are the economic foci amid mountains made formidably difficult by erosion, drought and steep slopes. Outside the Fen depression, Shansi has a stern countryside of low agricultural potential, obliging local people to live as traders and bankers for the movements of goods and people which pass Shansi *en route* between Central Asia and the Yellow Plain. The barrier-like Shansi massifs are without east–west routes through them apart from the Pingting Gap, which permits rail and road movements between Tung-kwan (in the Fen trough) and Peking.

Shansi has assumed modern importance because its sedimentary rocks include great coal-seams and beds of iron ore made accessible by faulting: at many places they can be mined open-cast. Anthracite occurs on the scarps west of the Ho Shan and bituminous coal towards its east. From mines near Tatung at the northern end of the block, coal is railed to the Taiyuan and Peking blast-furnaces. Shansi coal also serves the Peking–Tungkwan railway line, and is the power basis for industrialisation plans in Peking.

(b) Shantung does not maintain any great altitude (5,000 feet in the west), and is a hilly, eroded upland rising abruptly from the Yellow Plain and tilting downwards to the coast. It has a roughly rectangular shape on a N.E.–S.W. axis, divided midway (at Weihsien) by a fault depression, now drained of swamps and well farmed. The igneous Tai Range, which overlooks the Yellow Plain, has been a pilgrimage centre for plainsmen.

The southwestern part of Shantung is land-locked, with the North China Plain on three sides. Deforested and eroded, it supports little except sparse grass and shrubs. Springs from limestone outcrops on its northwestern edge have attracted tourism. Its northern edges contain coalfields which are mined at Poshan and Weihsien, whence 10 million tons a year are normally railed to Peking and Tientsin. The proximity of these mines to the coast has led to making this China's third largest coal-producing region, though its reserves are not of similar rank.

The northeastern part of the Shantung block is a peninsula thrust well out into the Yellow Sea, which laps three of its sides. Generally below 700 feet in altitude, its landscapes are weathered to rounded shapes with coasts of barren, rocky cliffs. Peninsular Shantung has about a fifth of its surface cultivated in the manner of the Yellow Plain, but climatic conditions are milder and farming less precarious. Considerable fruit production is possible, and Cheefoo is famous for its vineyards. The coastal people engage in fishing and have become sea traders. Pressure of population on the small areas of agricultural land is as high here as anywhere in China. Weihaiwei and Cheefoo on the extreme north have good harbours without hinterlands, and there is a great natural harbour at Kiaochow Bay, where Tsingtao has this century grown to "million" rank. Linked to Peking and Tientsin by the road and rail route through the Weihsien depression, Tsingtao functions as a major port for the Yellow Plain, with connections to Nagasaki, Shanghai and Liaotung.

THE KOREAN PENINSULA

Structurally and climatically of the mainland, Korea is isolated overland by distance accentuated by harsh, thinly peopled, thickly wooded mountains at the root of its peninsula. Until late last century it was an "outlier" of an older Chinese mode of living, and was then colonised by the Japanese, whose cultural and economic impact was both intense and sustained so that the countryside today is more Japanese than Chinese.

Spreading astride the new boundary at the 38th Parallel, Korea ranges over the same latitudes as Honshu and, as in that island, the greatest agricultural development is in small lowlands to the southwest round Seoul and the little plains south of it. The bare uplands are subject to bitterly cold northwesterlies. Coasts to the south and east are rocky and much indented. Consisting of a block of old sedimentary and granitic rocks in rounded forms, the country tilts downwards to the west, its outline, relief and river pattern reflecting two fault-lines, one running N.E.–S.W. and the other at right-angles.

The western coastal plain of South Korea has a mild climate, permitting a summer crop of padi and a winter crop of barley or beans. American cotton and sweet potatoes are also grown, the latter helping to release rice for sale. The mulberry is extensively grown for rearing silkworms.

Cultivation in North Korea is restricted by prolonged winter cold to one crop a year. Short-term padis, evolved in Japan, occupy the best soils, but barley, millet, soya and other beans dominate. Northern mountains and hills are heavily wooded, but support "shifting cultivation", involving burning the trees, taking a catch-crop and then leaving to natural regrowth for some years.

The eroded structure includes mineralised intrusive rocks. Lode and placer gold are lightly worked. Large iron-ore deposits lie to the north along a belt from Haeju to Pyongyang, at Iwon and Nanam. Coal is worked near Samchok on the east and at Pyongyang. Mining for lead and zinc takes place at Kumhwain in the north and Onggin in the south.

The Korean people, off the main tracks of international trade, have continued farming with difficulty near the limit of rice. Physically they resemble both the Chinese and the Japanese. In their colonial period about three-quarters of a million Japanese lived in Korean towns. The peninsula contains about 30 million people, nearly three-quarters in South Korea, where continuous, intensive farming supports dangerously great densities in small, tightly packed hamlets of single-storied wooden buildings. The demand for rice in Japan stimulated commerce in Korean rice and weakened the self-contained system. Some industries have developed in Japanese-style small units, and a tenth of the people live in little towns. *Seoul* is a "million" city; *Pyongyang* contains half a million. The former is the focus of the largest farming zone in South Korea; the latter, now capital of North Korea, has hydro-electric power from Supung on the Yalu River and considerable paper-making and rayon factories. At Chinan-pohang are copper, lead and zinc smelters and a large chemical plant. Commerce with Japan and old fishing interests cause port towns to be numerous. Mokpo harbour on the southwest has overland rail links and sea contacts with China, but Pusan is Korea's chief port, terminus of its main railway, ferry port for Shimonoseki and with shipbuilding facilities. Fishing concentrates on the harsher east coast, fish being used directly as food, canned for export or converted into fertiliser.

The main internal lines of movement on the roads and railways are between Seoul, the plains around it and the southern coastal plain, where there are dense populations and major ports. In North Korea are railways originally built to fan northwards from Seoul to Pyongyang and Wansan, whence western lines connect Antung and Mukden. The changed relations between the two parts of Korea and their neighbours imply changed orientation of transport movements.

CHAPTER THIRTEEN

Insular Eastern Asia—Japan

THE ISLANDS of Eastern Asia include large ones such as Hokkaido, Honshu, Taiwan (Formosa) and Luzon, together with thousands of small onces. Structurally, east Taiwan resembles South Japan and Luzon, each being much fractured and with volcanic mountains adjoining great oceanic deeps. Agriculturally South Honshu is more analogous to Western Taiwan and the Central Philippines than it is to north Honshu and Hokkaido. Distances alone divide the festoon of islands into three parts—Japan, Taiwan and the Philippines—and relates Taiwan more to the continent than the others.

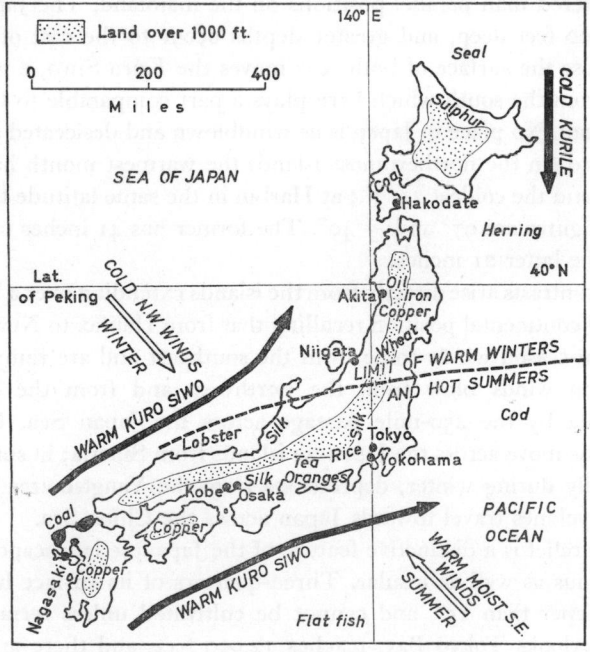

FIG. 33—Japan: physical features, climate, economy, and towns

The scale of every natural and economic feature on the islands is much smaller than in Continental East Asia. Japan could easily be fitted into the space of the North China Plain. Taiwan is no bigger than the Tungting Lake Plain. The rich and productive plains of the Central Philippines combine to little more than the area of the Tai Lake on the Yangtse Delta. The total population of Japan is about half that of the Yangtse Plains. Taiwan contains less people than Peking and Shanghai together. Filipinos number about half the population of the Szechuan Basin. On the other hand, Taiwanese are about as numerous as Belgians, Japanese total about twice the population of France and the Philippines contain as many people as Egypt.

JAPAN

The four major Japanese islands are arranged in the shape of a boomerang with one tip only 120 miles from Korea. They spread between the latitudes of Shanghai and of Harbin, but are milder in climate and better watered than parallel positions on the mainland. The Japan Sea is over 10,000 feet deep, and greater depths occur to the east of Honshu; while across the surface of both seas moves the Kuro Siwo, a warm drift moving from the south which here plays a part comparable to that of the Gulf Stream. No place in Japan is as windblown and desiccated as Peking. At Sapporo (in the northernmost island) the warmest month has a mean of 69° F. and the coldest 21° F.; at Harbin in the same latitude the corresponding figures are 97° and − 40°. The former has 41 inches of rain per annum, the latter 21 inches.

These contrasts arise directly from the islands extending over a latitudinal range and continental position recalling that from Halifax to New Orleans. The warm-season winds come from the southeast and are rainy, and the cold-season winds blow from the northwest and from the continent, ameliorated by the 250-mile passage across the Japan Sea. In winter, depressions move across the Japanese islands from Siberia; in summer and occasionally during winter, depressions from the Yangtse area and some tropical cyclones travel towards Japan across the China Sea.

Broken relief is a distinctive feature of the Japanese landscape, which is mountainous as well as insular. Three-quarters of its surface has rugged slopes steeper than 15°, and cannot be cultivated unless terraced. Fuji, which overlooks Tokyo Bay, reaches 12,000 feet, and there are a dozen peaks of 10,000 feet. Southeast of Tokyo Bay the ocean reaches 35,000 feet deep, an abrupt descent hindering the development of deltaic fans.

Rocks forming Japan's surface are jumbled by prolonged structural instability, involving thrusts and over-thrusts, foldings, tensions and metamorphoses. Alluvial plains constitute less than a fifth of the country, another tenth is of older, higher alluvials (diluvials) on natural terraces, and an eighth is granitic. Volcanic materials, lava flows, ash and other ejecta at different phases of evolution occupy a quarter of the land in forms derived from conical shapes. About 500 volcanic cones are recognisable and nearly 50 still active. The steepness of the terrain, the lava flows and the slumps due to earthquakes contribute to make bare rock common on the Japanese landscape, whose natural forests have been intensively cut for the wood which is the basis of Japan's domestic crafts. Volcanoes and earthquakes have been the Japanese counterpart of the floods and droughts which have scourged North China, and the instability led to frequent changes of level which formed the natural terraces common along rivers and coasts.

Hills, whether of fold or block structures, volcanic groups and valleys are arranged in slightly curving lines, giving rise to complex nodes where two or more meet. The winged form of Hokkaido relates to such a node where a N.–S. structural line extending from Sakhalin meets a N.E.–S.W. one showing as the Kurile Islands and another which is an extension of the Eastern Honshu arc on a N.N.W.–S.S.W. trend. Kyushu has nodal structure where the Ryukyu volcanic island arc meets another in extension from Shikoku. The node north of Gifu makes a specially dramatic landscape, where the Bonin volcanic island arc meets other arcs from Shikoku and from eastern and western Honshu.

That these landscapes so frequently contain "much within little" is accentuated by the narrow land masses which are never broader than 150 miles; opposite coasts of Japan are at places less than 50 miles apart. High relief together with this narrow form means that the run-off is as mountain streams, short, small in catchment area, swift, violently erosive, deeply incised for much of their length, subject to torrential spates of brief duration ("flash spates"), and able to carry heavy gravels and boulders almost to the sea. Such rivers are clearly more suited for power than for agriculture: they present difficult problems of control whether against flood or for irrigation; many contain too little water to justify hydro-electric installations, and yet have too much "head" for irrigation. Rivers play little part in domestic transport.

THE LOWLANDS

Because the Japanese lowlands are small, they have vital agricultural importance. Half the total cultivated area is on alluvial plains and another quarter on the diluvial terraces. A setting of steep hills and mountains is always evident to people on the lowlands, many of which are alluvial fillings of small bays or gulfs. Ribbon-like, narrow coastal plains occur, often wave-levelled, sometimes slightly raised above sea-level. Unlike the great depositional plains of the mainland, here the slope of the alluvial fans is perceptible, making run-off control necessary even in the lowlands. Most small plains have the coast close at hand, bringing farming and fishing close together. Beach ridges and wave-built sand-dunes fringe the coastal lowlands except in protected bays, where the effects of wind and wave are minimised. Small salty lagoons are common and some rivers move in braided patterns behind a beach ridge, paralleling the coast for miles before entering the sea. Often the beach ridges are planted with conifers to fix them and to shield crops from blown salt and sand. Others are laid out with orchards or vegetable gardens.

Upon the little plains, river-beds are frequently raised by continuing deposition within artificial levees, complicated by the substantial deviation of upstream water into contour canals for irrigation. Thus the road approach to a river is commonly uphill because Japan's rivers stand upon its plains rather than in them. The risk of catastrophic break-out of river water is always present, though the dykes are carefully maintained. Upstream dams and reforested hills are devices in use to control the water before its reaches the plain.

The diluvial terraces have a low water-table and drier, coarser soils, and are often subdivided by incised rivers. Waterfalls occur where the terrace breaks to the lowland. While flat enough for cultivation, the upper levels present difficulties to irrigating their dry surfaces and the technique is to construct local ponds or dam the river farther upstream.

Piedmont alluvial fans spread among the hills and mountains, but they are always small. The well-marked fault valleys, as in the N.–S. basins of northern Honshu, form narrow depressions filled with multiple fans.

COASTS

Over 95% of the coast is unapproachable by sea or by land so that there is great pressure on the accessible stretches. Many cliffed coasts are structural by origin, hence wave-eroded indentations are small and few. The large complex bays of Seto or Setouchi (the Inland Sea), Ise, Saganu, Wasaka and western Kyushu owe their reticulated outlines to fault-lines and vents, providing deep arms of sea and facilities for water transport. Road transport over Japan's rocky, broken landscape is far less easy than movement by sea which has become the most important highway, coastal tramp services regularly connecting over 700 little ports. The most used overland routes are those of Tokai, linking the Tokyo area with Nagoya and Osaka by several skilfully engineered railways through complex mountainous country.

CLIMATE

Two main types of climate occur in Japan. To the north the characteristic is severe winters and short growing seasons. South of about 37° N. there is sub-tropical climate modified inland by high relief.

The best known landscapes of Japan are those subject to the southern climate. Here summer is as warm and wet as that of Shanghai or New Orleans, and most rain (60–100 inches per annum) derives from on-shore southerly winds. This is "monsoon" Japan, which has a cool season with a January mean about 40°, unpleasantly raw, moist winds from the north and northeast and many days overcast. Snow falls on twelve days a year. Despite only 240 frost-free days a year, rice is the staple food crop. In climate, Northern Japan resembles New England modified by the effects of insularity. It lies north of the January 32° mean, and suffers from heavy snowfalls, with a growing season mostly too short for widespread rice growing. Some sheltered valleys have aspects which permit crops of special short-term padis. Ice drifts down the east coast of Hokkaido from January to April, but the west is drift-free due to the Kuro Siwo.

Japan's mountains greatly modify local climates by effects of altitude, "rain shadows" and föhn winds. Localities round the Inland Sea, sheltered by ranges to the north and south, have a noticeably smaller rainfall than exposed coasts, causing greater need for irrigation than the sub-tropical surroundings suggest. Mountain air and converging ocean currents cause extensive coastal fogs. Although the typhoons or tropical cyclones are dramatic weather events in South Japan capable of destroying crops and houses, causing "flash spates" in rivers and wrecking ships, they are not always catastrophic. Two or three occur each autumn, but a warning system and protective devices minimise their effects, which have assumed vital importance chiefly because the margin of food is small.

The broken surface of Japan is constituted of a mossaic of small units which differ considerably in size, appearance and development from neighbouring ones. Intensive farming has explored the variations to such an extent that their economic effects are exaggerated. This results from an extremely dense population confined to the few gentle slopes. Each little lowland is a cluster of people, closely settled and farming intensively, while the adjoining unit of upland or hill stands practically bare of natural or cultivated vegetation and of settlements.

Three regions can be recognised: (a) Japan south of Lat. 37°. (b) The Northern Island of Hokkaido. (c) The transitional zone of Honshu north of Lat. 37°.

SOUTHERN JAPAN

The southern zone of warmth, rain, small lowlands and sea contacts has set the pattern of the Japanese way of life. Intensive farming, bamboos, orange trees, fans, silkworms, factories and cities within mountain-girt plains dominate the landscape upon which are settled five-sixths of all Japanese people, living in such congestion that the little plains overflow with people, causing migration and exports. Tea-growing is confined to the south, as also is winter-cropping of fields which in summer contain padi.

The core of the region lies round the Seto, an elongated inland sea open at three points to the ocean, dotted with small steep-sided islands and flanked to north and east by mountainous peninsulas of Honshu, and to the south by rocky, mountainous Shikoku and Kyushu. People and farms are clustered close to the coast which, shielded from the open ocean, is linked by shipping routes. About 28 million people live around Seto, over two-thirds of them rurally, but over 50 towns exceed 40,000 people each, one being the city of Osaka (3 million people). Only one-eighth of the landscape can be cultivated, and even this has required tremendous effort and ingenuity from the local farmers, who support an average of six persons from each cultivated acre. The regional density is eight people to the cultivated acre. The Seto is intensively harvested for fish. Many hill-sides have been laid out in narrow terraces for tea and other bush or tree crops. Two-thirds of the cultivated area is irrigated, the rainfall of about 60 inches per annum being irregular though the growing season is almost continuous.

The little lowlands have been levelled into water-filled padi-fields without tracks across them and often without houses. Hamlets are mostly withdrawn to the foothills or gravel patches. A hamlet consists of tightly compacted huddles of four or five wood-built farms without paddock or barn. Some preserve signs of old moats now serving to drain field-water away from the houses. Other hamlets are evenly scattered within a geometric grid of canals and drains, sign of a regionally planned development. The Westerner is impressed by the appearance of using every square inch of ground, and by the absence of waste patches at corners of fields or even at the foot of telegraph-poles. Farms are usually without grazing cattle, watch-dogs or other animals. Every handkerchief-patch is made to yield something, and the local saying is, "Even the stones show finger-prints", as though the pressure of man on the earth has worn through to the rock. While the plains stand empty of trees unless at shrines, the upper slopes are wooded. The pressing need for firewood means a constant attack on woodlands. Bare rock shows in every vista, and volcanic cones and sheets of sterile volcanic ash and lava appear on every horizon. Railway-lines are more prominent than roads, the latter built outside the plains and poorly surfaced; most land movement is by railway, which often runs close to the water edge and has many tunnels and cuttings. This whole landscape is more exactly and precisely exploited than many a horticultural show-place in Europe, the Japanese doing their farming in the manner of gardeners. The country round the Seto was the nursery of Japan's civilization, and many shrines, temples and forts remain as relics of the feudal phase when each plain had its daimyo or overlord. In the east stand Kyoto and Nara, the earliest centres of Japan's imperial power evolved on the Kinki lowland.

THE KINKI LOWLAND

Kinki lies in a triangular frame, one side being the coast of Osaka Bay, the other two being sharp-rising uplands. The Omi–Iga forms its eastern edge, an extension of the faulted blocks arranged N.–S. in southeastern Honshu, and rises above 3,000 feet, its rounded, granites being much incised and nearly bare following intense erosion. A faulted upland with similar landscapes lies to the north, where the

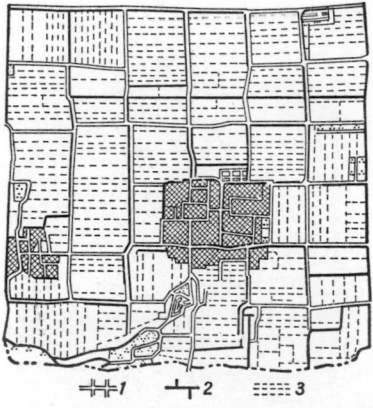

FIG. 34—Lay-out of a village on the Kinki Plain. The area shown is half a mile square; 1. indicates footpaths, 2. canals and ditches, 3. little ridges between properties

149

Tamba Upland terminates the hills of Southern Chugoku. Within Kinki rises an outlier, the Ikoma Hills, of similar N.–S. trend, dividing Osaka from the Nara Basin.

The lowland consists of the deltaic plains round Osaka opening out from the three alluviated fault-basins of Kyoto, Biwa and Nara, through which run tributaries of the Yodo River flowing from east to west.

Biwa, the largest lake in Japan, occupies much of the inner basin set between the E.–W. hills of West Honshu and the mountainous N.–S. pattern of Central Honshu. Biwa has cliffs to its west and, on its east side, an alluvial plain built from lacustrine deltas of small streams still rapidly silting the lake. Well-formed river-terraces are present on the east, though the streams across them are incised. Densest settlement and intensest farming is on the younger alluvials close to the lake. Rainfalls vary from point to point, depending whether the hills expose a locality to wind movements, particularly critical being the northwest winds which bring snow into the northern part during winter. South Biwa is more open to summer winds from the south. The northern lakeside farms must fallow in winter, cutting the padi early and drying it on poles owing to the dampness. Southern lakeside farms cultivate the padi-fields through the winter; wheat, barley and rape being sown in autumn for harvest in spring. Tea, mulberry, winter grains and summer vegetables are commonly cultivated on the terraces with irrigation from ponds. The lake has many fishing traps, and a canal cut through the western hills carries some water to Kyoto. The natural outlet (Seta River) flows south through a gorge. Local soft water has helped to attract a rayon-textile industry in small weaving and dyeing factories concentrated towards the south, where Otsu is the regional capital and historic rice market.

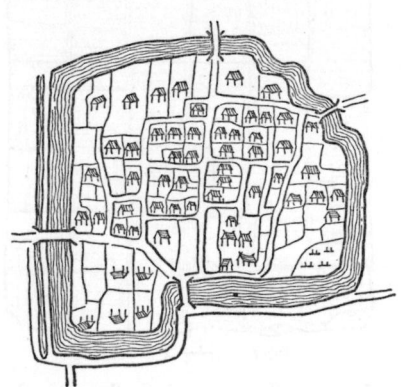

The *Nara Basin*, smaller and to the south, was nursery of the Yamato feudal tradition. Its focus, the city of Nara at its northern exit, was the first capital of Japan. Here grew the feudal system which dominated the Japanese until late last century. The Nara Basin contains large diluvial terraces, more especially to its north where they

FIG. 35—A moated village near Nara, taken from topographic map. The stilted symbols mark farm-houses set in garden plots. The village is about 100 yds. across

separate it from the Kyoto Plain. Antiquity is reflected in the many shrines, forts and palaces, and in the great density of farming population, here exceptionally high even for Japan. People live in small densely-compacted square villages, sometimes still moated and always edged by cultivated bushes. The villages are here evenly distributed over the landscape amid fields themselves squares owing to the lot boundaries being aligned to the four points of the compass according to geomancy. It gives a check pattern falsely suggesting a modern settlement, as in the U.S.A. Over three-quarters of the basin's floor carries winter crops as well as summer padi, and one-tenth is cropped three times a year. The slopes are in trees or unused. The historic association draws much tourism to Nara.

The *Kyoto Basin*, combining features of Biwa and Nara, is almost surrounded by steep hills and sheltered from the north. Its lake Ogura has been reclaimed for padi-fields. Bamboo groves mark the wetter spots, and the surrounding hills have been extensively reforested as a protection from sheet-floods. Fruit is a feature of local production. Tea

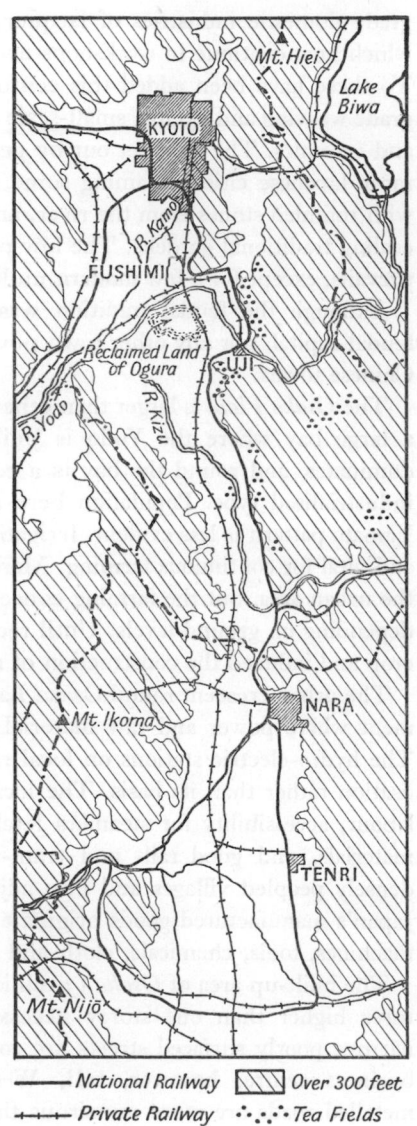

FIG. 36—The Kyoto and Nara plains from which the River Yodo flows to Osaka. The low-lying areas are padiland with continuous rotation of other crops; tea is grown on the hillsides. The Tokai route to Tokyo is by way of Lake Biwa. The map covers an area of 15¼ × 4¼ miles

——— *National Railway*   ▨ *Over 300 feet*
+—+—+ *Private Railway*   ∴∴∴ *Tea Fields*

occupies the diluvial terraces. The pattern of fields and villages repeats the Yamato style of Nara.

Kyoto, at the far north of its plain and on higher, coarser diluvials, is the only one of Japan's major cities located inland. Capital for many centuries, its cultural and religious tradition is indicated by shrines, forts and high-grade domestic industries of lacquer, enamel, bronze and silk-weaving, which now continue in workshops averaging less than twenty employees. To these have been added this century cotton and woollen mills, high-grade weaving and dyeing, small-scale metalwork, quality printing, pottery and ceramics. The city, set out by geomancy, has the squared lay-out of most Japanese cities, retaining some narrow, countrified streets cobbled with rounded stones from the river, and with plaited bamboo hedges concealing traditional gardens. The low profile of one-storied wooden houses prevails, except for a few modern multi-storied cement buildings.

Although the feudal tradition was strong, neither Kyoto, the great feudal capital, nor any other town now has the defensive wall common to Chinese towns.

The *Osaka Plain* is larger than other parts of Kinki, and reaches Seto in a large bay where the Yodo is building a delta. Urban development dominates, and round the bay is a conurbation called Honshi of highly industrialised type. Population here is dense, and in the rural area the Yamato pattern is less evident. Irrigation ponds are prominent everywhere and vital for continuous farming. Market gardens are numerous and serve the urban area, but the farming concentrates on rice and orange growing, depending on ground levels. Until recently cotton was a prominent cash-crop and induced the construction of many ponds.

The urban crescent round Osaka Bay exemplifies an industrial development where power and raw material resources were always inadequate. The hydro-electric stations on local rivers were consequent to industrialisation rather than its basis. The location factors were the huge pool of labour, accessibility for steamers fetching coal, oil and other heavy raw materials, and good rail- and tram-ways for connections both to the densely peopled villages and into adjoining regions. About one-third of Japan's manufactured goods originate here, where metal goods, cameras, machines, tools, chemicals, cloth and artificial silks are produced.

The built-up area of *Osaka* (3 million) is almost at sea-level, and structures higher than one storey necessitate piling. Flimsy buildings and narrow, poorly surfaced streets are common in the older sections; at the business centre, however, tall, Western-style cement structures and metalled roads are more numerous than in other Japanese cities. Earth-

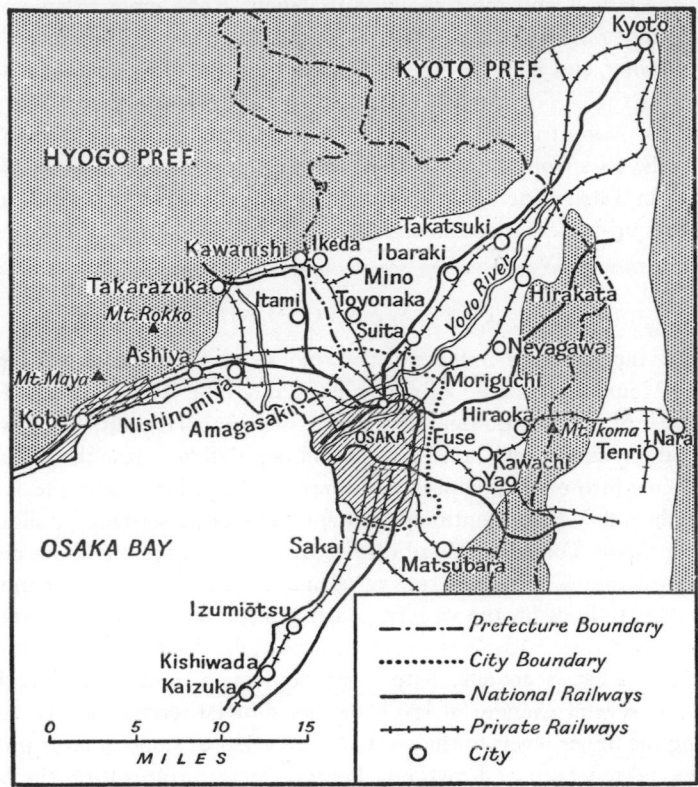

FIG. 37—Osaka and Kobe, the old and new centres of industry on the
Kinki Plain

quakes and fires have not so far necessitated rebuilding in Osaka (as contrasted with Tokyo and Yokohama). The Yodo distributaries provide
much-used urban waterways, making the city a smoky, industrialised
"Venice". Early Osaka developed round a gently sloping beach suiting
junks trading with imperial Kyoto. The modern harbour is artificial, yet
continual dredging is necessary. Lighterage is done direct between steamer
and factory, thus reducing off-loading to quays. There is an enormous
trade in thousands of small boats plying between Osaka and the dense
populations round the Inland Sea, particularly Kyushu whence comes the
city's vital coal. The limitations of the harbour are such that ocean-going
vessels now use the deep-water facilities of *Kobe*, 60 miles away and already
the terminus of many shipping services, its dock and warehouse facilities

being the largest and most modern in Japan. Kobe grew as an outport consequent to the industrialisation of Osaka. Here foreign influences were always strong, and Kobe is Japan's leading port, handling 40% of national exports in 1956. The town is restricted to a narrow site, but it has good electrified, many-tracked railway services inland. Much lighterage and junk traffic plies from the ships at Kobe to other ports round Seto. Metal-working industries, including shipbuilding and chemicals, are the foundation of its up-to-date manufacturing.

THE KWANTO PLAIN

West of the unstable much-shuffled blocks and volcanoes of Japan's Central Mountain Knot of Chibu (which includes the Great Foss and Fuji), and south of the longitudinal mountains of North Honshu, the Kwanto Plain, largest single lowland in area and in population, forms the "heel" of Japan. One-fifth of all Japanese live there in a location facing the Pacific rather than the Asian continent. Kwanto has been formed by alluvials from the River Tone and its tributaries from north and west. The deltaic extension has now linked the rocky "island" of Chiba to the mainland and forms arcuate lines on the eastern coast. To its south Kwanto comes to the sea as a great circular bay in a recent crustal subsidence. The alluvials have filled what is actually a tectonic depression, and they have been subject to several changes of level, so that diluvial terraces are common, forming the upper levels to the west where breaks of slope in river profiles and general relief are well-marked. These western terraces form the bluffs overlooking Yokohama.

The larger part of Kwanto consists of a diluvial terrace about 120 feet above the young, wet, low-lying alluvials; it carries a cover of porous volcanic ash, which causes water difficulties. The upper storey is much incised and eroded, which itself induces a low water-table, but the ash is of a kind which holds water colloidally, so that rain quickly disappears from the surface and the soil behaves like a clay. Upon the terrace wet-farming is practically impossible without the more expensive forms of irrigation, a fact which, combined with fairly severe winters, contributed to make this plain one of the last to be colonised by the Japanese, who were more expert with conditions around Seto. Major agricultural settlements in Kwanto began from about the sixteenth century. The difficulties continue and, though Kwanto contains the greatest single cluster of Japanese, its density is only half that of the Seto lowlands which are more fertile, lower in level, less colloidal and easier to irrigate. Polders for reclamation are common along the Kwanto coast, and rivers much be controlled with dykes to contain them during the rains. The Tone has been diverted to relieve Tokyo of flood risks and to spread water farther across the plain.

Two-storied land-use is a feature of Kwanto. Upon the upper levels, arranged in a rough arc and built of older, difficult alluvials, the availability of water dominates settlement. Houses commonly line the canals which provide domestic and field water. Tree and bush crops, the drier cereals (wheat and barley) and soya beans are common, and the mulberry is so widely grown that the western half of Kwanto has become Japan's greatest single silk-producing area. Upon the lower levels, intensive wet-farming for rice, vegetables and winter wheat (with multiple cropping and inter-tilling) make possible a huge production for Tokyo and Yokohama. The severe winter cold and violent winds from north and west are offset by screening the fields, and farms have hedges or trees as wind-breaks. Tea is a feature of the south and west, tobacco of the eastern half of the plain. Kwanto is noteworthy as the chief wheat-farming region, a sign of its climate being more difficult for rice-growing, and of the large area of natural terraces.

About thirty urban units of at least 25,000 people each stand upon the Kwanto Plain, the largest being Tokyo, Yokohama and Chiba which form one conurbation (known as Keihin). Three other major towns, Maebashi, Otsunomiya and Mito, stand inland where major valleys debouch to the plain. North Honshu is part of the hinterland of Kwanto, and is closely linked to it by railways. There are also multiple lines overland through the hilly west to Nagoya and Kinki.

Tokyo, one of the world's six largest cities and containing about 9 million people, stands at the head of a shallow bay. Its overseas trade and shipping interest have led to the growth of Yokohama as its deep-water outport. Tokyo has a digital form, the result of growth along highways radiating from the Imperial Palace. Its canals and old river channels are much used within the city, which has a more open and more sturdily built appearance than most Japanese cities following reconstruction after fires and earth-quakes. In the business sections, multi-storied buildings, broad metalled roads full of buses, trams and road vehicles strike a modern Western note. Manufacturing has gravitated to the low-lying flood plains between the Sumida and Arakawa rivers and along the coasts. Cheap transport, par-ticularly by lighters, and cheap labour are the critical location factors for industry, there being little local raw material except silk (no longer a key in-dustry of the city) and cotton. Manufacturing centres on metals, machines and tools, chemicals and textiles in that order, together with optical goods,

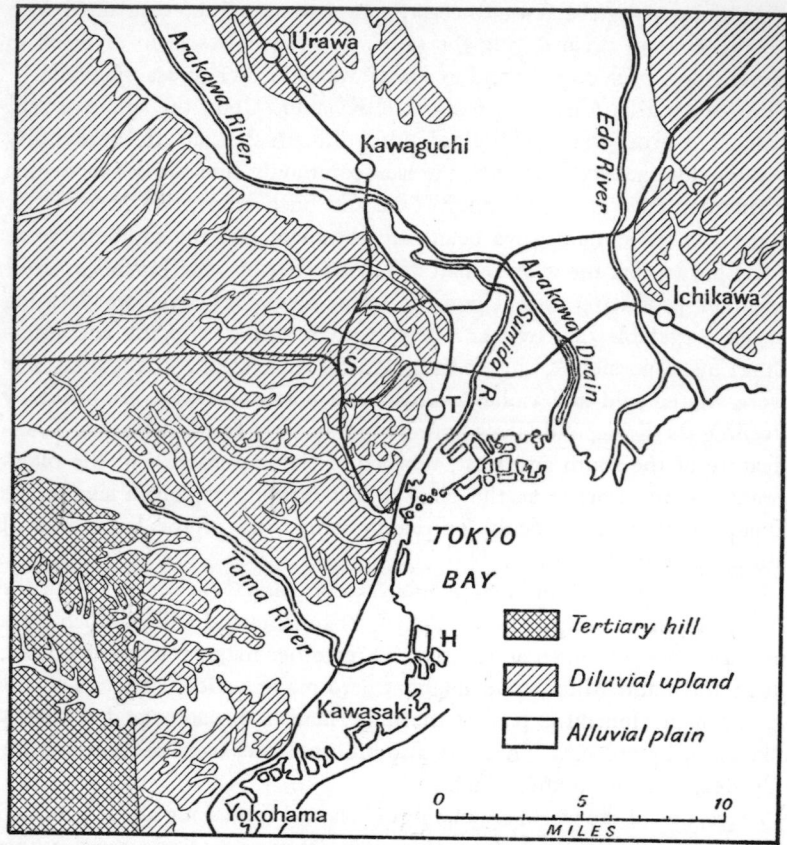

FIG. 38—Landform and transport around Tokyo. The diluvial upland is a terrace of older alluvium. To prevent urban floods, the Tone River has been diverted into the Arakawa Drain and the old delta extensively reclaimed. S. Shinjuko; T. Tokyo, and H. Haneda (location of the international airport)

cameras and binoculars. Blast-furnaces, steel mills, oil refineries, cement plants and shipbuilding yards contribute to the industrial landscape. The source of power is coal imported from Kyushu, Hokkaido and Manchuria in large quantities. Local rivers are harnessed for hydro-electric power back in the hills, whence high-tension cables run across the plain to the conurbation.

Yokohama has by no means displaced Tokyo as a port. It has merely taken much of its increase over the last two decades. Even in Yokohama, much freight is handled by lighters which ply direct to factories anywhere round the bay. The city dates back only about a century and, like Kobe, has specialised in dealing with foreign as opposed to domestic water-borne trade, handling one-fifth of Japan's foreign trade in 1956. Its exports include silk, foods and textiles for the Asian mainland, and its imports are raw cotton, rubber, wool and coal for the major industries. A trading rather than a manufacturing centre, Yokohama's associations are usually with North America and North China.

The Kwanto coasts are intensively fishing, both inshore and at a distance, the great industrial market being an incentive. Fish canneries are numerous.

THE NOBI PLAIN

Between the foci of population and industrial development centring on Kinki and Kwanto, there has for centuries been much coming and going, thus establishing the classic Tokai routes through the difficult N.–S. mountains of South Honshu. Modern motor roads and railways follow closely the historic route, hug the coast and must often tunnel through the steep hills separating the densely populated basins.

The largest plain along the Tokai route is that of Nobi bordering the deep, fault-sided Ise Bay. Near the bay head is *Nagoya*, one of Japan's four major industrial cities, reproducing landscapes like those of Osaka and Tokyo, but having no outport. Here cluster 6 to 7 million people, a fifth in Nagoya itself. More subject to disastrous flash-floods than either Kinki or Kwanto, the Nobi Plain has much the same aspect, grows similar crops on a similarly intensive, irrigated basis. Its speciality is the mulberry and silk. Silk-weaving on a cottage basis grew into not only mechanised industry but also general weaving of cotton, wool and artificial silk in factories spread along the Nagoya and Kiso rivers and round the towns of Gifu and Ichinomiya. Fine kaolin deposits have led to Nobi's second major industry—pottery. Nearly two-thirds of Japan's pottery products come from small factories on this plain.

Nagoya is about four miles from tidewater, indicating that land routes dominated its development. It stands on an old diluvial terrace which has protected it from the floods with which the erratic Kiso has scourged almost every foot of Nobi at some time. The inland location explains its slower industrial development. Cotton and wool for Nagoya mills now travel overland from Kobe and Yokohama, and its huge output of cloth goes into trade by the same routes.

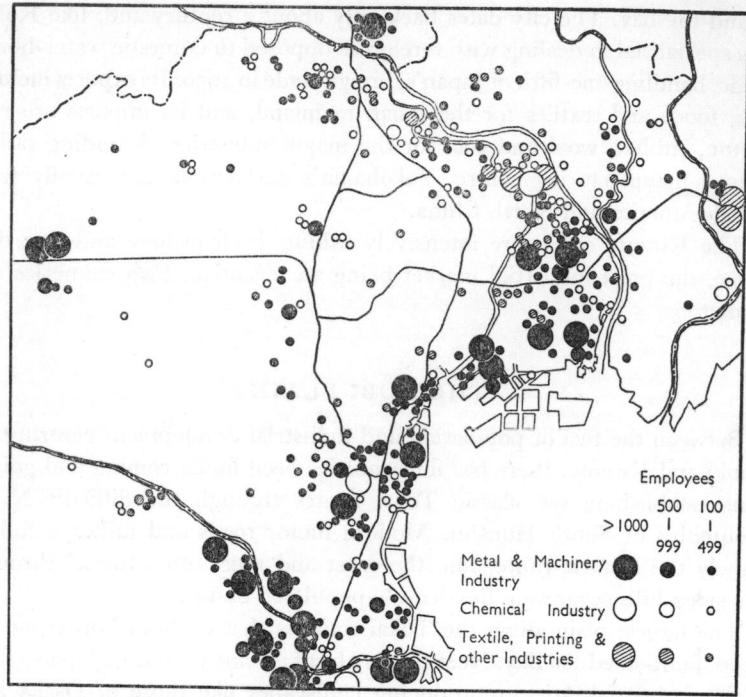

Employees

	500	100
>1000	I	I
	999	499

Metal & Machinery
Industry

Chemical Industry

Textile, Printing &
other Industries

FIG. 39—Distribution of Factories in Tokyo in 1955, showing size and type

NORTHERN HONSHU

Northern Honshu or Tohoku has a meridional alignment in its coasts, ranges and narrow valleys. Less indented than elsewhere in Japan, its bays and ports are few. The range of latitude means that Northern Honshu climate is transitional between the sub-tropical of Seto and the cool maritime of Hokkaido. North from Kwanto living is harsher, climatic conditions worsen for rice-growing and winter crops diminish because of frost and snow, leading to an increase of forest. The average farm area is double that farther south because yield is smaller and fallowing common. Across Tohoku run many limits of cultivation—sweet potatoes, tea, bamboo, the mulberry, citrus fruits disappear, the apple comes into cultivation, together with buckwheat, millet and the coarser beans. On the Pacific coast conditions are milder than at similar latitudes on the western side. This is a lumbering region, producing wood-pulp and rayon. In Kamaishi are Japan's chief domestic iron ores, giving rise to iron and steel works (using imported Hokkaido coals) and ore exports to South Honshu. Near Akita are a few petroleum wells and copper mines, and there is a coalfield at Joban. Tohoku is not industrialised and contains only 2% of Japan's factory workers. The population is low and located inland. There are a few poor fishing-ports and the ferry town of Aomori which links to Hakodate in Hokkaido. Sendai, the regional capital, contains over 250,000 people. The Tohoku railway is arranged N.–S. in longitudinal valleys with a few trans-verse links.

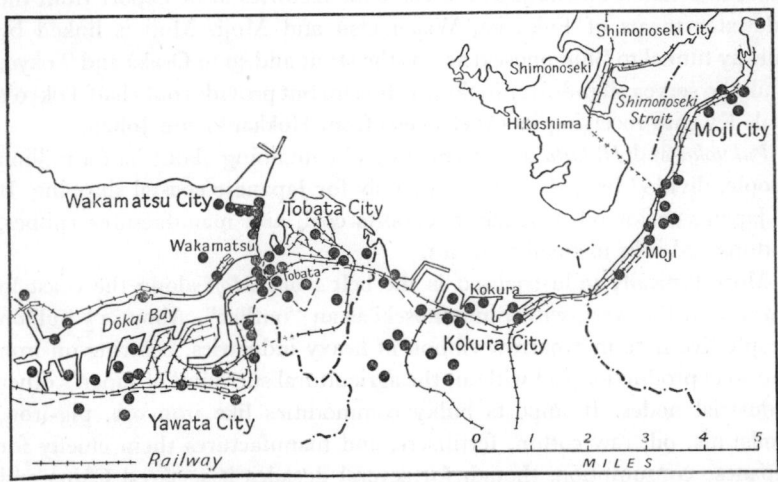

FIG. 40—The Kyushu industrial belt from Moji to Yawata, beside the Shimono-seki Strait. Each dot represents an industrial installation, the types included being, iron smelters, shipyards, steel-rolling mills, glassworks, chemicals, electrical machines, rolling stock, paper, ceramics, sugar refining, cement, flour-milling, and distilling. "Course" marks the main road

INDUSTRIAL LANDSCAPES OF KYUSHU

While Kyushu repeats many features of South Honshu, it is more moun-tainous and has smaller, intensively farmed fluvial plains, it is more emphatically tropical, reaching almost as much farther *south* of Tokyo as Sapporo *north* of it. The Kyushu climate is comparable to that of the Shanghai Delta only 500 miles to the west. Kyushu contains Japan's chief coalfield (Chikuho), lying close to its western seaboard and conveniently placed for distribution by water round the Inland Sea. The coalfield lies in a tectonic basin among hills enclosing sedimentary rocks in a belt about 25 by 7 miles. The coal, some of which is anthracite, has been frequently faulted, the seams are much disturbed, often steeply tilted, or discontinuous, and worked in small units. Many mines are adit and open-cast so that pit-head works, dumps and long lines of coal trucks are not prominent —being scattered and small in scale upon a landscape which remains largely agricultural.

A railway with many feeder lines from the basin sides runs through the valley, almost duplicating the pattern of the Onga River tributaries which are too short, shallow and violent for transport. Little coal is used near pit-head, it is railed downhill to the coast for factories at or export from the tidewater towns of Fukuoka, Wakamatsu and Moji. Moji is linked by railway tunnel to Shimonoseki across the strait and so to Osaka and Tokyo. Chikuho serves all industry in South Honshu but provides only half Tokyo's coal, Kwanto receiving its other needs from Hokkaido and Joban.

Fukuoka and *Hakata* are "twin towns" containing about half a million people, divided by a strait adequate only for Japanese coastal shipping. It is Japan's major oil-distributor, exports coal, and manufactures rubber, cottons and silks in small factories.

More typically industrialised is the belt from *Moji* along the coast to *Yawata* in the west, with Shimonoseki as an "outlier". About $1\frac{1}{2}$ million people live here in a narrow ribbon of heavy industries, centring on iron and steel production and without the agricultural surround of Japan's other industrial nodes. It imports bulky commodities like iron ore, pig-iron, foodstuffs, oil, raw cotton, fertilisers, and manufactures them chiefly for Japanese consumption, though for several decades it serviced China and Manchuria. In these small harbours converge for Inland Sea distribution much trade from Eastern Asia, North America and Europe. The region has developed at a distance from the main population and impeded accordingly. Here is the quickly grown, cramped, squalid landscape of Oriental industrialisation at its worst. Blast-furnaces, flour mills, cement works, refineries of sugar and oil, piles of coal, great dumps of ore, reeking breweries, rice mills, shipbuilding yards and a maze of railway tracks exist side by side with a congestion of workers living in narrow, cobbled streets and flimsy houses. It is a "Black Country" in a tropical climate. Moji, one of the greatest shipping ports of Japan, is so closely related to Shimonoseki across the strait that the pair form the single port of *Kammon*, which has a large fishing industry and long association with Manchuria.

Nagasaki, at the head of a steep-sided three-mile ria, is an outlier of industry round an old port isolated from its meagrely populated surroundings. Industrial development has evolved from raw materials brought in by sea, processed and then distributed by sea. For many years it was a ferry-

VIII. In rural Japan bare hills are always in sight. Here, near Mount Shirane, may be seen the village house-types, rural electricity, coniferous trees and a scattering of snow which make the characteristic rural landscape of large areas of Honshu.

IX. Osaka from the air. Its elaborate waterways lead from the Yodo distributaries and necessitate many bridges as well as facilitating movements of materials to complex, modern factories scattered throughout the city.

X. Tokyo street scene of workers leaving a factory. Western style dress is commonly used for work and business, partly because the traditional kimono is expensive. Concrete buildings, tramways and electric wiring are constant features of this bustling city.

XI. In Filipino villages the houses are usually stilted with palm thatch for walls as well as for roofs. Nearly every background includes the coconut palm.

port for Shanghai and had been the sole entry of earlier European contacts. It is a narrow-streeted town built on steep slopes which, while looking attractive, severely restrict its expansion. Nagasaki is the site of the great industrial organisation "Mitsubishi", which operates a shipbuilding yard, steel works, factories, and electrical plant upon which the place assumed modern significance despite its isolation. Its heavy coal intake comes by water from the Sasebo coalfield on another peninsula farther north, a source of power on which Sasebo became a naval dockyard. Nagasaki has become static by comparison with rapidly growing industrial cities in Honshu.

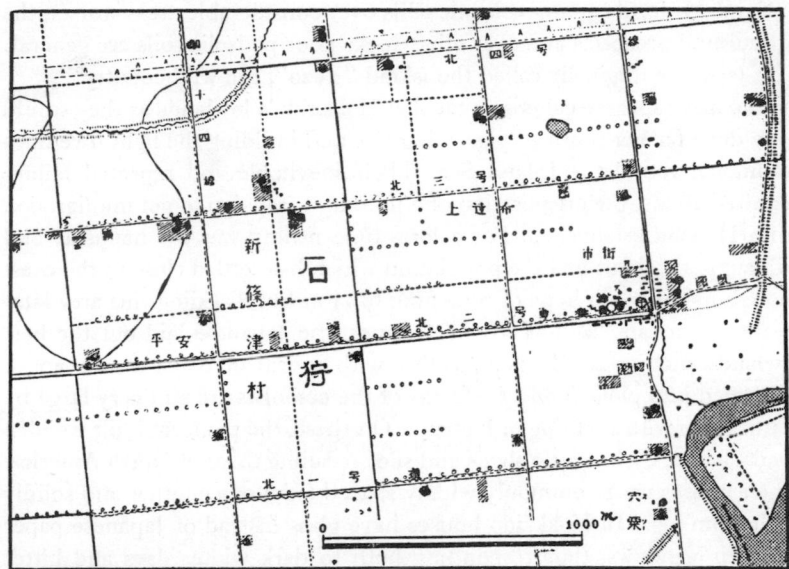

Fig. 41—Hokkaido landscape north-east of Ebetsu showing the pioneer settlement pattern of large square holdings and widely separated farmhouses

HOKKAIDO

The volcanic mountainous island of Hokkaido, comparable in climate and vegetation to the Maritime Provinces of Canada, is part of Japan yet hardly of it. Its landscape resembles the North Korean mountains, but the climate is milder. It has been settled since 1850 by a people who brought to it techniques perfected in more tropical landscapes round Seto.

Shaped like a ray with a twisted tail, Hokkaido consists of a much-faulted irregular knot of mountains (including twenty active volcanoes), which are extensions of structures in North Honshu and Sakhalin. The tail (Ohima Peninsula) is formed round a series of volcanoes reaching 6,000 feet. Alluvial plains are few and often mere wave-cut terraces without much soil, swampy and of little agricultural value. Coastal alluvial areas are either of coarse soil or poorly drained peaty lowlands. Severe climate makes this a very different setting from the densely peopled parts of Japan. At best only about 120 days a year have temperatures averaging above 40°. Dense deciduous forest (beeches, oaks, ashes and elms) still stand on much of the southwest, but to the centre and northeast the forests are of firs and spruces. Moors, grasses, sedges and mosses are common in lowlands. Infertile young volcanic soils over considerable areas worsen the agricultural prospects and over other rocks poor podsolic soils are general. The Japanese originally called the island "Yezo", the wild country.

The first Japanese colonisers tackled Hokkaido's lowlands as they would have done farther south—by growing rice and building the light dwellings traditional round the Inland Sea. Their inevitable and repeated failure required almost the organisation of a military campaign to get immigration from Honshu established. For a long time fishing was the mainstay and still supports about half the population which has settled close to the coast though no longer in hope of returning to Honshu. Tackling this area later in the American "Middle West" manner, the Japanese laid out the best lowlands such as the Ishikari Valley with a grid of roads a mile apart, quartered into plots. Thus the farms of the colonists are still very large by comparison with anything in Honshu. On these, the pioneers built wooden sheds, barns, byres, cattle sheds and silos recalling those of North America. Their houses were commonly widely spaced from one another and solidly built from logs. In Hokkaido houses have glass instead of Japanese paper for their windows, thus responding both to dark winter days and bitter cold from Arctic winds. With large farms to handle, settlers needed draught animals, and the horse has become prominent everywhere, drawing wagons and similar heavy farm equipment.

Along the Hokkaido coast, fishing communities spread in ramshackle lines of houses paralleling the coast, salting, boiling and pickling arrangements reflecting the problems of a fishing industry far from major populations. In the uplands, shifting lumbering goes on.

The major cluster of people is in the Y-shaped lowland centring upon Sapporo, practically isolating the "tail" from the main mountain zone. The cluster extends through the N.–S. Ishikari Valley. Here is Hokkaido's best farming land, but there is none of the usual Japanese intensive farming. Winter fallowing is universal but, despite the climate, padi is the leading crop (occupying only a fifth of the cultivated area), using strains evolved to suit Hokkaido by maturing in about a hundred days. All padi is sown broadcast and yields are the least in Japan. Beans, oats, potatoes are the supplementary crops in that order of acreage. Clover and alfalfa are grown for the farm animals. About a quarter of Japan's milch cows are in this area, one or two to a farm. Though the climate and terrain suggest that wheat should be grown, it ranks low in Japanese esteem. The significant factor in this anomaly is that, while the Chinese were a wheat-eating people who migrated into the tropics, the Japanese, nursed round the Inland Sea, had subtropical modes which they tried to apply as they moved into the cool temperate environment of Hokkaido.

Hokkaido forests supply most of Japan's wood for structures, houses and factories. They are the basis for a large production of paper and rayon. Hokkaido has substantial coal reserves, chiefly in a N.–S. belt east of the Ishikari depression, where seams as much as 50 feet thick are worked. Railway lines serve the mines which are more modernised than in South Japan. The coal is shipped from Otaru and Muroran. The latter also has a large smelter and iron and steel works.

After about ninety years of effort and subsidised immigation, the island now numbers about 4·8 million people, 5% of all Japanese. This migration has not greatly relieved the sub-tropical zone. More people live in towns than in rural areas, recalling conditions in Australia. A third of the people are in eight towns exceeding 25,000 each and mostly ports. *Sapporo* is the focus of the densely peopled Ishikari Valley, though there are only about 150 persons per square mile. Like *Hakodate*, the ferry port on the Ohima Peninsula, Sapporo contains a quarter of a million people.

Ainus, the indigenes of a stock radically different from the ordinary Japanese, are now scanty (about 15,000 in the whole island) and they live in remoter hilly districts following a primitive way of life recalling that of tribes in Eastern Siberia.

CHAPTER FOURTEEN

Insular Eastern Asia—Taiwan and the Philippines

IN SEVERAL arcuate lines south of Japan extend the Ryukyu group of islands, physically unstable and mostly volcanic, which have been settled by Japanese farmers and fishermen. Their landscapes recall those of South Japan, but their resources are limited by small size and isolation. They have had little significance except for island-hopping movements, such as millennia ago carried trickles of Malays and Polynesians to the Japanese islands, and such as in the World War II enabled military forces to separate Japan from its overseas positions and to mount attacks on the core area of Japan. One of the Ryukyus, Okinawa extends over a thousand square miles, and remains a major military base and a key-point on international airways.

TAIWAN

Of a different order of size is Taiwan (which Portuguese discoverers called Formosa), spreading its 14,000 square miles across the Tropic and aligned almost N.–S. paralleling the Fukien coast. Its eastern two-thirds is a mountainous, volcanic country with ranges rising above 10,000 feet and continuous down the length of the island. This relief descends steeply to the Pacific, and marks it as part of a block tilted in pressure against the edge of the Continental Shelf, a structure emphasising the link of Taiwan with the continent about a hundred miles to the west across the fairly shallow, island-dotted Taiwan Strait. While for the first half of this century Taiwan was a Japanese colony, it had historic connection with China, having been peopled with Hokiens and Hakkas from across the strait.

The mountain zone has a climate and landscape resembling that of the southern Himalyas. Heavily forested, it has small pockets of alluvium, and the main economic interest is the foothill production of black tea. Camphor trees are a feature of Taiwan forests, which include continuous stands of oaks, evergreens and cypress. Lumbering is slight and aboriginal tribes primitively in more inaccessible places.

Alluvial plains lie west of the mountains. The foothill zone is well-peopled by a million Hakka farmers, the main lowlands by about 5 million

Hokkiens. These long-settled communities were much influenced by Japanese colonists, and frequently intermarried with them. To them since World War II have been added several million refugees from all parts of China, including remnants of the civil service and Nationalist Army. Heavy erosion by west-flowing rivers has dissected the plain, across which for long stretches the drainage is slightly incised, making irrigation problems for the basic crop—padi. Rainfall rapidly changes from 50 inches per annum at the coast to over 200 inches near the mountains, and varies with aspect. Winter winds come largely from the north, summer winds from the south, so that the northern part of the island has more cool season rain and the southern has warm season rain. The south suffers considerably from drought, and is occasionally afflicted by tropical cyclones. Japanese markets during the first half of the

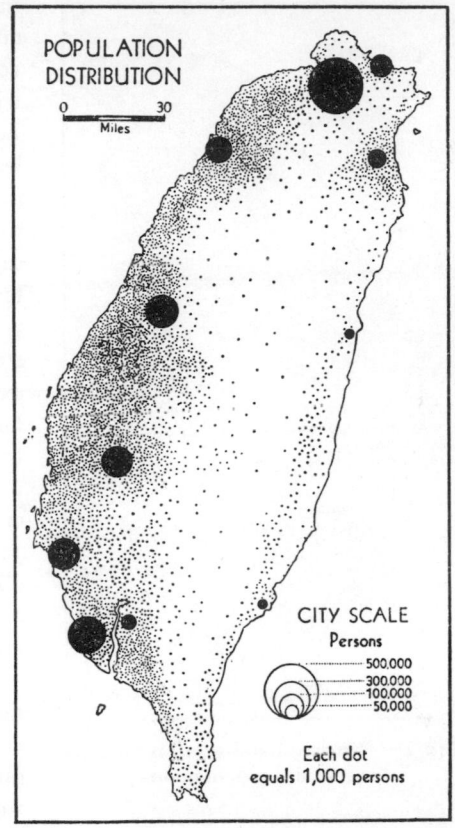

FIG. 42—Taiwan: Population. The largest city to the north is Taipeh with Keelung farther north as its outport. The largest southern city is Kaohsiung (Takao)

century gave rise to a well-organised commercial agriculture in West Taiwan, differing greatly from South China. Padi, sugar-cane and sweet potatoes, together with tea and tropical fruits, are still the basis of intensive farming. The western plain is dotted with rice and sugar mills linked by many roads and light railways to the farms and ports. Two-thirds of the cultivated area carries padi, stimulated by the huge prewar export to Japan; rice is again being exported though in lesser quantity owing to the refugee population. Probably the limit of cultivation has almost been reached, since scarcely more than 1% has been added to the cultivable area

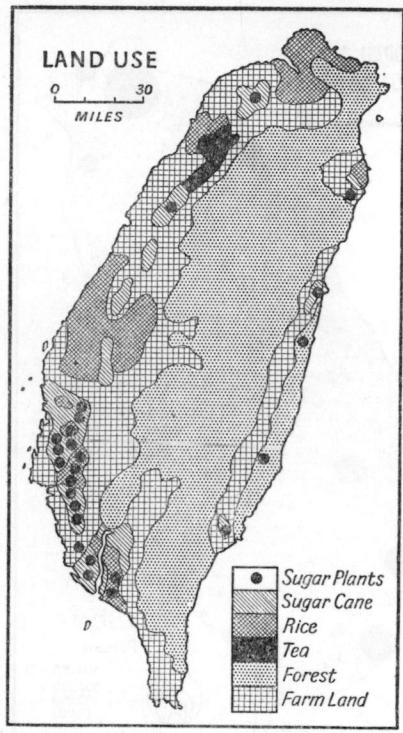

LAND USE

0   30
MILES

● Sugar Plants
Sugar Cane
Rice
Tea
Forest
Farm Land

FIG. 43—Taiwan: Land-use. The forested area is also mountainous

since 1938 despite the population doubling since then to the present 10 million. Multiple cropping is widely practised in Japanese style. Farms are small (three-fourths are less than 5 acres) and fertiliser in great demand to sustain continuous production. Both beancake (from soy) and chemical fertilisers came from Japan prewar; procuring fertiliser is a constant problem for Taiwanese, since the traditional nightsoil is no longer adequate. The island now features the production of chemical fertiliser (about 128,000 tons annually) and imports a further 30,000 tons, a consumption of about 38 lb. per inhabitant per annum—second highest rate among Asian countries. The second crop is sugar, the island ranking now as Asia's second largest exporter; in 1957 it had an output of 930,000 tons refined sugar, three-quarters of which went into international trade, largely by way of Hong Kong, Japan being a major customer.

Coal is a feature of the island's mineral exploitation, but it has only average quality. Local copper ores yield a few hundred tons a year, and over 8,000 tons of tin concentrates are produced. Evaporating pans are laid out on the dry west coast producing about 400,000 tons of salt, part of which is exported to Japanese heavy industry.

Several large towns of modern type grew up in the Japanese colonial period, mostly to the west and near the coast in response to trade in bulky farmstuffs. The capital is *Taipeh* in the far north (containing about a million people). Heavy silting has rendered it useless as a seaport, and the shipping function is now served by the port Keelung, nearly 15 miles away. Taipeh is the main trading and administrative centre, swollen by its postwar international significance. *Kaohsiung* lies at the southern end of the plain, and ranks as the second largest city (350,000 people) and a major port, as well as the island's chief manufacturing centre. It refines imported oil and aluminium ores, the latter relating to hydro-electricity from the Sun-Moon Lake harnessed by the Japanese.

Although Taiwan has few natural harbours off the west coast, much fishing goes on, engaging about 200,000 people. Fish forms a significant part of local diet. The influence of the Japanese is evident in the numerous power-driven fishing-boats. In addition, there are 75,000 acres of ponds, chiefly near the Taoyuan Delta on the southwest coast, used for both fresh- and salt-water fish. Suao on the northeast is a major port for deep-sea bonito and tuna fisheries at mid-year.

THE PHILIPPINES

In its landforms and physical environment, the Republic of the Philippines resembles Japan (1,600 miles farther north) more than South China (550 miles to the west).

The Philippines, a mountainous, volcanic archipelago a little smaller than Japan, has only a small proportion of flat, irregularly scattered lowlands, so that population is in dense clusters separated by little-used uplands. Luzon has roughly the shape and structural lines of Honshu. Mindanao is as sparsely settled and poorly developed as Hokkaido. The seas of Sibuyan, Visayan and Mindanao provide the Philippines with sheltered domestic waterways like Japan's Inland Sea, and the densely peopled lowlands round the Visayan Sea recall those round Seto. Because the Philippines is much farther south and surrounded by broad expanses of tropical sea, the islands are warmer, rainier and more equable than South Japan. Both the archipelagos suffer from earthquakes, typhoons and sudden local floods from short, violent rivers. Both have heritages of a dense natural forest cover, parts in the Philippines have been cut beyond recognition, the rest almost untouched. Wet-farming, rice-growing and sea-fishing are activities which the Japanese and the Filipinos have in common. Houses and dwellings in both are flimsy, simple, small and mostly wooden and thatched. Bamboo, reeds and leaves appear prominently in household equipment, together with many relics of self-contained farming systems. The environments being similar in the Philippines and Japan, the techniques of farming are also similar.

There are, however, significant contrasts. Half of Japan is aligned latitudinally, the Philippines is more longitudinal. No part of the Philippines is restricted by harsh winters as in Hokkaido: the deterrents to development in Mindanao are equatorial rather than sub-arctic. In the Philippines mid-summer days are 2 hours shorter than in Honshu, and Manila has a mid-winter day about 1·5 hours longer than Tokyo. While the narrow Korean Strait has given Japan much contact with the East Asian mainland, the Philippines is farther out into the Pacific, and less in contact with China than with other islands north and south. As a corollary Japan has a strong Buddhist tradition, whereas the Filipinos are mostly Catholics by contact with Mexico and Spain, and Muslim by association with traders from Borneo and the south. But the remarkable contrast with Japan is that, though the climate of the Philippines is so much more benign and the cultivated land larger, the Filipino population is one-fifth that of the Japanese. Land-use is strikingly less intense in the Philippines where the average holding is four times that in Japan, rice being basic in both countries. The Philippines has nothing to compare with Japan's industrial development or exploitation of minerals. The former exports agricultural produce, Japan imports it.

The layout of the Philippines is simple. Northern Luzon is a compact, rectangular block of mountains built of sandstones, limestones and a N.–S. belt of crystalline rocks. Mindanao is a similar block of mountains, covered with great sheets of basalt and old lava. East Mindanao is physically continuous with an arc of islands on the Pacific side, including Samar, Leyte and the volcanic "tail" of Luzon. A parallel feature on the west is the detached range of Zambales (westernmost Luzon), an arc of islands including Mindoro and Negros, and ranges in west Mindanao. Palawan, the Peninsula of Zamboanga and the Sulu Islands are aligned N.W.–S.W., being residual edges of the rift beneath the Sulu Sea.

The oldest and most productive settlement of the Philippines is a group of middle-sized islands round the Visayan Sea; i.e. Panay, Negros, Cebu, Bohol and Leyte, four of these being actively volcanic and owing their fertility to soil weathered from basic lava. A later nucleus developed by the Spaniards is the highly productive and well-settled lowland from the Lingayan Gulf through the lake plains round Manila Bay as far as Bicol. Mindanao in the far south and mountainous Luzon in the far north are regions of scant development, least population and large areas of forest—tropical deciduous in Luzon and evergreen equatorial in Mindanao.

While most economic interests centre on eleven large islands, there are 6,800 islands each less than a square mile, a pulverisation which sets major economic problems.

The Visayan Islands

Samar, Negros, Cebu, Panay and Bohol, lying roughly fanwise round the "Inland Sea" of the Philippines, total about 19,000 square miles with a cultivated area of 2½ million acres and 7 million people. Here one-sixth of the national area supports three-eighths of the population. On Bohol and Cebu nearly half the surface is farmed, but less than 5% of the cultivated

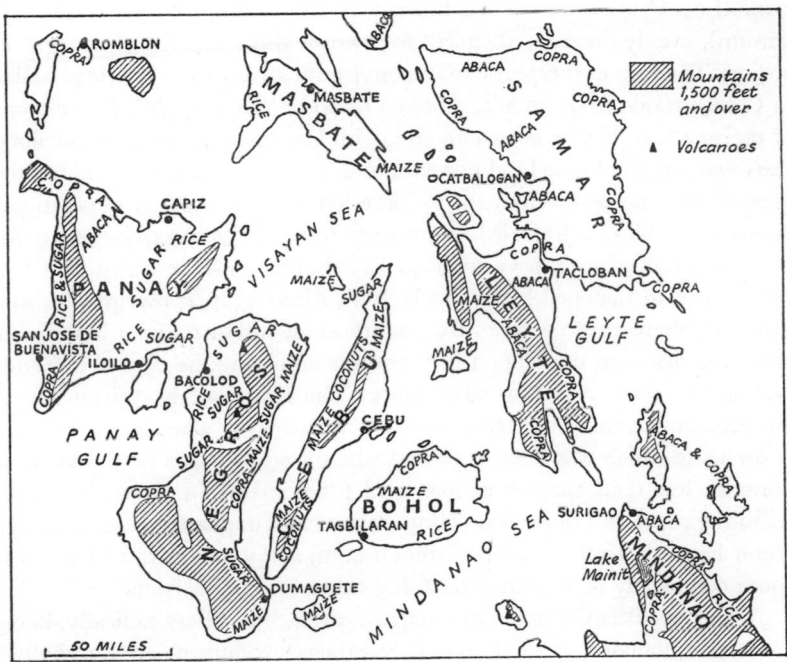

FIG. 44—The Visayan Islands around the "inland sea" of the Philippines

area is irrigated. On Panay over three-quarters of the farms concentrate on padi which occupies half its cultivated area. On Cebu, three-quarters of the farms specialise in maize and coconuts, maize occupying 60% of the cultivated area. Negros has about 40% of its farmed area under sugar-cane. Samar specialises in coconuts and 80% continues in forest. On the Visayan group, at least two people live from each cultivated acre; Cebu alone supports four to the acre. Samar, the biggest of the Visayas, contains about half as many people as Cebu, the smallest.

Thus there is diversity in the development of these nearby islands which at first glance have similar environments and have been tackled by people of a similar culture and a distinctive speech (known as the Visayan dialect). What underlies the diversity may be exemplified by comparing Negros, Cebu and Samar. *Cebu* is a hilly and elongated island built of limestone and sandstone strata upon which are scattered much broken, weathered coral. Hence its uplands are dry and often bare of anything except scrub. Erosion and weathering of the coral and limestone has helped create in the narrow lowlands soils of high-calcium content unsuited for padi. The rainfall on Cebu is one of the lightest in the Philippines (61 inches per annum), evenly distributed except for two or three months of drought in spring. The farming response to the environment is maize growing. Maize in Cebu's staple food, eaten as a boiled mash or "on the cob". Three crops of maize a year may be grown on one field. Coconuts are widespread along the coast, providing the local protein food. The high calcium content of the ground and the waste from maize have led to large chicken populations. Among the hills, a fibre called maguey (resembling sisal) is grown for export. Local tobacco has a high quality though small in quantity. Cebu people live in thatched huts usually built directly upon the ground, and grouped where a spring issues from a limestone hill or round a well. Some terracing has been done upon the foothills adjoining the coastal lowlands and much in-shore fishing takes place. The limestone has given rise to substantial cement production. Cebu City half-way along the east coast is on a site which was already settled when the Spaniards first arrived. It contains less than 200,000 people, and functions as an inter-island port handling copra and fibres, exporting cement and importing rice. Although Cebu has a difficult terrain and much high, rocky uncultivated land, it is more completely used than almost any other Philippine island.

Negros parallels Cebu across a narrow strait, but differs radically, being more mountainous, with dormant volcanoes prominent on its skyline. Masses of igneous rock dominate the structure, and the plains have fertile soils derived from weathered, volcanic material of recent date. On its west spreads the broad plain of Bacolod (about 75 by 15 miles), where farming and settlement concentrate. The mountains are thinly peopled and consistently exploited for timber, which is in great local demand for domestic buildings. The mountains create "rain shadow" effects in eastern Negros, where the climate is like that of Cebu; west of them heavy rains occur during the summer southwesterlies. Parts of the Bacolod Plain have 120 inches of rain per annum which, in conjunction with river-borne soils, has led to an economy dominated by padi and sugar-cane. East of the mountains maize, coconut and some abaca occur, repeating the economy of

Cebu, except round San Carlos and Bais which are outliers of the padi-sugar economy. The western plain dates its cane growing from this century, when Filipino sugar enjoyed a tariff protection in the U.S.A. Previously Negros had specialised in padi, which continues to occupy a large area as subsistence crop. The plain had been divided into large estates during the Spanish colonial period, and the customs of these "haciendas" continued. Parts were let to share-croppers and half the harvest went to the landlord. Sugar growing was done on this basis and, since any one smallholding had to include both food and commercial crops (some padi and some cane), it conveniently equalised the labour demand which is so uneven in cane growing. Processing the cane is done in "centrals", modern highly mechanised refineries on the lines of those in Hawaii, the older U.S. sugar-growing colony. A refinery does not grow cane, but contracts in advance with landlords and smallholders. There are eight centrals on the western plain and one in each of the east coast sugar-growing strips. Each central is the focus of light field-railways, which move the bulky cane from the fields.

While the Negros coast lends itself to in-shore fishing, it suffers from wide coral reefs which impede the approach of steamers handling the sugar. Long jetties have been built to overcome this difficulty at Pulu Pandan, but timber from the far north and the far south still send their logs in rafts across the Guimaras Strait to Iloilo on Panay, where a good, sheltered harbour facilitates loading the logs on to steamers. The name "Negros" comes from "negritos" a short, primitive, hill community still wandering in the more isolated forests of Negros.

Samar, the least developed and third largest island of the Philippines, is ruggedly mountainous and thickly forested. There are only two or three small settled valleys close to little harbours on the sheltered west coast. Standing well to the east of the archipelago, it receives the first violence of the winds and seas from the Pacific so that it has a very heavy rainfall (over 160 inches per annum). Samar has frequent typhoons; these develop at a point roughly east of it so that one in four of all Eastern Asia's typhoons cross Samar. The island is subject several times a year to storms with winds upwards of a hundred miles per hour, accompanied by torrential rains and dangerously high seas. Whole stretches of its isolated and dangerous east coast have virtually been abandoned; on its more sheltered west small-holders grow abaca, a banana-like plant from which comes "Manila hemp". Copra is the leading product, with a little padi and sweet potatoes for subsistence. A local sedge is collected for making mats which have fame throughout the islands. Lumbering here has no significance.

The Luzon Lowland

The core zone both of Luzon and of the whole archipelago is a longitudinal lowland (about 150 by 40 miles), running from the Lingayen Gulf to Tayabas Bay, through which rise two isolated volcanic mountains (Arayat and Banahao). It is flanked by faults and much-disturbed mountains, the western ranges being interrupted by a structual depression forming Manila Bay and by Lake Taal in a large round crater.

Upon this, the largest continuous stretch of lowland in the country, live about 13 million people, mainly engaged in farming rice and sugar-cane, and for whom Manila is the administrative and commercial capital central to the plain, standing where its land routes converge on a narrow neck with access to the sea.

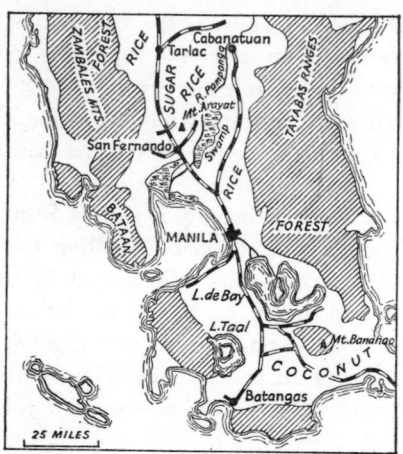

FIG. 45—The Lowland of Luzon

The plain is well exemplified north of Manila, whereas its southern half has a surface broken not only by Banahao (7,170 feet), but also by Laguna de Bay, a large fresh-water lake separated from Manila Bay by only narrow sandspits practically at sea-level. In the northern half the structure includes alternately porous and impervious materials, suiting artesian wells of which there are over 350 in Pampanga Province alone, mostly used for irrigation. Laguna de Bay is only a few feet deep but changes level according to the seasonal rains, and on its seasonally flooded edges are wide belts of swamp plants.

On the plain the climate is distinctly monsoonal. In the cool half of the year, dry northerlies blow; in the warm half, moist southwesterlies. The Pacific air stream of winter reaches Lowland Luzon after crossing the high eastern ranges, so that November to April receives less than 14% of the annual rain, bright sunlight and shrivelled vegetation marking the cool season. Summer in the lowland is very rainy, July being the wettest month with an average of 21·5 inches. Hence the warm season is one of vigorous plant growth, vegetation is lush and green, and the landscape often water-logged or flooded. Cultivation continues during the cool season wherever there is irrigation, which is well developed in thirteen regional systems.

Weathered volcanic soils are now widely spread over the plain, deriving directly from near-by vents and transported by rivers. Piedmont fans are prominent in the detailed surface modelling, and most streams press well towards the west, combining to form the Pampanga River flowing south to Manila Bay or the Agno River moving north to Lingayan Bay.

Apart from padi and sugar, the food and cash-crops, there are local specialities. The mangrove coast has much nipah palm, whose sap is distilled for alcohol; salt pans and fish ponds are common. Huge areas of coconut spread round the flanks of Banahao, where local conditions induce rains at all seasons, giving rise to large-scale copra production. Another specialisation is tobacco-growing which is most extensive towards Lingayan Bay.

But the plain is overwhelmingly a padi-farming region and contains at least a third of all Filipino padi-land. The intensity of farming is unusually high, local padi yields being half as much again as the national average (which is only about a quarter of the Japanese). The plain produces over half the Filipino padi, and the regional surplus constitutes the chief source of rice in domestic trade.

Wet padi-farming takes place on about three-quarters of the cultivated area, but only a third of it is irrigated, the rest depending on rainfall. Continuous cropping is possible, and two crops of padi each year are common, one crop being planted at the beginning of January and harvested by the end of May, the other planted in June for harvesting about December. These cycles are fairly constant on irrigated lands, but more flexible on other fields whose dependence upon rain causes the main padi crop to be grown during the wetter second half of the year followed sometimes by padi and more commonly by short-term "catch" crops such as maize, which tolerate erratic rains. Luzon padi is transplanted, and hand-cutting and hand-threshing are usual. Padi entering trade is usually treated at modern mills scattered over the plain, but the subsistence farms still use foot pounding and home milling. Maize is not a major crop, being an insurance against dry spells and a means of using poorer fields and is commonest in the foothills of Nueva Ecija, a comparatively new province where some large naciendas or estates exist.

Owing to the latitudinal range of the Philippines, the timing of peak field work differs slightly from south to north and consequently a little inter-island migration of labour takes place between the more crowded Visayan islands and Luzon.

Mountainous Luzon and Mindanao

Outside the islands and lowlands already described, the Philippines is much less extensively developed and large areas are as little peopled as Borneo. North Luzon and Mindanao, at opposite ends of the archipelago, resemble one another in having extensive forest-covered mountains whose timber is scarcely touched and where a few primitive jungle tribes still wander. Agriculture there is only in discontinuous patches, fringing the coast or in a few valleys, such as the Cagayan Valley of North Luzon, where the original Igorot terrace farming for padi goes on, largely for local subsistence only but now including high-grade tobacco as cash crop. Another isolated development near Davao in South Mindanao evolved from an earlier Japanese abaca estate which has led to pineapple canning, both being highly commercialised, worked by migrants from other islands and exclusively for export.

Mining is also scattered in these outer areas, impeded by transport difficulties and distance from markets. In Mountain Province of Luzon, gold has for a long time been mined at Baguio. From Camarines Norte in southeast Luzon and Surigao in Mindanao iron ore is being shipped to Japan. Chrome ore is worked from an exceptionally large deposit at Zambales in Western Luzon. While interesting as attempts to diversify Filipino activities, these mineral workings usually value only about a quarter of the coconut products exported from the Philippines.

Part III

Southeast Asia

CHAPTER FIFTEEN

Continental Southeast Asia

THE CONTINENTAL Southeast Asian countries include Burma, Siam, North and South Vietnam and Cambodia, and form a skew parallelogram with the Arakan Yoma and the Annamite Chain as roughly opposite sides. The Gulfs of Martaban and Siam limit it to the south while to the north high and frequently bare mountains form the scantily peopled limit merging into Yunnan and East Tibet. It is a compact unit of 750,000 square miles and 75 million people. From Rangoon to Saigon it is almost as far as from London to Rome or from New York to Florida.

PHYSICAL ENVIRONMENT

The landward mountains, still heavily forested, are more difficult to cross than the surrounding seas, and the people are isolated not only from associations northward out of the region, but also from neighbours within the region. Thus the Akyab people are separated by the forested, closely folded Arakon Yoma from the Burmese in the Irrawaddy Valley, and those in turn by the skew palisade ranges (few reaching higher than 5,000 feet),

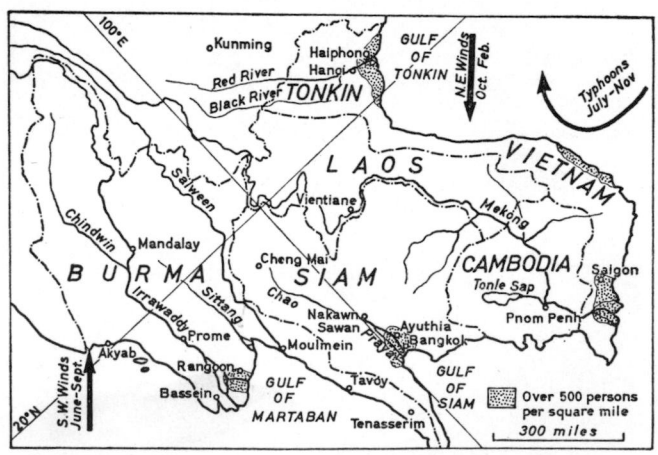

FIG. 46—Places and People in Continental Southeast Asia

XII. At Zamboanga in Mindanao, Eastern Asia merges with Southeast Asia. Inter-island trade is handled by small steamers but local people move along the coast and streams in catamarans—small craft with outriggers. Here two Mindanao passengers are wearing Muslim fez-type headgear.

XIII. An air view of rice-carrying junks at a klong junction with the Chao Praya, where stand a Chinese rice mill and warehouse.

XIV. The Bangkok Plain. A road can be seen crossing the flat plain and close to it are the seed beds. Note that dwellings are withdrawn to clusters of trees.

XV. Rangoon from the air. Steamers exporting the rice are handled by lighters in the Rangoon River whose shores are so gentle that the lighters are serviced from jetties.

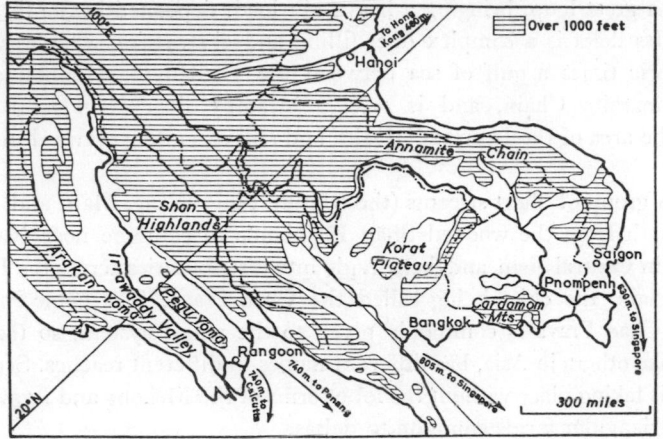

FIG. 47—The landform and river pattern of Continental Southeast Asia

north and south through the Shan Highlands, from the Siamese; the less forested Annamite Chain, which exceeds 5,000 feet only in patches, hinders connection between coastal Annamites or Vietnamese and the Cambodians and other communities of the Mekong Valley. The Korat Plateau, while by no means so high, so forested or so negative as the ranges, acts as an obstacle between Siamese, Laotians and Cambodians.

All lowlands in this continental region have mean monthly temperatures always higher than 50°, and the daylight remains fairly equal throughout the year—from 13 hours daily at mid-summer to 11 hours at mid-winter. The landscapes which have attracted most people and activity are those of the alluvial plains built up by the rivers coming to the coast under conditions which, though varying in detail, produce sedimentation and deltaic land-forms of different types and sizes. The distributions of people and agri-culture are dominated by the river valleys, particularly their deltaic parts. Three river systems set the master pattern:

(a) The Irrawaddy forms the core of Burma, rising far within Tibet, and fed steadily by snows and mountain rains, moving southwards in great zigzags through a large structural depression between sections of low, folded hills to form a huge delta which is steadily extending.

(b) The Mekong, one of the world's largest rivers (nearly twice the length of the Ganges, only slightly shorter than the Yangtse and far longer than any river in Europe) has most of its course outside Southeast Asia, runs for 300 miles parallel to and not far from the Irrawaddy, and then curves east in a great loop, bringing a heavy silt load, deposited in South Indo-china. Its delta is a complex one, filling and obstructing what was even in historic times a gulf of sea between the Cardamom Mountains and the Annamite Chain, and is now a swampy flood-plain more than twice the area of the Irrawaddy Delta and still extending seaward in great lobes.

(c) A group of short streams (the Metun, Ping, Wang, Man, and Yom) flow south from the wooded Shan Highlands to combine near Nakawn Sawan in Central Siam, and then divide into distributaries across the Lower Siam Plain, the chief being called the Chao Praya. The name Menam (river) Chao Praya is commonly given to the whole system, so that the river, like others in Asia, has different names in different reaches. Seaward silting is taking place without the lobe forms of the Mekong and Irrawaddy or the triangular forms common to deltas.

Though the Salween is one of the region's long rivers, it flows through a gorge course almost as far as the sea, and has no true delta so that it has less significance for settlement, farming and transport than many short streams.

RÉGIMES OF RAIN AND WORK

The position of the high relief is such that the prevailing winds of both seasons blow askew to the ranges, greatly affecting the rainfall pattern either side of them while inducing fairly even humidity throughout the year at higher levels, helping to account for the continuous broad-leaved evergreen forests on them. The northeasterlies of the cool season are here mostly continental winds so that to the valleys they bring bright, mild, dry weather, and to east-facing slopes of the Annamite Chain, Arakan Yoma and West Siam Ranges they bring rainy weather. The southwesterlies (commonly southerlies as has been explained) bring widespread equatorial rains, especially on western slopes and at the southern ends of the main river valleys: inland valleys and the Vietnam coast are still in rain-shadow, and drought prevails round Mandalay and in Lower Siam. The Middle Irrawaddy and the Chao Praya Valley receive least rain in Southeast Asia, the former averaging only 33 inches per annum. Thus two of the most densely settled and heavily farmed areas are the driest.

The rainfall variations and different river régimes produce very different cycles of farm activity. In Burma's Dry Zone round Mandalay padi depends chiefly on ponded water in artificial tanks resembling those of Southern India; the padi is planted in late April for harvesting in June.

TABLE 2

SOUTHEAST ASIA'S RAINFALLS

	J.	F.	M.	Ap.	My.	Ju.	Jy.	Ag.	S.	O.	N.	D.	Mid-year Daylight Hours[1]
Continental:													
Hue	7·0	3·1	4·1	2·1	4·4	3·2	3·3	4·6	14·4	25·5	29·1	15·2	13·0
Saigon	0·7	0·1	0·6	1·6	8·4	13·7	12·3	11·3	14·1	11·4	4·4	2·5	12·7
Cheng Mai	0·4	0·1	1·0	1·6	6·0	5·1	5·7	9·1	9·5	6·7	2·3	0·5	13·1
Bangkok	0·9	1·0	1·3	1·9	6·9	6·4	6·9	7·3	11·6	7·8	2·1	0·7	12·8
Mandalay	0·1	0·1	0·2	1·1	5·8	5·5	3·3	4·6	5·7	4·7	1·6	0·4	13·4
Rangoon	0·2	0·2	0·3	1·4	12·0	18·0	21·4	19·4	15·3	6·9	7·8	0·4	13·0
Moulmein	0·2	0·1	0·5	2·8	20·3	37·2	46·2	43·6	27·7	8·7	2·2	0·3	13·0
Insular:													
Kuching	26·2	19·3	14·0	9·7	9·3	8·7	7·3	8·5	9·7	12·9	13·5	19·1	12·05
Balikpapan	7·7	7·5	9·0	7·6	8·7	8·3	7·8	6·9	4·8	5·7	6·4	7·5	11·9[2]
Jakarta	11·9	13·4	8·0	5·6	4·1	3·7	7·6	1·6	2·8	4·5	5·7	7·6	11·7[2]
Pasoeroean	9·6	11·8	8·0	5·2	3·5	2·3	1·1	0·2	0·3	0·8	2·5	7·3	11·6[2]
Kuala Lumpur	6·8	6·3	9·3	10·8	8·4	5·0	4·0	6·2	7·4	11·1	10·1	9·3	12·1
Singapore	9·9	6·8	7·9	7·7	7·0	6·7	6·5	7·5	7·2	8·2	9·9	10·3	12·0
Padang	13·4	10·9	11·4	14·3	12·0	12·8	10·9	13·4	16·4	19·4	19·9	18·7	12·0

[1] June Solstice   [2] Shortest day because in Southern Hemisphere

On the Irrawaddy Delta padi depends on local rainfall which occurs well before the Irrawaddy spate; planting is in early July for harvesting in late November. In the Bangkok area, padi depends entirely on floodwater coming from the Chao Praya and other distributaries deriving from monsoon rains in the northern hills: sowing is in July for harvesting in December. On the Mekong Delta, padi depends on river flood which arrives belatedly from snow melt in Tibet; sowing in in April for harvesting in December. In the small deltas of Vietnam, elaborate irrigation from rivers is practised to make full use of warm-season rains on the Annamite Chain, as well as of the cool-season rains on the east coast; the double cropping thus made possible needs one planting in December for harvesting in May and another in June for harvesting in November.

Further consequence of the landforms is that each valley community is drawn towards the river for farming and for movement, and separated from the adjoining valley by formidable terrain. The valley peoples thus develop or keep differences of speech, custom and even of farming techniques. In Burma are preserved the culturally distinct Burmese, Karen, Shan, Chin, Palaung and Kachin clans; in Siam, the Siamese (or Thais), Shan, Karen and Laotians; in Indochina, Annamites, Cambodians, Chams and Siamese. Additionally there are many smaller, isolated groups commonly called "hill tribes". On the coast have settled other outsiders, Chinese in Indochina and Siam, Annamites in the Mekong Delta and Indians in Burma. The isolation of the interiors is long-standing, and today little produce from far inland moves into trade: few roads or railways provide modern links, and most of the streams are too rocky, too swift or too shallow and erratic for regular transport.

RICE BOWL OF ASIA

In all parts of this region farming is for food, only a minor fraction going into commerce. Exporting rice is, nevertheless, the basic national economy in Burma, Siam and Indochinese countries. To be self-contained, the farmers grow other things besides rice—spices, fruits, and fowls occurring on most farms with coconut as the chief protein coastally, and beans, sesame and pulses inland. A little wheat, maize or millet is grown in Dry Burma and Siam, and retained locally. Oxen and buffaloes, one or two to a farm, are kept everywhere; more oxen inland, more buffaloes near rivers and coasts, but neither much used for meat. The chief flesh intake is river fish or salt fish from the coasts. Wherever the Chinese settle pig-rearing occurs, this being the largest meat-eating community of the region.

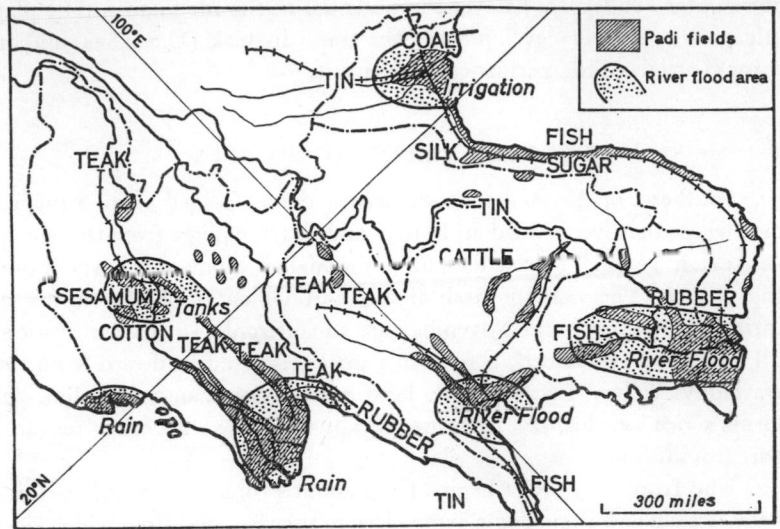

FIG. 48—The economic pattern of Continental Southeast Asia

Deltaic Burma, the Bangkok Plain and the Mekong Delta have continuous areas of padi-farming, source of the rice which goes into trade. The combined outflow of rice is a little over 3 million tons annually, Burma contributing half, Siam nearly a half and the Indochinese countries less than 6%. Burma exports 44% of its production, Siam 24%, Cambodia 2%. The yield everywhere is below Asia's average, the surplus arising more from extent than from intensity. The rice traded internationally is less than a fortieth of what Asia produces yet, since it comes from continental Southeast Asia, the region regulates rice supplies for urban and commercial populations, for workers in the oilfields of Sumatra and Borneo, the rubber plantations and tin mines of Malaya, Indonesia and Ceylon, and the factories of India and Japan. Hence this region is called the "Great Rice Bowl", and it supplies Asian staple food much as the Americas and Australia has supplied bread for the industrial populations of Europe. When looking at Fig. 48 indicating the main padi areas, which are only small fractions of each country, it is necessary to remember that the bulk export of rice draws much shipping to Rangoon, Bangkok and Saigon. Another consequence is the inflow of sacks (gunny bags) from Calcutta and East Pakistan.

For people and economic activities, the important landscapes of continental Southeast Asia are the deltaic plains, and to a lesser degree the intermontane valleys. Whatever the potential of the mountains, they play little part in current development; the trade in teak (U.S. $24 million in 1958) attracts little permanent settlement.

DELTAIC PLAINS OF BURMA

1. Southeast of Akyab are small, narrow deltas formed along a rugged coast where the rivers Kaladan, Lemyo and Mayu emerge from troughs in the Arakan Yoma. Their sediments are modelled by on-shore winds into long shapes. The risks of flash floods and violent typhoon storms in April, May, October and November are considerable, so that cultivation, still largely self-contained, is only in patches, isolated landward from the Irrawaddy Valley. Local people here are predominantly Muslim. Of Burma's rice surplus, 6% is from Akyab, which has no other resource apart from fishing.

2. The Irrawaddy Delta begins from about Prome, where the foothills of the Arakan and Pegu Yoma come close to the river and from which rice-growing is continuous. Distributaries start near Henzada; of these the Bassein River also carries regular water from the southern Arakan Yoma, and has become an important transport channel. Seaward the great tongues of sediment end in a confusion of swamps, silt bars and casuarina trees. The lobe form is most extensive to the west and least near Rangoon, where Pegu Yoma streams have only small, slow-growing deltas and where tidal scour is fairly strong. Slower sedimentation there enables Rangoon to handle river and sea shipping. The delta covers 12,000 square miles, a sixth below high-tide level and another sixth only a foot above. The surface is complexly modelled by slow-changing distributaries with criss-crossing levees of many ages and by hundreds of natural drains and swamp patches. Reshaping takes place each flood-time and on exposure the surface has runnels.

Here rice is almost the sole crop, grown largely for commerce. Until recently large farms were quite common, not always worked by the owners, sometimes let in parts to families who cultivate on a sharing basis. The delta was brought under cultivation rapidly following the entry of the British in the 1850s, and attracted Burmese farmers from upstream and from the Sittang Valley. The tremendous work of clearing the delta's swamp forest and evolving the mode of cultivation suitable for this delta was largely done by pioneer Burmese squatters, using manual methods and buffaloes. The "Rice Rush" to the Irrawaddy Delta was the earliest of its kind in Southeast Asia, the expansions in Lower Siam and Indochina

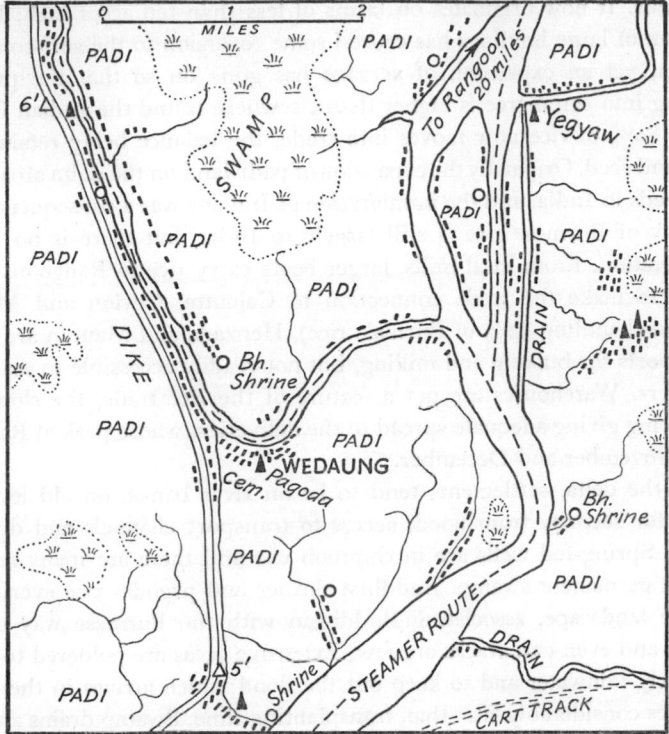

FIG. 49—Landscape of the Irrawaddy Delta, from a topographic map. The large distributary is the "China Bakir", a name of Indian origin referring to its use by the Chinese. It shows undrained swamps away from river channels, and a dike preventing a meander from pressing into padi-fields. A steamer route to Rangoon is marked. The small black rectangles represent huts, and the triangles pagodas.

following this example. The scarcity of labour was inevitably acute. Holdings mostly exceeded the capacity of a Burmese family to deal with on its own, and Indian labourers began to come in. At first they came seasonally, to help during peak work periods; later they came to settle. The transition from self-contained padi farming, to which the Burmese were accustomed, to commerce in rice set in train an entry of Indian labourers, different by race, culture and language, later led to the appearance of Indians and Chinese as traders and as moneylenders, some exacting stiff terms for the short-term loans normal to agricultural production, and in time acquiring large holdings from foreclosed mortgages.

Delta padi moves firstly along the river channels beside which stand the mills. It now originates on farms of less than ten acres each. Recent division of large holdings has caused some reversion to the self-contained system, yet an expansion of acreage has gone on so that the produce flowing into commerce is higher than elsewhere round the Indian Ocean: about 80% of rice now moves into trade, the balance being retained for food and seed. Originally the expansion of padi-land on the delta arose from the needs in India, and the immigration of Indians was a consequence; the outflow of Burmese rice is still largely to India, but there is no Indian immigration. From local mills, larger boats carry rice to Rangoon, where steamers make the trade connection to Calcutta, Ceylon and Madras. Bassein (handling 12% of Burma's rice), Henzada and Maubin are minor river ports for bulking and milling, but not readily accessible to sea-going steamers. Warehouses are not a feature of the rice trade, the slow local freighting giving adequate spread to the deliveries, whose peak at Rangoon is in November and December.

On the delta, settlements tend to be on river banks, on old levees or spits, for security from flood, access to transport channels and drinking water. Spring-fed wells are in common use and there are many areas of almost permanent swamp. Buddhist shrines and pagodas rise everywhere on the landscape, associating Buddhism with the Burmese way of life. Roads and even cart tracks are few. Extensive areas are poldered to retain the early rainwater and to keep out the flood which arrives in the distributaries considerably later than transplanting time. Swamp drains and cuts also protect from river water. By keeping the river off their fields, Burmese incidentally induce greater silting at the seaward fringes, where extension is faster than field levels are raised.

To help provide sacks, jute has recently been farmed on about 30,000 acreas, but most sacking still comes from Bengal. While mono-cultivation and single cropping are characteristic of delta farming, on its margins rubber and fruit trees have been introduced. Teak floats across the delta without affecting its economy.

Rangoon, one of Asia's "million" cities, is located on a low rocky extension from the Pegu Yoma, facilitating road and rail connections to Mandalay and North Burma by way of the Sittang Valley and a dead-end line to Prome. Waterways linking the Rangoon River to the Irrawaddy enable it to be terminus of paddle-boats from Myitkyina. The river connects the country lengthwise, and is the freight link between the "new" delta and the "historic" interior round Mandalay. Its breadth accentuates other hindrances to east–west movement. Rangoon, modern in the sense that it grew with the British administration beginning from about a century ago, has few urban amenities. Damaged considerably during the war, it was disturbed afterwards and attracted from the guerilla infested rural areas many refugees who set up squalid huts which, thatched and tattered, give the town a more rural appearance than its rank as national capital might suggest, yet indicates its function as a farmer's market town. It handles the rice exports and a diminishing outgoing of teak. The refinery at Syriam nearby has resumed activity, handling crude oil piped from the Yenang-yaung field.

3. Farther eastward, the Sittang has no true delta. Its low, well-watered valley provides a wide belt of fine rice-growing country extending inland from the edge of the Irawaddy Delta as far as Mandalay. The misfit river meanders intricately, being an abandoned course of the Irrawaddy. The Rangoon–Mandalay railway, located along the western side of the valley, handles its rice. Tides in the Gulf of Martaban partially scour the Sittang estuary. *Pegu*, placed well south and west of the river, is the local market, and was capital of an old kingdom and port of call for early Portuguese sailing ships. A tradition of resistance to Irrawaddy Burmese continues in this valley, where guerillas have been attacking the arterial routes to Rangoon.

4. The Salween discharges its great flow near *Moulmein* from a deep-set valley parallel to the coast almost to its mouth, then sharply turning west-ward. Its speed prevents deposition along the river itself and silts are swept north and south by tides to settle along the coast. From these long-settled alluvial belts 5% of Burma's rice production is obtained, supplying the mining and planting communities near by.

5. Farther south in Tavoy and Tenasserim strings of rocky islands are rapidly becoming connected by silting to the mainland. Isolated padi farming takes place. Here in a more equable climate of substantial rains a few European plantations and mines produce rubber, tin and wolfram (tungsten ore) from alluvial deposits. The tin is south of Mergui, but barely a thousand tons of concentrates are produced annually; the wolfram is near Tavoy, its production fluctuating widely with world prices.

ALLUVIAL PLAIN OF LOWER SIAM

1. Lower Siam, or the Bangkok Plain, is the low-lying, alluvial surface forming a rough rectangle between Prachinburi, Saraburi, Peiyuakiri and Ratchburi, and with extension inland to the confluence near Paknampoh. These towns are located inland on the rivers Prachin, Pasak, Chao Praya and Meklong, coming respectively from the east, northeast, north and

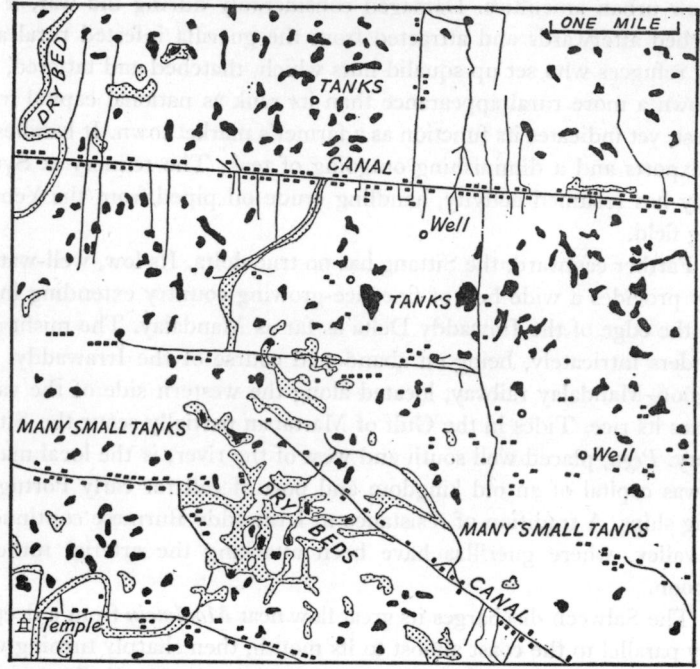

FIG. 50—The alluvial plain of Lower Siam, taken from a topographic map centred on 14° 8′ N., 100° 24′ E. showing a confusion of old dry water channels, drainage canals, small scattered tanks and wells, with bunds (beside drains) settlement

west; all contribute to the sediments now partly filling a large structural trough. Seas beating into the Bight of Bangkok from the south keep the seaward edge of the sediments straight, and partly account for the plain being more above sea-level than the Lower Irrawaddy. The rivers flowing to the plain are short, their flow is as erratic as the local rainfall. They vary quickly and directly with the rains which, like those of India, begin abruptly, starting in April after a four- or five-month drought. The fall on the plain averages 50 inches per annum, and is not significantly greater in the northern hills whence come the streams. The low rainfalls, worsened by low effectiveness in the bright, hot weather, show wide variability. Many "streams" across the plain are only strings of pools for several months a year. The Chao Praya is the only perennial distributary. When spates occur, the parched, dusty top-soil is quickly washed into the streams, whose heavy loads are dropped irregularly in spits and levees, quickly filling drains and beds of distributaries. Because the rainfall is inadequate for wet-farming, the crop depends on the streams. The rush of water from the north first fills the main distributary, gradually pours into the other distributaries, and in good years all overflow to form a sheet-flood over the whole plain, which is then receiving its rain. Sheet-flooding, which to be adequate must maintain for several months at Ayuthya a level 11·5 feet higher than the sea in the bight 35 miles away, seasonally endangers the farms which cluster on small mounds, on levees or beside streams. It obliges the farmers to maintain small puntlike boats to get about among their flooded fields. Stilted houses are usual, and the dwellings of some short-lease farmers are on rafts, which provide both safety and mobility. The plain is covered not only with a complex of old water-courses, but also with drainage ditches (klongs), dug to spread the flood rather than control it and commonly with W.–E. alignments.

How great the water variation may be is exemplified from the Chao Praya at Paknampoh, which in the dry first three months of the year has a mean flow of 4,000 cubic feet a second and increases by about July to 54,000 cubic feet per second. At Chainat the average change of level is 38 feet. On-shore waves induce sandbars across the distributary mouths, and in the dry season tidal water may be felt as far as 50 miles upstream.

The distributaries have changed considerably during historic times. Main channels were once those farther west, but streams from the Western Mountains have added substantial silt so that the alluvial surface is now higher in the west, less affected by sheet-floods and less reliable for padi. Some "tanks" have been built as an alternative, but prove inadequate. Large areas of bush are common in the west, and offer coarse grazing for cattle moved over in that direction seasonally from the central and eastern padi farms which lack fodder grasses. Several centuries ago the western distributaries were the centres of farming activity, marked by historic ruins. The Tachin, however, is no longer regularly full. East of the Chao Praya modern water controls and irrigation canals have been constructed in large grid patterns round Rangsit and Chainat, the latter having an irrigation barrage across the Chao Praya itself. These modernised zones on the plain are the scene of great commercial mono-cultivation of high-grade padi, on large properties using only Siamese labourers or sharecroppers. Elsewhere the padi is from smaller farms, often sharecropped or owner worked and close to self-containment. Settlement concentrates on the water-lines, away from which regular domestic water is scarce. Overall density of people is low. To each house group, characteristically linear, the social centre is the Buddhist temple, marked by sharp-pointed pagodas standing on slightly higher levels and often a refuge from flood.

Development on the Bangkok Plain has been most recent, the greatest rate of extending its riceland having been in the last fifteen years. Commerce in rice led to immigration of the South Chinese, who play a large part as middlemen, collecting, bulking, milling and shipping the rice. About a thousand small oil-driven mills, mostly Chinese, are scattered along the waterways in and around Bangkok, where also the Chinese concentrate, and whither move thousands of small farm boats coming from the klongs. The exported rice derives from a zone not greater than 30 miles radius from the city, which has so many waterways that it is also called "the Venice of East Asia"! Cattle and supplementary foods are purchased by the plainsmen. The canals serve needs in fields and transport, and act as "high street", public water supply and public sewer. All village houses are of wood and thatch, the pagodas of plaster or stone.

About 60% of Siamese padi and all its exported rice come from this dry plain. Owing to variations of surface and of flood, methods of cultivating differ from place to place. Where local water is more dependable or showers precede the flood, transplanting is practised. Where rain and spate are coincident or long delayed, broadcast sowing must be used since the ground cannot be worked until softened. In less reliably watered areas padi cannot always be grown, so farmers crop vegetables, maize, pepper and tobacco for local use. Neither off-season cropping nor rotation are usual in the commercial farming areas. Cattle may be seen everywhere on the rural landscape, a couple per farm being needed to work the heavy ground quickly.

The Meklong and Prachin Rivers have direct natural outlets to the bight, but much of their water is diverted into the E.–W. canals and out across the plain.

Bangkok is the only city in this rural region where live two out of three Siamese. It is too far within the Chao Praya (called "the Bangkok River" below the city) to be directly accessible to ocean-going steamers, which cannot cross the bar and operate with Chinese lighters. Unlike Rangoon, Bangkok is not a river port, since the Chao Praya carries inland only punts and rafts. Siam's coastwise shipping is negligible. Yet Bangkok is reaching the "million" category, and functions as the political, social and commercial capital, reflected in its mixture of building styles and peoples. Large palaces and gilded Buddhist temples adjoin modern office buildings and "amphibious" wooden houses beside or floating on the canals. Teak rafts float down from far north during the wet season. The plain has no other outlet except Bangkok, and its mangrove coast has some salt pans. The road system is discontinuous, partly because rice moves by water. Railways link Bangkok north to Cheng Mai, northeast across Korat and south through Kra. A major international airport indicates Bangkok's position on the global air-routes from Europe and India to Japan and Australia.

A few market towns are spread across the plain, chief being *Ayuthya*, the previous capital and silted river port, now a marketplace for farmers using its maze of shallow klongs. Set within a cut-off loop, Ayuthya is not easily reached now even from Bangkok.

Prachinburi and Ratchaburi are countrified market towns in the lower parts of their respective rivers. Nakawn Sawan is head of the river towards the northern fringe of the plain, where rocky outcrops from below the alluvium act as a funnel through which the upper water pours before dividing across the plain.

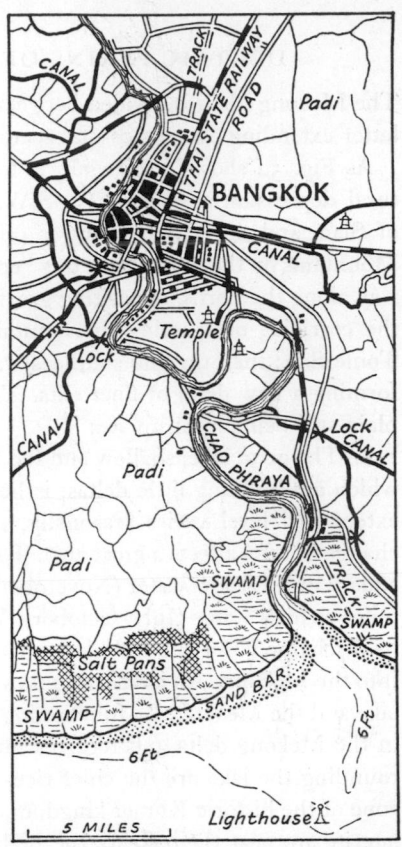

FIG. 51—Bangkok and the coast of the Bight. The lighthouse marks a bar where the sea is shallower than the actual river mouth

East of the bight are small coastal plains built by short streams from the Cardamoms, where small, reliable padi-farming goes on in an isolated economy more self-contained than on the Bangkok Plain and centring on Chantaburi.

189

DELTAIC PLAINS OF SOUTH INDOCHINA

The Mekong Plain is divided between Cambodia and South Vietnam, the latter extending over its coastal sector.

As Fig. 52 shows, the region is formed by the filling of a long structural depression aligned N.W.–S.W. between the Dang Rek Mountains of Siam and the Vietnam ranges on the north side and the Cardamom Mountains on the south. Into this "corridor" the Mekong enters from half-way along the north, depositing great loads of silt as an "old delta" across the corridor, obstructing the natural drainage to form the large lake of Tonle Sap: then turning southeastwards, dividing into distributaries and forming a new delta of finer silts. The three distinct parts of the alluvial plain still being built up are:

1. The great lake, shallow and fed by short streams from north and west which are building little deltas, is heavily colonised by aquatic plants. Its extent and level varies seasonally, the banks being so flat that a small change of level affects a great area. Tonle Sap has an area of less than 1,000 square miles at low water (November–June), and may exceed 4,000 square miles at high water (July–October). When the Mekong is in spate, part of its discharge flows into the lake; when it falls, the lake discharges southeast into the Mekong. An alternating flow takes place in the channel linking the lake and the Mekong. By functioning as a sump, Tonle Sap regulates flood in the Mekong delta and receives much silt which hastens its infill. Surrounding the lake are the chief rice-growing areas of Cambodia and core zone of the historic Khmer kingdom, whose archless, Hindu ruins built of laterite are near Siem Reap, the highwater limit of the lake. Greatest extents of padi-farming are to the northwest. Tonle Sap teams with life and is extensively fished. The fish are dried, smoked, fermented into sauce or floated alive in cages to coastal markets 250 miles away. More fish are produced annually from this lake than from the North Sea.

2. The "old delta" has a surface of clays and gravels irregularly spread and dumped across the lowland. The patterns are very confused, and variations of level are considerable, partly because the streams which model the surface change direction and intensity seasonally. The surface carries much padi-land amid swamps and forest patches; the substantial surplus from this discontinuous cultivation moves by water to Pnom Penh, at the confluence of the Mekong and the Tonle Sap River. Many ruins and shrines of the massive pyramid type recall an ancient Hindu

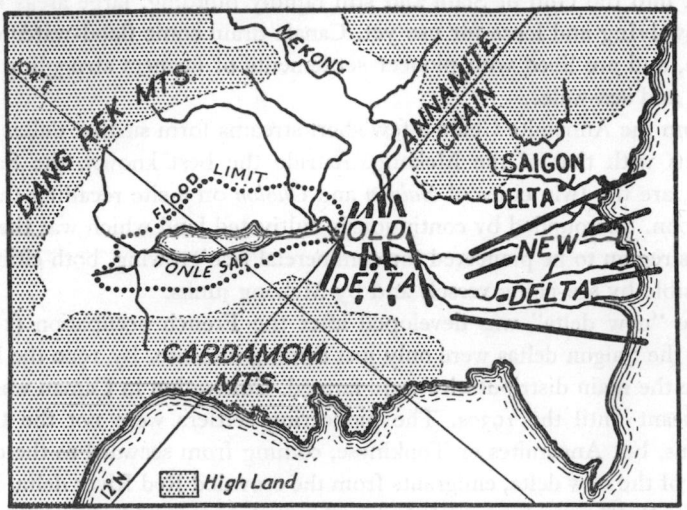

FIG. 52—The Lower Mekong Plain and Tonle Sap

colonisation on this inner delta. At *Pnom Penh* converge waterways from the lake, from the north along the Mekong and from the southeast along the distribuatries. Shallow steamers can reach this little town, but, though the Mekong is broad, it is not traversed commercially much beyond this point, because the irregularities of sandbanks are little known. Often the channel from Tonle Sap to Pnom Penh is so mud filled that even native craft have to be slid through it.

3. The "new delta" has an eastern portion laid out by large distributaries (none named "Mekong"), which have formed long lobes seemingly twisted to the left by the discharging water. Their surfaces are crossed from side to side by drainage canals with strings of wooden huts beside them; these distribute flood-water like Siamese klongs. Sheet-flooding is the basis of local wet-farming. Rural people here are as waterborne as those in Siam. Local rains occur from April to December, and are supplemented by river spates from October to January when the delta may be 15 feet under water for hundreds of square miles. To padi farmers this flood, of a scale beyond control by local people, presents a problem which they have solved by evolving a long-stalked padi able to grow through deep inundation.

A different condition exists southwest of the delta, where longshore sea movements have swept the silts into a great cuspate peninsula (of Camau), thrust into the Gulf of Siam and still rapidly building, large areas being too low-lying and loose for use yet. Canals drain some flood-water westwards, and are lined with pioneer settlements of farmers struggling with river- and sea-water.

From the Annamite Chain a few short streams form smaller deltas continuous with that of the Mekong. Astride the best known, the Saigon River, are the twin cities of *Saigon* and *Cholon* on a site recalling that of Rangoon. Surrounded by continuously cultivated land which was the first in this region to be pioneered for commercial rice growing, both cities are accessible by sea-going vessels and by Mekong junks.

The "new delta" was developed after the French occupation (1860), when the Saigon deltas were only just coming into use. By 1900 the lobes beside the main distributaries were farmed. Cultivation in Camau was not significant until the 1930s. The pioneering settlers were not the Cambodians, but Annamites or Tonkinese, coming from seaward to the outer edges of the new delta, emigrants from the crowded Red River delta. Here too, South Chinese have settled, now dominating in middleman activities. The sector round Saigon has been the scene of farming other than that mono-cultivation of padi prevailing along the Mekong. Rubber and tea plantations were established by French companies after the Malayan pattern, and pepper, pig farming and vegetable growing by the Chinese. In the outer new delta, large holdings were managed by the French for padi cultivation, a unique European participation in Asian-style farming which has now ended.

Population on the Mekong Plain is as irregular as the modelling of its surface. Large empty areas are still left in swamp-forest, generally indicating difficulties with flood-water. Over 12 million farming people are living here, greatest density being on the new delta whose outer lobes are almost as densely peopled as the Red River Delta. People are fewer in Cambodia, where disease has offset—and perhaps been a consequence of—long occupation. Everywhere the dispersed farmers live in wood and thatch huts loosely grouped. *Saigon* is a Western-style city of roughly a million people, and *Cholon*, also of "million" size, is Chinese in people and building styles. These cities handled the huge prewar trade in rice from Southern Indochina and were linked with other Asian countries as well as to France. Saigon is now only the capital of South Vietnam. Cambodia is developing *Pnom Penh* for exporting its rice and as national capital, though it retains the open pattern of market town. It was always connected by shallow river vessels to Saigon, to which there are also a deteriorating road and railway. Another railway line goes from Pnom Penh to Battem-

XVI. Padi for export is carried towards the Irrawaddy in sacks, often to slow-moving sailing craft which take it downstream to a mill and the wholesale exporters.

XVII. Insular Southeast Asia has the world's most extensive workings of alluvial tin. Here a Chinese miner directs a jet of water against an ore-bearing gravel which in Malaya may contain nearly a pound of tin ore per cubic yard. The jet is partly balanced by a tray of rocks.

XVIII. Singapore from the air. It is a modernised city with well-equipped docks but the flow of traffic is generally so heavy that many steamers anchor off shore and deal with Chinese lighters. As many as three hundred steamers at a time may be lying in Singapore waters . . . and in sight of Indonesian islands on the horizon.

bang, a rice market northwest of Tonle Sap. Air routes link Saigon, Pnom Penh, Siem Reap and Bangkok.

Between Saigon and the Red River, the rock-bound coast of Central Vietnam has small embayments containing the deltas and flood-plains of many short streams from the Annamite Chain, which are violent because rains are intense and the near by hills deforested. Connected by road and railway, these little lowlands contain dense populations exploiting the deltas intensively, using multiple cropping and year-round cultivation, irrigating in the warm, dry season and taking advantage of the cool-season rains. Rice is the dominant interest, yet maize, millet, vegetables, tea, yams, sugar cane and fruits are grown and pigs kept. Much sea fishing takes place, but heavy seas in autumn isolate the coast for weeks at a time. The deltas yield little surplus because the populations are dense and confined. The Annamite people of these little deltas are long-standing settlers from Tonkin, but they have become so congested that they are migrating to the Mekong Delta.

INTERMONTANE VALLEYS OF BURMA

The longitudinal valleys of the folded Arakan Yoma have only primitive settlement, and they remain largely unused. Rivers make a trellis pattern through the ranges, often creating swamps along fever-ridden valley bottoms avoided by hill-people. Many non-Burmese "hill tribes", with distinct languages, religions and cultures, are scattered in these valleys, commonly dwelling on the healthier slopes and hill-tops. Shifting cultivation and the hunting associations occur. No significant routes traverse the Yomas, the Ledo Road from Assam to Myitkyina being now abandoned. The Chindwin, a major tributary helping to regularise the Irrawaddy, is the largest stream, only farmed where its flood-plain adjoins the Dry Zone, round the market town of Monywa (see Fig. 74).

The Dry Zone. Burma's largest intermontane valley is the Dry Zone which, though suffering from a long drought season and low rainfalls, was the core zone of Burmese people. A variety of surroundings and contacts meet there, making possible an agriculture more mixed and self-contained than in the Delta. It is easier to deal with environmental problems in the Dry Zone: here are little plains at several levels, streams of several régimes and several kinds of unleached soil. The broken terrain has its counterpart in small farms. Padi is grown in limited localities (totalling $2\frac{1}{2}$ million acres) at valley bottom below the general level. Large tanks for water storage are common everywhere (Fig. 53), and planting is in late April for harvesting

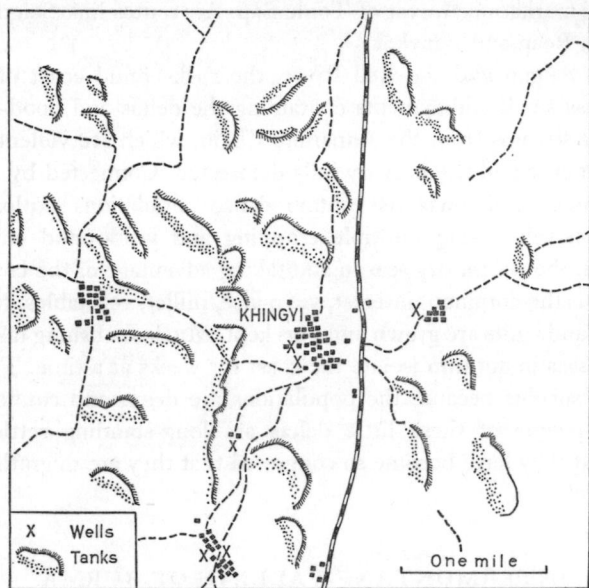

FIG. 53—The Dry Burma landscape, from a topographic map. Note the nucleated settlement, and the absence of streams. Mandalay is a few miles to the north

in July, a régime different from that on the Delta. A black waxy soil is derived from volcanic materials (the volcanic Mount Popa overlooks Dry Burma from the Pegu Yoma), enabling the cropping of a poor-grade cotton, relevant to local clothing though some is still traded overland into Yunnan. Groundnuts and sesame for staple edible oils are widely grown as short-term rotation crops in small lots, producing a regional surplus. Four million acres are under millet, here a more reliable crop than padi. Rotation is a feature and involves bean and pulse crops. Cattle are numerous and necessary for the heavy field work in dry fields; they graze on the savannah. Dry Burma rears the cattle used on the Delta.

The Dry Zone is nearly self-contained. Its population per cultivated acre is two or three times that of the Delta, so that the regional net surplus is small. Rafts of teak float through from the north en route to the coast. Cottage industry enables highly decorative silk and cotton fabrics to be produced for the local market only.

Fingers of development like that in the Dry Zone extend into the mountains round it, the largest being along the Sittang which has continous cultivation down to its mouth. The banks of the Irrawaddy southward are not continuously cultivated or settled. Beyond the Dry Zone, near Pakokku where the Irrawaddy turns south again, are the oilfields of Chauk and Yenangyaung, linked by pipelines to the Syriam refinery. Now partly nationalised, the field produced 470,000 tons of crude oil in 1958.

Mandalay, with ruins of historic grandeur, is the largest town of the Dry Zone, suffering from increasing isolation as transport deteriorates. Its moats and walls mark its strategic significance to movements along the Upper Irrawaddy, the Shan Valleys and the Chindwin, by restless hill peoples from the north and along the Sittang Valley to the once-powerful kingdom of Pegu whence came Siamese invasions. Other little towns in the zone, along the rivers which dominate transport, are markets for local oil-seeds.

East of "Dry Burma" is the cooler, more complex hill and valley country of the Shan Highlands and their extensions north and south, where a little subsistence farming goes on together with a little tea-growing trade. Once popular for holidays from the centre and south, the Shan country is reverting to self-containment. Its teak moves into commerce, but the lead-silver mines of Bawdwin are nearly exhausted. The Shans constitute the largest non-Burmese group in the country, and extend beyond Burma into Siam, Laos and Yunnan. *Lashio*, chief town of Eastern Burma, is the railhead from Mandalay and terminus of a caravan route into Southwest China.

INTERMONTANE VALLEYS OF SIAM

(a) The thickly forested Western Mountains of Siam contain long, dead-end valleys, irregularly settled and cultivated except close to the Bangkok Plain.

(b) North of Nakawn Sawan are valleys converging southward and carrying the Chao Praya headwaters. Subject to "flash floods", they contain pockets of alluvial soil discontinuously cultivated. Their climate differs little from that of the Bangkok Plain. At *Cheng Mai*, a little northern fort and second largest town of Siam, the rainfall régime resembles that of Bangkok. Padi farming is only possible with simple irrigation along the rivers. Remoteness here obliged the scattered farmers to be diversified to maintain themselves. They show many transitions between shifting cultivators and settled farmers. Teak is the chief product in trade with Lower Siam. Cheng Mai is centre of the lumbering, half of which goes on in the Man Valley and a quarter in each of the Wang and Ping Valleys. Where the main headwaters converge, towards Paknampoh, settlements keep back from the rivers because the combined streams form large seasonal "lakes" owing to the narrows near Nakawn Sawan; together with the slight variations of régime from stream to stream, the ponded waters help regularise the floods delivered to the Bangkok Plain. This confluence was the centre of an old Thai kingdom, before the Siamese occupation of the Plain.

The strategic railway to Cheng Mai carries only light traffic, but gives a timber outlet during the dry season when the streams have little water. So isolated is this zone that elephants are still used in the timber trade.

The Pasak River running separately southward and parallel to the Korat Scarp is continuously farmed only where it adjoins the Bangkok Plain. Farther east and south of Korat, the Prachin Valley is widely farmed, almost imperceptibly merging into the Tonle Sap rice-lands.

(c) Different from most of the intermontane units is the low, sandstone plateau of Korat, tilted eastwards from the scarps separating it west and south from the plains. Its inset rivers, typical of sandstone landscapes, drain east to the Mekong; yet commerce in that direction is negligible. The Korat landscape carries savannah with coarse thorn and bush vegetation used for cattle rearing. The flat-bottomed, steep-sided valleys contain swamps difficult to clear owing to their erratic fluctuation, but considerable poor-grade padi is now produced in places. An open-patterned market town, *Korat*, capital of the thinly peopled, poorly watered region, is located to the southwest, significant of the ties to the Bangkok Plain now emphasised by the railway. From the plateau come cattle replacements for lowland padi farms, and also the inferior padi which releases better qualities to trade.

THE VALLEYS OF LAOS

The riverine state of Laos consists of many intermontane valleys tributary to the Middle Mekong. They are less settled than their counterparts in Burma and Siam. While the Mekong is their link, local self-containment implies little use of it. Primitive hill people (including Man, Liao, Moi and Lolo) are grouped in valley chieftaincies, cultivating dry padi and maize, often on a shifting basis, and keeping cattle, their chief trade product. Confluence locations give rise to a few regional market-places. Farther downstream several larger valleys from the Annamite Chain have considerable acreages of scattered wet-farming merging with the economy of the old Mekong delta; each has a confluence town on the Mekong, whose rocky rapids near Stung Treng hinders transport through Laos.

It is probable that these little-visited, thinly settled and little-known intermontane valleys and the adjoining hills contain mineral resources. To difficulty of access is now added the danger of insecurity and infiltration from Yunnan, so that bringing the area into fuller use is increasingly unlikely. Settlement is restricted by the prevalence of a type of malarial mosquito notorious among the hill people and infesting the foothill vegetations everywhere from the Annamite Chain to the Arakan Yoma.

KRA—THE ISTHMUS OF TRANSITION

Siam's Western Ranges continue southward and, becoming maritime, take on a different character. The skew ranges form so narrow an isthmus that in places less than 20 miles of land divide the Bay of Bengal from the Gulf of Siam. Rain comes from both winter northeasterlies and summer southwesterlies, which in combination with insularity create a climate of equable raininess and temperature. Heavy silting occurs on both coasts, which have shallow shores and steep rocky islands. Here and there small deltas have been formed by the short streams. The isthmus was a well-used portage route between either side at times when sailors feared the detour round Malaya. South Indian traders and settlers moved this way long before European shipping reached Asia, and by this now-abandoned route Hindu cultural influences came to Siam and Indochina. European traders used Kra routes as late as the Napoleonic wars, and building a sea-level canal there was often talked about until World War II.

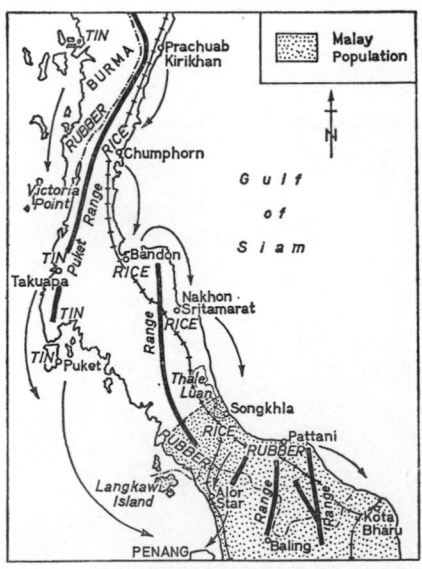

So equatorial is the climate of this isthmus that 100,000 acres of rubber have been planted. Much alluvial tin is mined at Puket, so that the economy is more Malayan than Siamese. Immigrant Chinese

FIG. 54—The Kra Isthmus showing relief, race, products and the direction of trade in rubber and tin

and Indian labourers are prominent because Siamese keep to their subsistence farming on the small deltas. Always on the outer fringe of Burmese and Siamese interests, the isthmus is now shared by them. Here Siamese come into contact with the Malays, the outer community of Insular Southeast Asia. A railway runs along the isthmus carrying a light trade and few passengers; it serves to move 13,000 tons of tin concentrates and 90,000 tons of rubber to market yearly in Penang or Singapore. Roads are discontinuous, and coastwise shipping movements hindered by the rapidly silting shores.

CHAPTER SIXTEEN

Insular Southeast Asia

INSULAR SOUTHEAST ASIA spreads on both sides of the Equator and is subdivided by large seas. Its land area (747,000 square miles) roughly equals its continental counterpart, but the islands sprawl over a space as large as the United States. From westernmost Sumatra to the eastern tip of Celebes is as far as from London to Cairo; from North Malaya to Jakarta is as far as London to Rome. Over 100 million people live here, averaging a denser population than Continental Southeast Asia. The region is mostly equable in temperature and uniform in rainfall, with roughly equal daylight throughout the year.

Having a high proportion of mountain, its landscapes are chiefly "hill and valley", but there are some plains built from deltaic alluvium by swift streams from small catchments. Much coastal plain is still swamp or only recently cultivated. Thousands of rocky islands jut through the shallow Sunda Platform seas, few having economic significance, mangrove and coral surrounds hindering access to them. Their smallness means that they can support few people: domestic water is often in short supply. Java, Malaya,

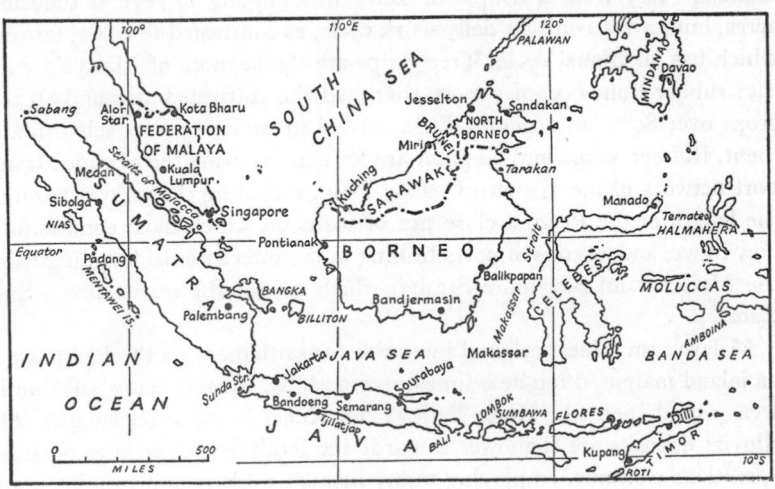

FIG. 55—Insular Southeast Asia

Sumatra, Borneo and Celebes are so large that they are best considered separately. Parts of each are as isolated as the islands are from one another. Java now contains 60 million people, Sumatra 12 million, Malaya 7½ million, Celebes 6½ million and Borneo 5 million.

THE MALAY PENINSULA

Substantially broader than Kra and reaching within 80 miles of the Equator, Malaya has granite-cored skew ranges and some karst limestone landscapes, flanked with broad alluvial coastal plains laid down by small rivers whose deltas have been reshaped by the sea into compact swampy belts. Warm throughout the year, it has no season of drought. Thick evergreen Equatorial Rain-forest still covers four-fifths of its surface, and its mountains are not high enough to break the continuity of tree-cover.

Coastal sections to the northeast and northwest are deltaic plains densely peopled by Muslim Malays who, physically resembling Sumatrans and Javanese, continue self-contained padi-farming and casual fishing. Beside the open padi-fields are clumps of coconut and fruit trees beneath which are stilted wood-and-thatch huts. Tree patches containing houses are called kampong, a form of land use and settlement characteristic in Insular Southeast Asia.

Landscapes on Malaya's western plain are dominated by commercial tree crops (rubber, coconut and oil palm) and by alluvial tin mining. Holdings vary from a couple of acres in kampong to several thousand acres, but have a constant daily work cycle, as contrasted to cereal farming which has an annual cycle. Tree crops are the keynote of Malaya's rural life; rubber alone occupies more than half the cultivated area and all tree crops over 80%, an economy little related to subsistence or self-containment. Rubber, copra and oil palm are for export, using the complex transport network of the Western Coastal Plain, including the railway running the length of the Plain, a close net of roads on which most commodities now move, and a series of ports linking to the international shipping using the Malacca and Singapore Straits, which act for the region like a Suez Canal.

Malayan tin mines, original incentive for settlement on the Plain, are at its inland margin, often near limestone foothills. Mines occupy substantial areas round Ipoh (the Kinta Valley) and Kuala Lumpur (Selangor). The alluvial deposits are shallower towards the foothills, where true opencast operations continue, employing many manual workers and running water to sift out the grains of tin ore, which average ten ounces per cubic yard of

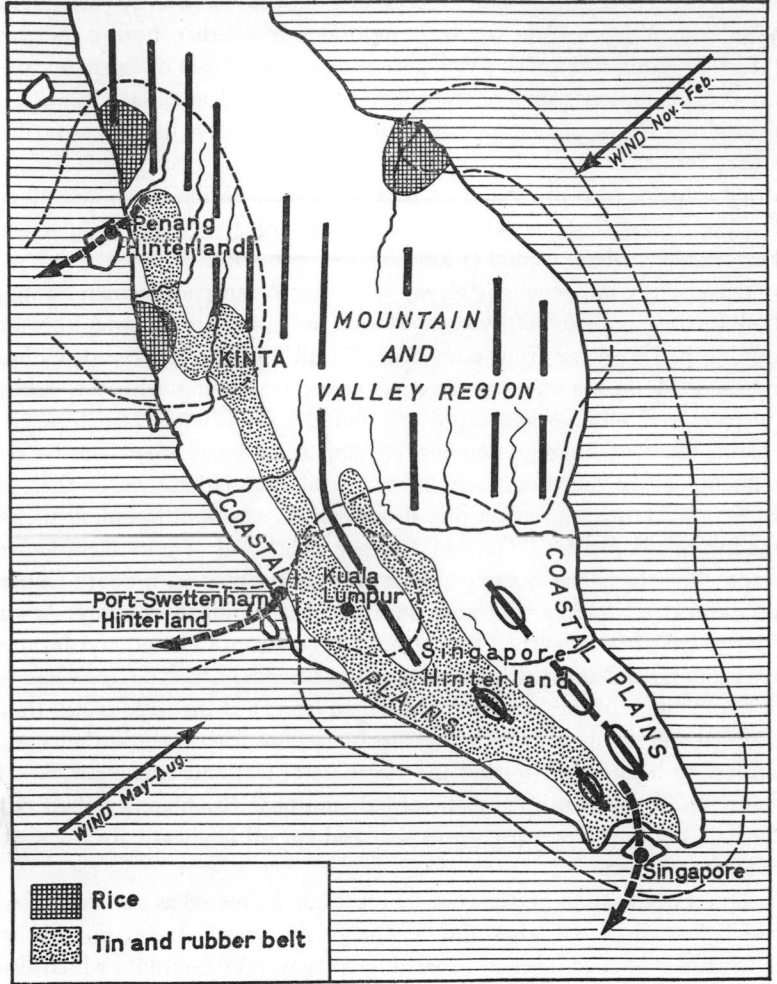

FIG. 56—Economic features of Malaya, its ports and hinterlands

gravel. Deep-set ores are now extracted by dredges slowly floating from point to point, filling in as they go, making small mark on the countryside and needing less labour and water. Dredges produce high values in proportion to running expenses, but they are costly. Tin-ore tonnage exported is only a tenth that of Malayan rubber, so its transport and labour significance is less.

The "Tin and Rubber Belt" is a creation of the last seventy years, before which the Western Plain was little more developed than Borneo today. In it now live four-fifths of the Malayan people. Apart from maintenance work on the plantations, mines, transport services and smelters, industry is negligible. Every plantation has a processing factory, usually electrified, where rubber is changed from liquid to sheet form or coconut kernels are dried or palm nuts pressed. The Belt is dotted with markets, since all rice for the Asian labour is imported, and the largest—*Kuala Lumpur*—has become the Federal capital (1960 pop. est. 350,000).

Because the indigenous Malaya, like other Asian padi-farmers, were so tied to their subsistence system, labour for commercial agriculture and mining had to come from elsewhere. South Indians and South Chinese immigrated during the last seventy years, explaining why the rubber, oil palm and mining landscapes are dotted with Chinese cemeteries and Hindu temples. Immigration was at first temporary, then became permanent. These outsiders form now a total population greater than the Malays, creating a peculiar plural society. In the mushrooming of new market towns for the "Tin and Rubber Belt" and of port facilities and trade, the urban areas became almost entirely peopled with South Chinese producers and traders who now dominate the national economy. Among Malays have been absorbed Sumatrans, Bugis (from Celebes) and Javanese who immigrated in small groups at many periods.

Exploitation of the Eastern Plain began later, but that side is still thinly peopled and much remains in swamp forest, not least because the coast is subject to heavy seas (during the northeasterlies) and is shallow far offshore. In Trengganu iron ore is mined, and near Kuantan is a shaft mine for lode tin, both operating for export and cut off landward. In the south, bauxite is mined.

The concentration of Malayan Chinese has increased as an effect of war which first dispersed large numbers from the towns. Later, guerilla war in the forest obliged defensive roadside villages to be built into which since 1950 over half a million rural Chinese have been withdrawn from their lonely pioneer farms in the jungle. One in every five Chinese in the peninsula was twice shifted by events from 1941 to 1954. The 500 "new villages" thus created were part of an unprecedented massive rural resettlement.

Of the ports which handle Malayan commodities, Singapore and *Penang*, at opposite ends of the "Tin and Rubber Belt", are on islands where rocky coasts provide deep draught approaches. Each has a smelter, though most tin leaves the country as concentrates. Port Swettenham, a

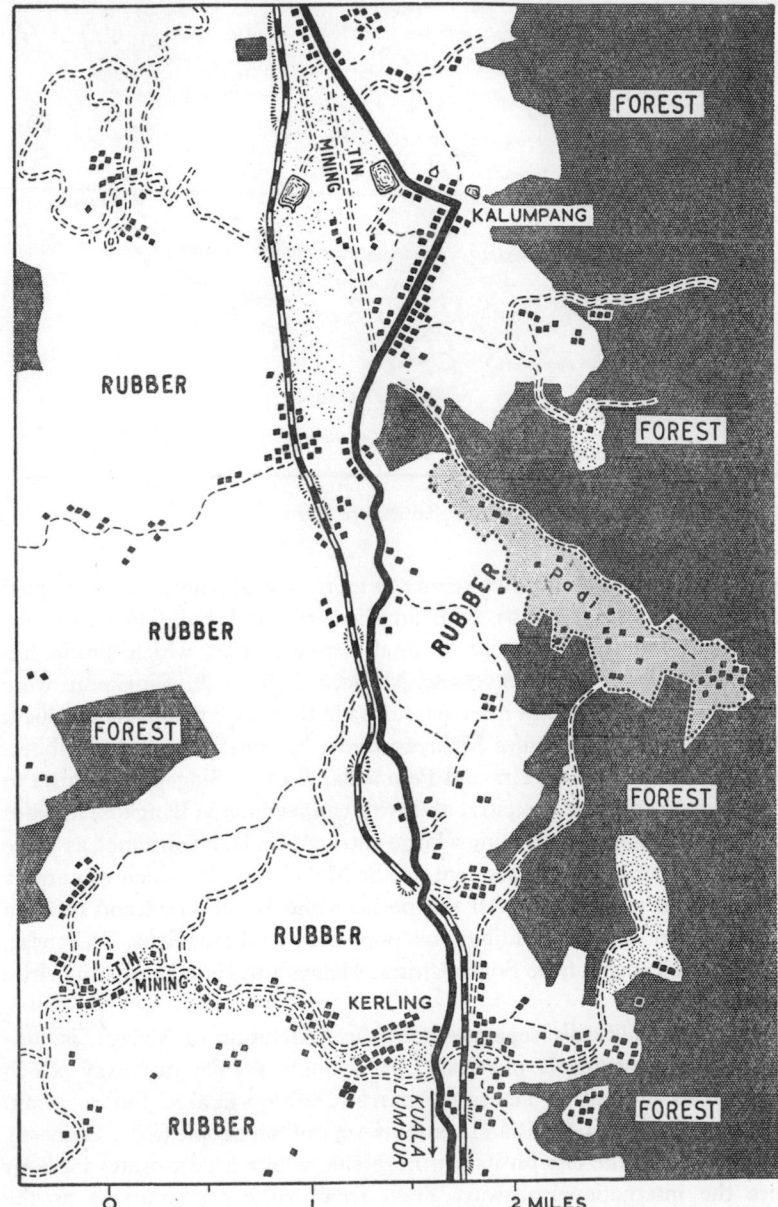

FIG. 57—Topographic detail in the Tin and Rubber Belt of Malaya. Transport, tin and rubber are worked by Chinese and Indians, the isolated valley of padi by Malays

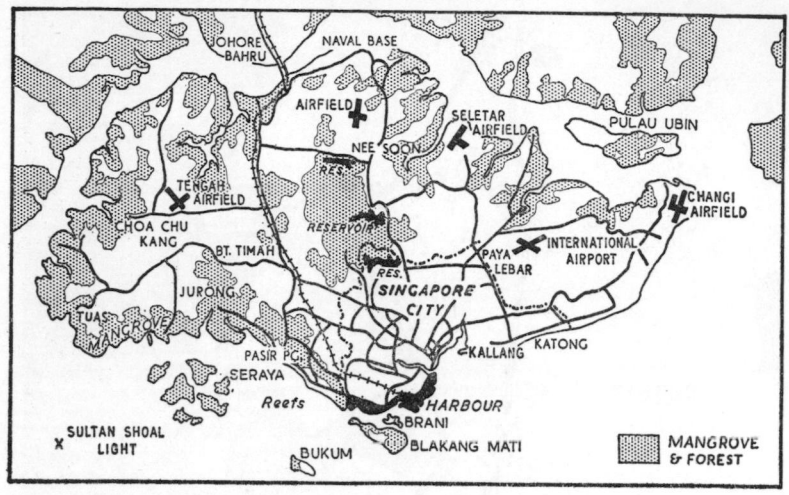

FIG. 58—Singapore Island

creation of the last twenty-five years at a more central point, is on a channel through mangrove swamps with implied silt and building problems. Malacca is four centuries old, a small estuarial port which silting has rendered useless for modern vessels. Malacca, Penang and Singapore were originally more engaged in inter-island trade than with peninsula produce; Penang, now chiefly handles Malayan trade, but deals also in the rubber, copra and tin of Medan, Kra and Peninsular Burma. Singapore, central to West Borneo and East Sumatra, and with connections to Bangkok, handles a huge transit shipping. Having a large entrepôt trade, it continued as a free port, but is increasingly dependent on the Malayan trade, which was once a lesser part of its entrepôt. All the ports, while Westernised and modern in facilities and public buildings, are populated with Hokkiens, Cantonese, Hakkas and Teochiu from South China; Malays and Indians are minorities among them.

Singapore, politically separate from the Federation of Malaya, is connected to the peninsula physically by a single granite causeway which carries road and railway across the narrow, swamp-flanked Johore Strait. Only 25 miles broad, the island contains 1·9 million people (85% Chinese), concentrated in the city on its southern side where a deep-water harbour faces the international seaway. Such small rubber plantations as the island once had are fast becoming built-up areas and suburbs. The limited rural area produces neither vegetables, fruits nor meat sufficient for the urban food supplies which are almost entirely imported, rice from Siam, and other foods from Europe, America and Australia whose shipping passes this way. The island cannot even supply itself with water, most of which is piped across the causeway. Through Singapore Harbour passes the large tonnage of oil from Seria and Palembang, stored or in transit, but not refined on the island. A major airport adds further to the transport activity of Singapore which, being rail terminus and transhipment port, has many people engaged in international communications. Its trade involves the handling (in 1958) of 18 million tons of sea-borne freight including raw materials worth some U.S. $2,000 million annually, and a volume of in-and-out movement unequalled by any other single Asian port, giving rise to valuable insurance and banking transactions.

JAVA

Less than half the area of Britain and containing 10% more people, crowded and intensively farmed Java lies 7° south of the Equator. The trade winds playing over it become southeasterlies at mid-year and northwesterlies at year-end. The surface has as little lowland as Japan, and the mountains developed round high fault scarps aligned from east to west are modified by volcanic cones and ejects in such number that no Javanese locality is out of sight of volcanic landforms. Some 85 volcanoes have been identified, 17 active and 18 newly dormant. Interruption of drainage by ejecta leads to many lakes, including crater types. Prevailing winds create small rain-shadows in an intrictate pattern, so that rain and river régimes vary within short distances. On the northern coastal plain greatest rains are at year-end, least at mid-year, reversing the Continental Southeast Asia régime. In the

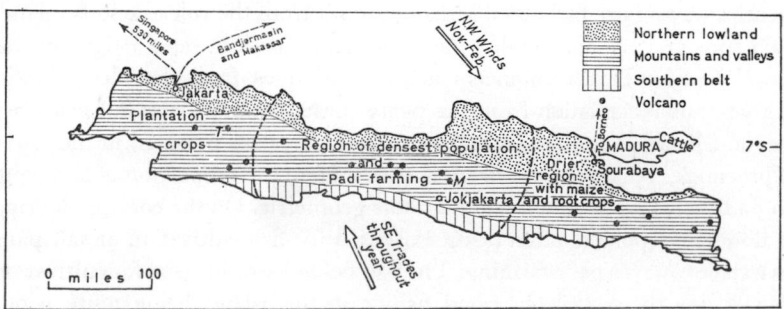

FIG. 59—Java: the broken lines mark the agricultural distinctions between the western, central and eastern sections

extreme east, the island has localities with July to October drought, inducing an "Indian monsoon" condition. At mid-island, the volcanic debris is of basic materials which weather to soils rich in calcium, nitrogen and phosphorus, able to maintain fertility despite prolonged cultivation. These are the basis for the highly productive valleys near Jokjakarta, and in the Solo, Brantas and Madicen basins, where concentrate a third of Java's farmers. The intermittent danger from volcanic ash and dust is negligible against their asset of fertility. Large stretches of middle and southern Java are still unused; much porous limestone occurs, some ejecta is acid and some levels are too cool or windy for farming. These zones are thinly peopled so that Java is densely settled only in restricted areas; a quarter remains forested, and bare rock and bush occur along the south coast which is battered by Indian Ocean waves.

The sloping surfaces of the densely peopled intermontane valleys are levelled into terraces for padi-growing. Direct rainfall is the source of most field-water, but devices like bamboo pipes bring water from the swift streams which tend to be incised. Native water control serves 6 million out of 25 million acres farmed; the soil porosity and steep slopes make drainage canals mostly unnecessary. The landscape retains a wooded appearance because kampong (coconuts, fruit, betel palm and houses) is placed in high proportion to the padi-fields. Other trees are at intervals between the fields, helping to prevent slumping. The topographic map shows radial patterns of settlement and cultivation owing to both volcanic landforms and piedmont fans, accentuated by swift flowing brooks from water-tables in the volcanic ejecta. Lower slopes have complicated water patterns due to conflicting trends, and valley bottoms are often canalised to prevent erosion by torrents.

Stretches of plain along the mid-north coast are where shallow seas and gentler waves have facilitated settling the silt from the volcanic soils inland. Old spits and lagoons parallel the coast. Here modern canal irrigation was developed by Dutch engineers using techniques from the Netherlands. Large-scale reclamation from the peaty coastal swamps were for centuries beyond Javanese means. Over 2·75 million acres are irrigated in the lower Tjimenoek, Tjitaroem and Brantas rivers. Here the proportion of kampong to padi-fields is less and the alignments geometric. On the coast, poldering is done, new polders often being exploited for fish cultivation or salt pans as a stage towards padi-farming. The wet fields are often used for cultivating fish during the padi cycle, pond fishing in this island being more widespread than sea fishing. An old alluvial terrace stands at higher levels inland and carries more tree crops than the newer alluvials to the north.

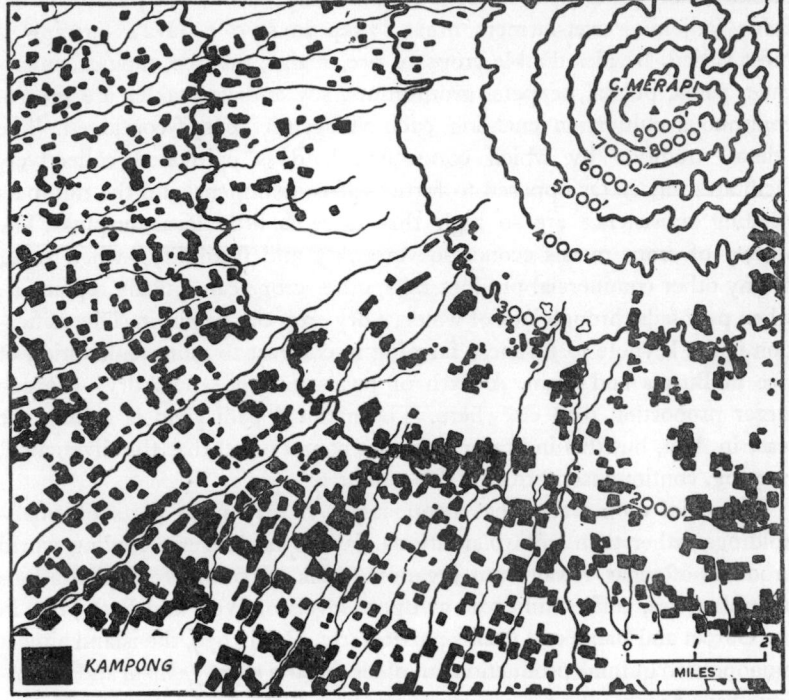

KAMPONG

FIG. 60—A topographic map of the flanks of the Merapi volcano in central Java. The kampongs are closely packed and between them is terraced padi. This is a basic volcano and its flanks are threaded by many streams which are avoided by the local villagers. Innumerable footpaths have been omitted for clarity

Two thinly peopled, dry limestone zones occur to the north, in Rembang and the island of Madura so that the plain is in part cut off from the coast as it extends between Semarang and Sourabaya. Madura, with a low rainfall as well as porous structure, has been a major cattle-rearing region, exporting many draught cattle to Java, where about 6 million head are kept.

In Java and Madura the mosque is the rural social focus; every clump of kampong contains one and dotted among the padi-fields are light shelters for Muslim field-workers to pray and rest. The name Madura, identical with that of the city in South India, recalls a Hindu colonisation in Roman times.

Because so many workers are available and because differences of relief permits many products to be tried without hindrance to or by surrounding fields (adjoining wet-farmers must "keep in step"), Java's farming is most varied. Besides double crops of rice, maize, tobacco, tapioca, sugar-cane, yams, pulses, peppers, groundnuts, soy and vegetables are grown, continuous cultivation enabling each village to be self-contained. The "desa" tradition by which communal land is cultivated collectively facilitates village (as opposed to farm) self-containment, and the numbers needing subsistence are so high that there is little local surplus. The variety of crops means economic versatility and flexibility—when sugar or any other commercial product fails, other crops can quickly replace it; when padi fails through lack of water, a dry crop can be put in. Diversification is the keynote to Javanese farming in contrast to mono-cultivation of rice in Burma and Siam. A sixth of Java's padi is grown dry—a much larger proportion than elsewhere. The national padi yield is among the least in Asia, but this indicator does not comprise all that the diversified, rotating, continuously farmed fields produce.

The chief crop traded has been sugar, mostly from parts of small-holdings rather than from plantations. Java is no longer a leading world producer of sugar. Away from Javanese farms are commercial plantations of rubber, tea, coffee and cacao at upper levels of West and East Java, in the Garoet and Bandoeng Basins particularly. Until 1939, the island almost monopolised quinine production, an older malaria cure. *Jakarta* and *Soura-baya* have become the main ports of the island. Western estate production is diminishing and many plantations were taken over by squatters after the Second World War. So great has become the need for food that today barely 6% of the cultivated area is under crops for export, causing national financial difficulty and greater dependence on commercial production by the other islands. Sugar produced in 1957 was two thirds that of 1937.

Manual methods are universal in Java's rice production. Communal seed beds and communal stores are unique to the "desa" system. Variations of rainfall incidence help to even out the work cycle. Sowing the main padi crop begins in October, transplanting starts in January and harvesting may be taking place any time between April and July; the term of padi varies from $3\frac{1}{2}$ to 6 months. Sowing will, however, be going on any time somewhere in Java and harvesting somewhere else simultaneously, possibly even within sight. Despite ingenuity with the means available, production is less than the island needs and importing rice has become chronic. Java no longer can supply food to the other islands. Altogether 23 million acres of Java are in food crops, 10 million acres of padi, 5 million of maize and $2\frac{1}{2}$ million of tapioca. Sugar occupies little over

XIX. While lumbering is only slightly developed in the large forests of Southeast Asia, teak extraction is a feature of Thailand, Burma, Northern Borneo and Malaya. Here a Chinese operator is seen at work in a saw-mill near Bangkok. Thailand is now the biggest teak-exporting country in the world.

XX. In Indonesia the flanks of basic volcanoes are intensively farmed on terraces. On this landscape of ripening padi, the scale is indicated by the figures to the left; in the centre there is a little Muslim praying shelter serving also as a resting place for the fieldworkers. In the middle distance a stream is deeply incised in the soft terrain.

XXI. With self-contained rice farming goes cottage-weaving of cotton or silk—sometimes now promoted as a nationalist symbol. Here a Kelantanese peasant weaves the characteristic straight sarong cloth in use by both sexes through Malaya and Indonesia.

XXII. At Seria the oil derricks of the Brunei wells are close to the beach on a flat, swamp-forested coast which presents great problems of approach from both land and sea.

110,000 acres. Of the 1·4 million acres under commercial crops, two-fifths are in rubber and a third under tea or coffee.

Java's farming districts are so congested that the rural settlements have almost a suburban landscape of close occupation; some districts have densities exceeding 6,500 per square mile. Towns are few in proportion, most being like big kampong, a consequence of the slight internal trade. Earth road networks are close, serving farms rather than commercial traffic. Light railways or rural tramways, as in the Netherlands and Belgium, have been built yet are falling out of use now the need for moving sugar-cane to the mills has diminished. The coast is difficult to approach, both from the land (few villages are close to the shore) and from the sea, so that harbourage is limited and local shipping slight. Even fishing villages are few, underlining the Javanese disinterest in using the sea owing to their inland orientation, their inland principalities and the dense population tied to subsistence farming.

Craft industries serve rural domestic needs. Aiming at national self-sufficiency in the clothing staple, Jakarta and Pasoeroen contain several cotton mills using imported cotton to produce a minor fraction of the need. A factory for rubber tyres and another for electric lamps still operate.

Jakarta, national capital with about 2 million people, is located away from the greatest population concentrations, which are central to the island. Founded by the Dutch settlers, it continues eccentric to the island without being very central to Indonesia as a whole. Silting has ruined its original approaches, and sea-going vessels use the artificial harbour of its outport at Tanjong Priok. *Sourabaya* handles nearly half Java's exports, and has good access to the dense interior though remoter from world shipping routes.

All ports and market towns have Chinese traders, shop-keepers, sugar millers, middlemen, planters and bankers. The Chinese had arrived before the Dutch, but the early labour need on sugar plantations at a time when Javanese could not be interested, caused the importing of South Chinese labourers. Many degrees of Chinese absorption into local life are now evident. Hundreds of Chinese cemeteries lie round the towns and villages. That a plural society should exist despite the dense population indicates the prolonged disinterest of Javanese in commercial operations. The Chinese now number about 1½ millions, not a large proportion yet, concentrated in ports and towns, they have great weight in economic affairs.

SUMATRA

Second biggest Indonesian island, Sumatra has the second largest population. Its length is the distance from London to Gibraltar, its population
only a quarter more than Greater London. It has large virgin areas. Lying
askew the equator, its wet Equatorial Rain-forest is far more extensive
than that of Java. Seasonal rain-shadow effects are most pronounced either
side of the high faulted ranges running lengthwise through it close to the
western rocky, wave-beaten, unsheltered coast. Thousands of square
miles are covered with ejecta from over fifty volcanoes. An east coast belt
of tall, thick swamp forest, partly waterborne volcanic debris, occupies
half Sumatra. The swamp obstructs both development of its surface and
approach to its coast from landward or seaward. Until late last century this
island was almost ignored, and even today native farming concentrates at
few places inland, chiefly among the mountains where the hill communities
of Batak and Minangkerbau are indigenous. Their way of life, while highly
developed in relation to their setting, has been little touched by world
economy and remains self-contained. Radically different language, religions
and cultures correlate with the physical isolation of one group of Sumatrans
from the other. No metalled road or railway connects one side of the island
to the other or north to south. Isolated, discontinuous development is its
feature, equatorial forest still dominating its landscape. To the far north
are Achinese people in their simple, coastal villages of self-contained padi-
farming and fishing economy.

Inland from the silting port of *Medan* spread the rubber and tobacco
estates introduced by Dutch planters in the first quarter of this century,
exploiting a basic soil of volcanic origin where there is no great width of
coastal swamp. To these plantations Javanese, Chinese and Indian
labourers were brought from time to time, and an export trade established,
causing the growth of Medan and its outport, Belawan-Deli, served by
world shipping through the Malacca Strait. From this locality rubber
spread on smallholdings to remoter parts of Sumatra and the bulk of
Sumatran rubber is now from isolated smallholders. Many western estates
have been recently divided among more smallholders. Medan has trade
connections with Penang across the strait.

Round the volcanic Lake Toba is the indigenous farm economy of the
Bataks, a mountain people now largely Christianised and with smallholdings of rubber and coconut.

Farther south in the dales round *Bukit Tinggi* (older maps name it

Fort de Kock), Sumatra's capital, are the Minangkerbau, physically more Mongoloid than their neighbours; their customs, a curious mixture of Islamic and Hindu, recall early Indian and Arab associations with this island, which lies beside ancient sailing routes between India and China. Tortuous mountain roads connect this centre of rice growing to *Padang* on the difficult west coast. Now only accessible to steamers through a small outport, Padang is connected inland to the Oembilin mines by a twisting mineral railway, enabling Indonesia's only steam coal to be brought out. Bukit Tinggi has been producing tobacco, coffee, rubber and copra from smallholdings trading through Padang.

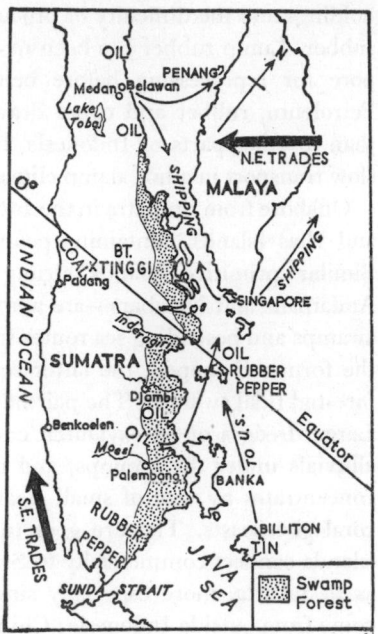

FIG. 61—Sumatra

Well inland on the Moesi River, which provides a steamer route through the forbidding swamp forest, is *Palembang*, exploiting oil formations along a series of low hills running towards Djambi on the Hari River. An American operation, this is the economic heart of Sumatra. Sea-going tankers, oil rigs, pipelines and a refinery stand near Palembang surrounded by swamp. Western techniques, imported foods, Chinese and Indian labourers and Chinese shopkeepers focus at this point, which has trade ties with Singapore. About 7 million tons of crude oil are produced here annually, inducing other production and settlement. Pioneers have moved along these river highways through the swamp to create rubber and coconut smallholdings on the banks. On the swamp coast, Chinese fishermen have settled, their colony of Bagansiapiapi being the greatest single sea-fishing centre in Southeast Asia, serving external markets with salted, dried and smoked fish.

Round the large bays of Lampoeng in South Sumatra, Javanese have been settling, stimulated by the Dutch administration. Lampoeng specialises in high-grade pepper which, like its rubber and copra, is from smallholders.

Medan, Padang and Palembang are Sumatra's chief towns. Much rubber is exported in crude lumps, whose low grade results from isolated smallholdings and the difficulty of procuring the acids necessary for high-grade rubber. Lump rubber has been moving, often in Chinese junks, to Singapore for reprocessing before being shipped to Europe and America. Petroleum, rubber and copra draw Sumatra into world economy rather than to other parts of Indonesia, being commodities which tolerate long, slow transport in a hot, damp climate.

Offshore from Sumatra in the India Ocean are the little-visited Mentawei and Nias Islands, containing people at a very low level of development. Similar primitive islands strung between Sumatra and Burma—the Andamans and Nicobars—are administered by India. Off East Sumatra's swamps and bestriding sea routes from Asia to Java are *Banka* and *Billiton*, the former S-shaped, the latter square. Each has granite hills skirted by forested tidal swamps. The pair have the landscapes of alluvial tin mining. Large dredges of an ex-Dutch company using Chinese labour work the alluvials under the swamps, and can annually export 30,000 tons of tin concentrates by way of small steamers loaded offshore from the shallow coral-girt coasts. The ore goes to Europe or U.S.A. for smelting. The islands connect commercially to Singapore, the major tin market, as much as to Jakarta, more especially since all supplies of food and equipment come from outside Indonesia; Chinese families originally drawn to Banka's mines have smallholdings for high-grade pepper traded in Singapore.

BORNEO

Borneo covers 280,000 square miles (3·5 times Britain), while containing only 5 million people (roughly half the population of Greater London), implying that it is the largest, least-developed and most-isolated island. Lying half-way across the Equator, almost to its mountain-tops it carries thick Equatorial Rain-forest, fringed with mangrove swamps and coral reefs. The backwardness of Borneo arises from being off the track of shipping ancient and modern and from poor soils. Without minerals accessible enough to draw "rushes" of people, it has dangerous coasts and few indigenes with farming traditions. Movement inland is chiefly by shallow river boats, the scarcity of people even impeding footpath travel. The indigenes are termed Dyaks though they include many communities (Kajan, Kenyah, Bahau, Kelabits, Punan, Muruts) living as hunters, collectors, river fishermen or shifting cultivators, some in "long houses", others in branch lean-tos. Close to the coast immigrant Chinese, Malays and Indonesians are pioneering for tapioca, pepper or rubber, or trade along the rivers in a little lumber, gums, canes and sago. Padi-farming is scanty and done chiefly by Malays living in stilted dwellings built over the water for protection and sanitation, as at Brunei. Oilfields are located on the coast at Seria and Balikpapan, connected more overseas than to the island. Balikpapan has a refinery handling 3 million tons of crude oil annually, a third being local oil and the rest from other parts of Indonesia.

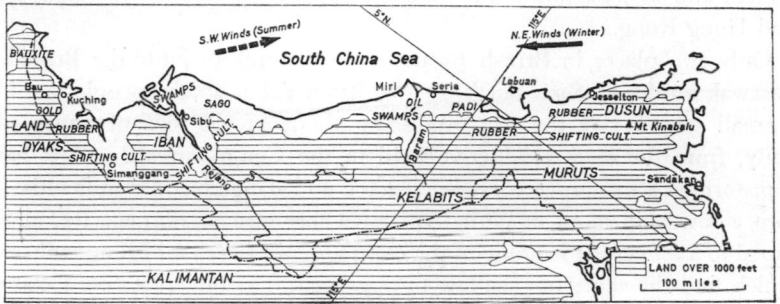

FIG. 62—Northern Borneo

British Borneo

The northwestern third is British Borneo with shallow seas, off-shore coral, mangrove-covered deltas and forested uplands, mostly unused. It is in three units: a small Malay sultanate of *Brunei* (55,000 people), a river mouth, rice-growing settlement; *Sarawak* with 600,000 people in 48,000 square miles, focused at Kuching; *North Borneo*, almost equal to Sarawak in area, but with only 400,000 people, centring on Jesselton. Small steamers connect these settlements along the coast. The only railway in Borneo is a few miles through the rubber plantations near Jesselton.

In *Sarawak*, the rivers Rejang and Baram run roughly westward in the interior and swing northward across large deltas smoothed by currents from the northeast. Villages and cultivation at wide intervals are scattered along these rivers. Sibu is a river market for Rejang Valley "Iban" shifting cultivators, Simanggang for those of the Lapar Valley and Marudi for Baram tribes of Kajan and Kenyah. Sarawak coastal people are Melanau, a fishing community mixed now with Malays. Dusun are self-contained rice farmers in North Borneo's western hills, inland from which live the tough mountain Muruts, shifting cultivators of tapioca and dry padi. Upon its high plateau are the Kelabits, an energetic clan of rice farmers and cattle keepers, unique in Borneo. A feature of Borneo is the "long house", a stilted wooden building of great length which is more a village than a house, occupied by many families living communally and self-contained at a low economic level.

213

Immigrants along the coast include Malays and Sumatrans concentrated in the market towns and especially in the country round Kuching where they once handled most inland trade. In Seria Malays are oil labourers as well as the majority in Brunei. About 250,000 Chinese, roughly a quarter of British Borneo people, are spread round Kuching, near Sibu, on the oilfield and in Jesselton and Sandakan. They trade with both Singapore and Hong Kong.

Only two places in British Borneo are westernised. Near the Brunei–Sarawak border at *Seria* north of the Baram delta, 20,000 people live in a small strip beside the sea, producing about 15,000 tons of crude oil daily, from the most productive field in the Commonwealth. This has transformed a mangrove coast—neglected and dangerous for millennia—into a township more modern than anywhere else in Borneo. Its oil is piped to a refinery at Lutong on the coast and out to sea for filling tankers, which find the shore too shallow to approach. The oilfield artisans come from Malaya, China and India, the technicians from Europe and America. The oil moves to Singapore to join that from Sumatra and Borneo and thence to refineries overseas. A few wells of diminishing output operate at Miri on the south side of the delta.

Kuching is river port and market for cash-crops from west and south of it. Chief interest is rubber, 90% from scattered smallholdings. The town is separated from the sea northward by 10 miles of mangrove over which meander streams large enough for sea-going steamers to use. Canoes travel to Kuching from hundreds of miles around, using the channels of the swamp which permit travelling along the coast without using the open sea. Sago, copra and pepper are also traded, their bulk needing much coastwise shipping. Timber is floated to sawmills scattered in the lower reaches of rivers. Gums, jelutong (for chewing gum), gutta percha, charcoal, incense, illipe fat (for chocolate making), tannin from mangrove trees and rattan canes are collected from the forest and move to the coast for export.

Padi-farming is not the focus of farming in North Borneo and occupies barely half a million low-yielding acres. Sago, tapioca and sweet potatoes are native staples and dry padi is common. Few minerals are mined though many occur. Gold-bearing sands worked by Chinese southwest of Kuching produce a thousand ounces a year.

Kalimantan

West, south and east Borneo form Indonesian Kalimantan whose features resemble those of British Borneo—broad peat-filled swamp coasts, wide coral fringes, great areas of Equatorial Rain-forest and few people, these being mostly in a simple stage of development except for immigrants from Sumatra, Java and Celebes, bringing new ways of farming. Rivers also dominate Kalimantan transport. On the west, where Borneo is close to the stream of trade moving to and from Singapore, Chinese have been settled for many centuries (at Sambas and at Pontianak), handling small-holder rubber, pepper and forest products, coming hundreds of miles along the Kapoeas River.

Bandjermasin, capital of Kalimantan, is on a distributary of the Barito, and trades in forest products—rubber from a belt of plantations round the Amoentai River, and rice from near Kandangan, the best-farmed section of all Borneo. Bandjermasin has ties with Jakarta; the Barito Valley behind it has largely been opened up by Javanese in response to schemes to relieve their population pressure.

On the southeast coast stands *Balikpapan*, on a sheltered deep-water bay 50 miles south of the Mahakam Delta oilfield, which pipes about three-quarters of a million tons of crude oil annually to the town's refinery and tankers. Here Bugis immigrants from Celebes are the main workers. An older oilfield to the north, at Tarakan near the mouth of the Kajan, has not been restored.

Celebes and the Eastern Islands

Half as large again as Java yet containing an eighth as many people, Celebes differs from other Southeast Asian islands not so much by its "octopus" outline as by being off the Sunda Platform and formed from volcanoes rising from oceanic depths. During periods of low sea-level, Celebes was never linked to Borneo or Asia, so that it has distinctive flora and fauna. Consequent to fairly easy canoe movements through these seas, Celebes people are of similar type to other islanders though with different language. Towards its node, studded with lakes and craters, the indigenous Toradjas live in simple self-containment, growing rice and coconuts in scattered patches. Other indigenes are not far from the head-hunting stage. Most development is at the outer ends of the Celebes arms, where immigrants have settled and external connections developed, isolated from the interior. At the southwestern tip, *Makassar* (85,000 people), despite the maze of coral at its approaches, markets for a small zone peopled by rubber smallholders, copra producers, maize growers and padi-farmers, and is entrepôt for inter-island trade maintained by the vigorous Bugis, historical pirates in these waters. Manado acts similarly at the north-eastern tip, where the Christian Minahasi trade with Mindanao as well as with outermost Indonesia. Its entrepôt includes *Halmahera*, whose Portuguese name recalls that the early European interest in these "spice islands" centred on the cloves of Ternate.

Celebes is increasing its population faster than any other Indonesian island, but immigration is quite small, few Dutch or Chinese having settled there.

Bali, like Celebes, has always been physically separate from Sunda Platform islands, and is a small volcano-packed island remarkable for its intensive, high-yielding, self-contained farming. Its cultural distinctiveness is famous: Hindu by religion, it maintains highly skilled cottage crafts, its own script and language and fine art tradition. On islands east of Bali, farming steadily decreases and the Muslim or Animist religions prevail. The strait between Bali and Lombok, safest deep-water channel through the Lesser Sundas, is used by shipping between East Asia and Australia.

Part IV

Southern Asia

CHAPTER SEVENTEEN

Landscape Types and the Northern Mountain Barrier

THE SOUTHERN Subcontinent forming the territories of India and Pakistan and variously named the Subcontinent, Pak–Ind or even Indo-Pak, is massively compact. Of every six people living on its surface, about four are spread over low-lying alluvial plains, the vast Indo-Gangetic Plain, or the deltaic plains edging the Deccan; another one lives on the higher plains and rolling surfaces of the Deccan, where weathering and erosion introduce their variants, as may be seen from examples in Figs. 63, 64 and 65, taken from inch to a mile topographic maps of India and Pakistan.

LANDSCAPE TYPES

Fig. 63 shows a landscape some distance northwest of Benares in the eastern Ganges plain, where about 50 inches of rain falls each year from June to September. The countryside is so flat that contours have been omitted because they do not reveal significant relief differences. Though only trees of economic value are marked, others grow along the roads, screening the houses and providing shade. That water is plentiful, and yet at the same time a focus of attention, is revealed by the many and widely scattered wells dug to the fairly high water-table in the alluvium, to serve fields rather than houses. Swamps are marked, adding evidence of flatness. Large "tanks", or artificial ponds, have been constructed behind earth bunds, and these also serve the padi-fields with water under control. Farming for padi and other crops goes on throughout the year, but seasonal alternations of rain and drought necessitate conserving water for the dry season. Tanks are characteristically square, often decoratively treated and flanked with trees and colourful plaster-and-brick temples, which frequently form the only distinctive vertical features on the otherwise low countryside. Tanks close to settlements are for bathing, washing and sitting—social centres comparable to the English village green. The map shows the nucleation of houses into tightly compact villages, yet there are no sign of defence. The sites are without a clear sign of attraction

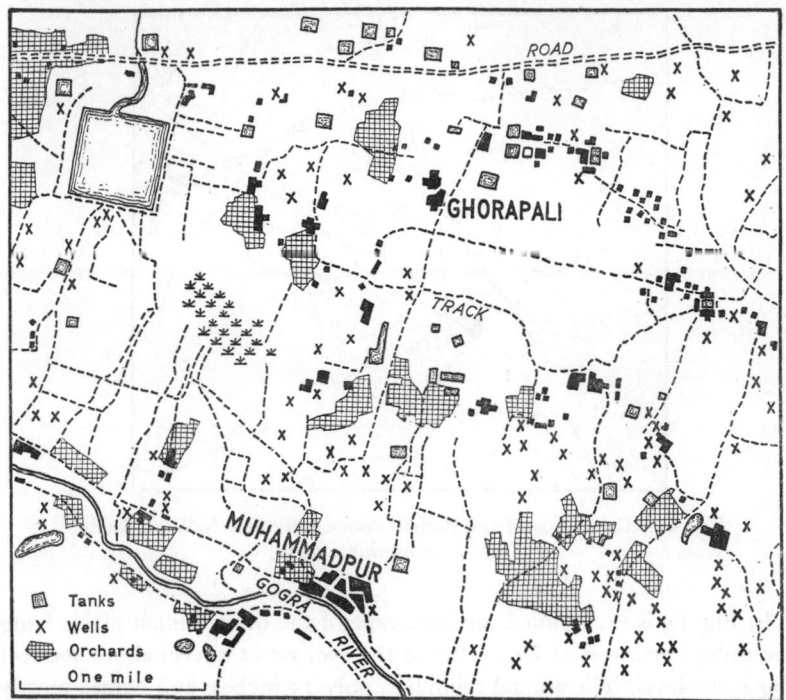

FIG. 63—Landscape about 100 miles N.W. of Benares, taken from
a topographic map

towards water. The houses have palm- or rice-thatch roofs, and
sun-dried brick or wooden walls which are commonly whitewashed
for coolness. Though a "road" is marked, it means a rutted track on
which nothing better than an ox-cart travels. The road will be un-
metalled, and motorable only in the dry season, because it is under a deep
mud during the wet season. The square pattern evident in the many tracks
reflects that bunding is necessary in padi-farming, and it is clear that
neither the road nor the Gogra banks is an attraction for settlement. No
substantial production for commerces takes place, so that the transport
system has continued thus for centuries. The farmers here operate smallholdings, producing throughout the year varying crops of padi, wheat,
sorghum, beans and sugar. The manually worked farms, close to self-
containment, often have skilled cottage spinners and weavers of local
cotton. The population averages some 950 persons per square mile, and
the place-names on the map show both Muslim and Hindu influences.

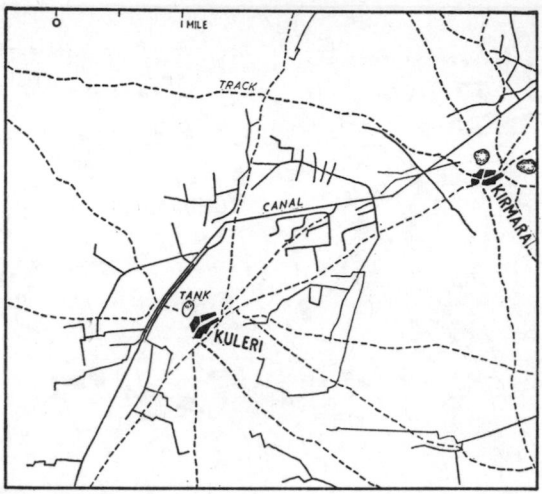

Fig. 64—Landscape of the Punjab about 120 miles N.W. of Delhi,
from a topographic map

In Fig. 64 is exemplified the landscape of the drier Punjab plains lying
120 miles northwest of Delhi, flat to the eye, yet at a level about 700 feet
above sea-level. The annual rainfall is only 15 inches, and comes mostly
in the third quarter. It is a countryside without trees except those planted
along sides of canals. A little natural dry scrub remains on which zebu
cattle and goats graze. The landform and soil relate to alluvium spread by
Himalayan rivers whose water content fluctuates widely each season. While
the need for water on the fields is great, the water-table is so far below this
porous surface that wells must be deeper than is practical for these people.
The villages shown depend entirely on tanks for potable water, here
irregular in shape, shallow and little more than scum by the end of the dry
season. High temperatures and desiccating winds greatly lower the
effectiveness of rain, except for the few showers in the winter. The slight
interfluves (doabs) of the alluvial fan, are used for a very old system of
canals which draw water from the stream at a point closer to the mountains; they distribute it along the tops of the interfluves, whence it discharges through the fields towards the hollows. As shown, the distributaries
peter out as the water in them evaporates or percolates away. The general
drainage trend is towards the Indus, but the local streams are practically
wadis, dry for most of the year, due partly to low rainfall, partly to diversion
of water to the doab canals. Nucleation of settlement is prominent, owing

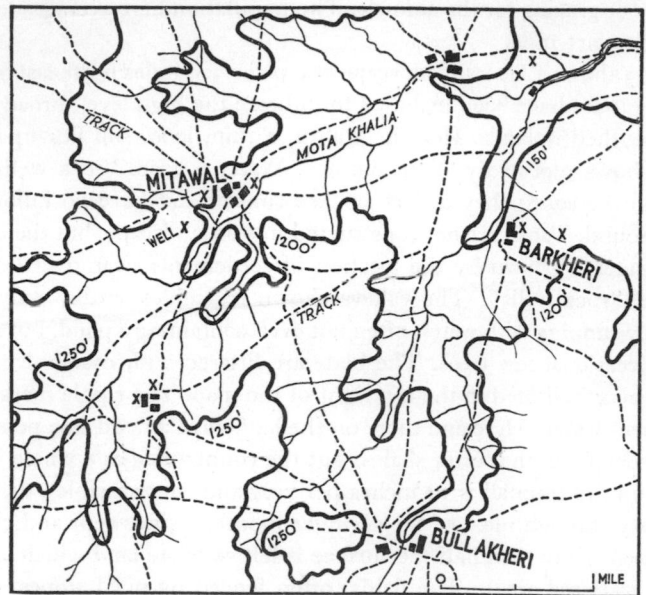

FIG. 65—Landscape of the Deccan about 300 miles N.E. of Bombay
(Crosses indicate wells)

to critical dependence on tanks and to an old need for protection. Frequent
droughts and famines, as well as location across the route used long ago by
tribesmen from the Northwest Frontier, leave their mark on this pattern
of villages, which have no walls, though such defences may still be seen
around towns. Houses on the edge of the village present blank walls to the
outside, often giving a defensive appearance.

The aridity means that the houses can have massive packed-earth walls
smoothed with sun-baked mud. Walls and houses may be thatched with
straw. Earth walls around little paddocks (for cattle or goats) are also
capped with a thatch to prevent crumbling during the rains. The map
shows not only the wide spacing of settlements and absence of isolated
homesteads, but also the open network of tracks, the sole lines of movement. Since Figs. 63 and 64 are similar in scale, the eye can compare the
settlement density. While Fig. 64 does not classify land use, the villagers of
Kuleri and Kirmara grow wheat, the coarser cereals (sorghum or jowrah or
bajra) and gram—the small bean which is basic protein food for the subcontinent. The canal serves to assure "dry" crops, because no wet-farming
is done. Considerable areas beyond reach of the canals are uncultivated or

left as poor grazing for the animals. The population here averages less than 180 per square mile.

Fig. 65 shows a Deccan landscape at a place 300 miles northeast of Bombay. Contours have been included to indicate the high level, broad valleys and smoothed uplands. Here in Malwa, a thin, loose soil lies upon rock which shows repeatedly at the surface. Water is from "rock-wells", pits dug into the solid; they collect surface run-off and have no inflow from underground. Tanks are not constructed in this landscape, but the concern about water is shown by the location of settlements near river-beds and close to "rock-wells". The valleys shown resembles wadis, only intermittently running with water, often not even containing a pond, but marked by an occasional few trees. The beds are littered with coarse debris, the width being indicated in the top right of the map. The ripple marks mean permanent water. Here and there on the landscape an odd tree persists by rooting deeply in the softer shales, but the countryside as a whole is bare, harsh and dry (rainfall is 14 inches per year and very variable), desiccated and dusty through most of the summer months, windswept and chilly in the winter. More than half the surface is left as waste land which carries a coarse, scattered scrub. The fields, often fenced by piled stones, contain wheat, the coarse grains and gram in rotation. Irrigation devices are absent, and crops are perilously dependent on direct rainfall whose efficiency here is lessened by shallow soils, prolonged heat and clear skies. Zebu cattle are kept, one or two per farm, but these animals are poorly fed owing to bare terrain. They have little economic value as Hindus do not eat meat, and the cattle have been described as little more than a few bones wrapped in a hide. Houses are small, one-storied and commonly built of irregular rock fragments or boulders from stream beds. Nucleated round wells, the house groups are the focus of a fan of tracks arranged without relation to topographic or drainage patterns, sign of the little movement between the parts of this poor territory, even though it has had a history of being strategically significant in relation to military movements across the Deccan from northwest to southeast. The general density of people is less than 120 per square mile.

THE NORTHERN MOUNTAIN BARRIER

North, east and west of the Subcontinent, there rise mountains and high hills which structurally are elaborate folds, draped round Central Asian blocks with the Indo-Gangetic plains occupying a foredeep, or trough, concealing where the Deccan block makes contact. The moun-

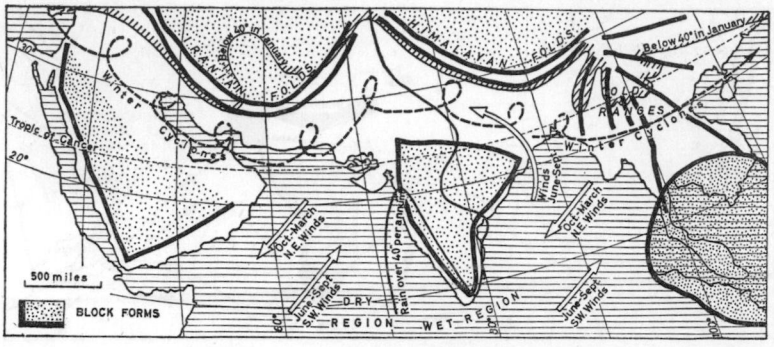

FIG. 66—The physical setting of Pak–Ind

tainous perimeter is at least 3,000 miles long—from Baluchistan to Arakan
—and has three distinct alignments. The westernmost section, arranged
roughly north–south, is 800 miles long. The Himalayan section has a
curved form with prominent east–west directions, and covers about 1,600
miles. The eastern portion is an arc of folds, dominently north–south for
about 600 miles.

Great variations occur within short distances among these mountains
which, alpine in character, stretch at least five times the length of the Alps,
covering a far greater area as well as reaching twice the altitude. Relief
induces changes in humidity and temperature, which, in conjunction with
the parallel folds and drainage lines, makes landforms dominant in the

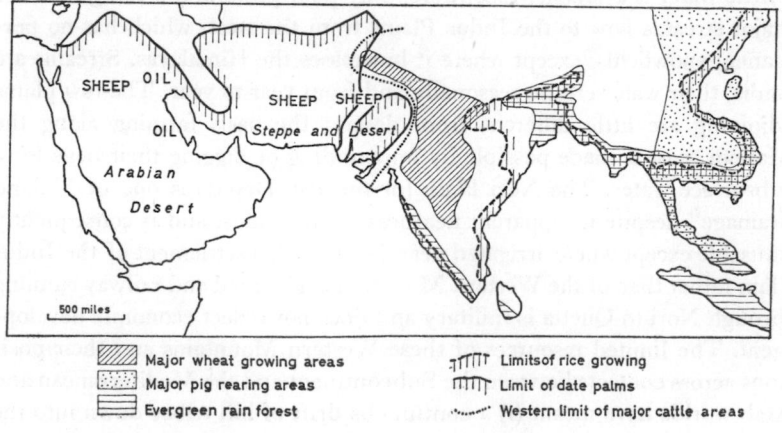

▨ Major wheat growing areas	⊤⊤⊤⊤ Limits of rice growing
⬚ Major pig rearing areas	⊓⊓⊓ Limit of date palms
▤ Evergreen rain forest	⋯⋯ Western limit of major cattle areas

FIG. 67—Pak–Ind agricultural features

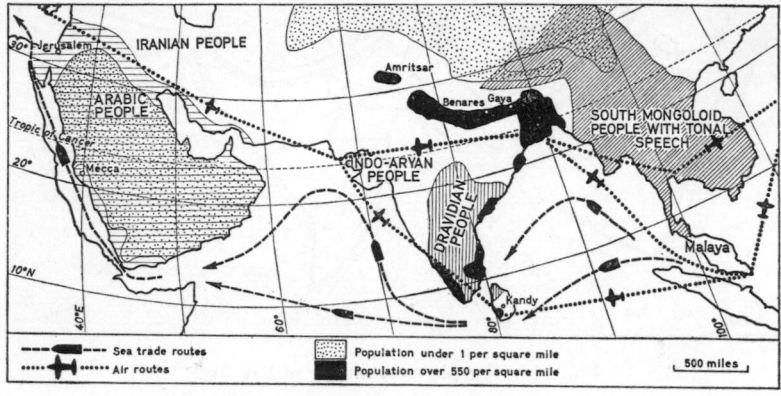

FIG. 68—Pak–Ind population, races and cultural links

pattern of natural and human distribution. These are cut across at many points by "cluses", steep-sided valleys carved by major rivers where they run transverse to the structure. The patterns are complicated by major climatic changes between south and north and between east and west.

I. The *Western Mountains* are characteristically bare and rocky, forming high desert variations, transitional between the dry Indus Plains and the dry Iran–Afghan plateau on either side. Earthquakes and old volcanic materials are common here and glacial landforms remain, though glaciers have disappeared. The consequence of the widespread aridity is that development, at its best, is oasis type and scattered in isolated valleys where a little water is available. Elsewhere, only poor pastoral life can go on. No major streams flow to the Indus Plains from the west, which has no permanent snowfields, except where it buttresses the Himalayas. Streams are wadis, their water erratic seasonally and from year to year. The few plains adjoining are little different from desert; the oasis farming along the Makran coast is made possible by impounding or digging their beds for a subsurface water. The Nori Plain (or the Pat Desert) is one of "inland drainage" despite its apparent nearness to the Indus, and is consequently unusable except where irrigated near Jacobabad, a settlement of the Indus Plain rather than of the Western Mountains. The road and railway running through Nori to Quetta is military and does not reflect economic development. The limited resources of these Western Mountains and their positions across contacts between the Subcontinent and the Mediterranean and Arab worlds have meant (i) a continuous drift of hill tribes down into the plains; (ii) caravan trade in wool and carpets of the hill people; (iii) periodic military pressures from west to east. Caravan routes, passes and fortified points controlling them are features of settlement, and the strong tribal structures of local society is the result of isolation within hard physical limits. The important routes are (*a*) along the Makran coast which is scattered with oases; (*b*) the Bolan and Harnai passes commanded by Quetta, railway-head for trade with Afghanistan; (*c*) the Zhob Valley, a pass linking Quetta to a line of forts on the way to Punjab across (*d*) the Gomal Pass which is the southwestern entry to the Province of the Northwest Frontier.

The Western Mountain zone west of the Indus and north of Gomal is complexly broken, jealously tribal and critical in position, a close network of roads and railways now running across it. The mountains, here affected by the Himalayan structures, have some east–west alignments, a few glaciers and frequently increased rivers. There are three plains, each probably formed as lake-beds—the Plain of Bannu, irrigated for wheat by Tochi water; the Plain of Kohat, rainier than elsewhere and supporting many wheat farmers; and the Vale of Peshawar, largest of all. The plains are virtually large oases of farming or sheep-rearing, continuously harassed by the tribes of the adjoining dry hills or mountains. Here went on for centuries the classic struggle between settled farmers and hill tribes, complicated by pressures from the

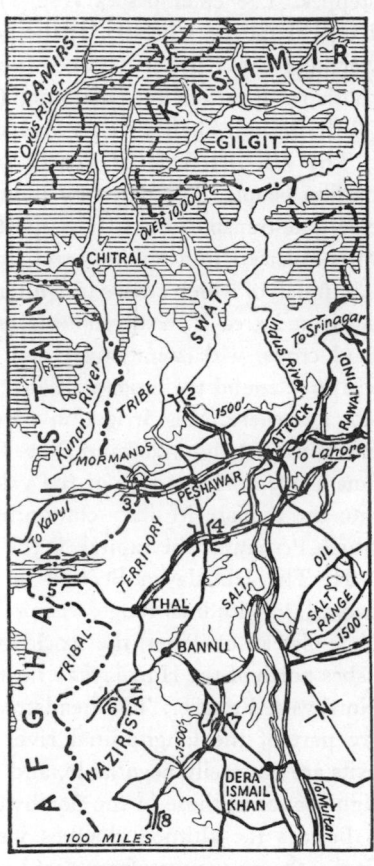

FIG. 69—The Western Mountains and the Northwest Frontier of Pakistan. The numbers indicate critical passes: 1. Kankhun, 2. Malakand, 3. Khyber, 4. Kohat, 5. Kurram or Parachinar, 6. Miram Shah, 7. Gomal, 8. Zhob Valley. Tribal groups in this area include Pathans, Chitralis, Bajouris, Utman Khel, Yusafzais, Hassanzais, Mohmands, Afridis, Jowakis, Mullagoris, Orakzais, Zaimukhts, Chamkannis, Bangashis, Turis, Wazirs and Sheranis

steppes of Central Asia, over a country which, while rugged and mountainous, has numerous routes well used by traders and horsemen from the steppes. The chief passes are: (1) the Kankhun between the Oxus and Kunar Valley in Chitral; (2) the Malakand, northern approach to Peshawar; (3) the Khyber between Kabul and Peshawar; (4) the Kohat, southern approach to Peshawar; (5) the Kurram, to Thal and Kohat; (6) the Miram Shah through Waziristan to Bannu.

The hill-girt Vale of Peshawar contains about one and a quarter million people, dominated by military interests with numerous forts and elaborate transport links. It supports 600 persons per square mile, and has three-quarters of a million acres in farmland, largely irrigated since rainfall, much of which comes in winter, is only about 12 inches per year. The cultivated area is mostly double cropped. Wheat and maize are the key food crops, with some sugar and cotton for commerce. Mulberries are scattered round the irrigated fields, contrasting with the treeless countryside elsewhere. Most irrigation water comes from the Upper Swat by way of a tunnel at the Malakand Pass. Oldest settlements are on the piedmont fans at the northern side of the vale, along which the Greek army moved into the Punjab. Military contonments are a feature of the townships, of which Peshawar, the capital, is the largest (about 120,000).

II. The Himalayan Section is more alpine in landscape; its closely packed, longitudinal ranges rising in tiers from the plains, buttressing the high plateau of Tibet, the world's largest "altitude desert" which establishes north of the Himalayas a no-man's-land narrowing westwards to the Northwest Frontier. The headstreams of the Indus and Ganges systems are part of the longitudinal river pattern; their precipitous, gorge-like exits are not easily negotiable, and they have not provided routes of such significance as those in the northwest.

Besides the altitude changes visible in the vegetation bands on their flanks, the ranges vary from east to west consequent to rainfall differences. Heavy rains during the southerly winds cause the Eastern Himalayan foothills to have a forest of almost equatorial variety and density. Foothills rising from the dry Punjab have thinner vegetation, with Mediterranean trees where not deforested. The successions northward are:

(a) In Bengal from tropical, largely evergreen, forest in the plain to wet sub-tropical forest in the foothills (duars or terai) to wet temperate forests in narrow bands succeeded at higher levels by alpine vegetation.

(b) In Uttar Pradesh, from sal forest rising to sub-tropical pine forest to moist and dry temperate types, finally to alpine vegetation.

(c) In the Punjab, the foothills have dry tropical scrub, then a little sub-tropical pine forest rising to dry temperate types, succeeded by the alpine.

These forests include at lower levels plants deciduous in response to monsoon droughts except in the Punjab. Sal trees at low levels, evergreen rhododendrons at higher levels and a great variety of needle-leaved trees are characteristic. These differences have their economic consequences: the evergreen tea is a feature of higher levels to the east, apricots, grapes and almonds at lower levels to the west. The compressed longitudinal ranges and valleys mean that anyone moving from south to north may be in the depths of thick forest for a few miles of terai, rise rapidly to alpines and rock plants, and descend to more hot-wet forest all within a few miles. Economic exploitation of the vegetation, mineral and water-power resources is negligible in the mountain zone. Much activity goes on in the foothill zones to establish headworks for irrigating the plains and for hydro-electric power. In the foothill area, exploration for mineral oil has reached the stage where oil is actually being produced at the new town of Nahark-atiya, near Digboi in Assam, and at Attock in the Punjab, the latter producing 290,000 tons crude oil in 1956.

In contrast with the western mountains, the Himalayas contain many snowfields and glaciers, but these have little human significance except as releasing precious water from snow-melt in spring. The mountain panorama in the Himalayas includes signs of snow and ice at all seasons. Large areas of high-level bare rock are only seasonally snow-covered.

Distinctive hill tribes of many languages and names have grown up in these mountains, strongly Muslim to the west by association with the Middle East, Hindu towards the foothills and Buddhist or "Tibetan" to the east. Little principalities, such as Nepal, Sikkim and Bhutan have persisted here, where population is in a few widely scattered and not easily accessible valleys. Nepal is the largest (8½ million people in 53,000 square miles), its border containing the famous peaks of Everest, Kanchenjunga and Annapurna, and the territory being sacred by association with Buddha and because it is thought to be a main source of the holy Ganges' water. One of its several tribes is the militant Gurkha. A hard country, it grows wheat, barley and potatoes, has much transhumance of sheep, goats and yaks, and remains largely in the self-contained subsistence economy despite a little transit caravan movement between India and Tibet.

Kashmir, until recently also one of the principalities, centres round a high, lake-studded basin in the Western Himalayas, marginal to West Pakistan, India and Tibet. Its strategic position recalls that of Switzerland

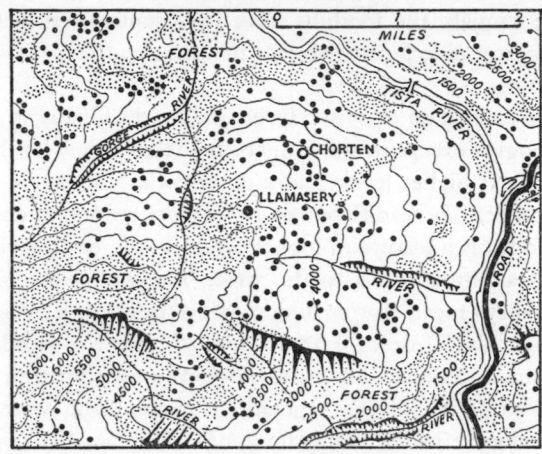

FIG. 70—A topographic map of the Himalayas near Kalimpong on the border of Sikkim, in Gurkha country. It shows dispersed settlement on higher levels, incised streams, and the avoidance of valley bottoms by Tibetan-type cultural centres (Llamasery is a Monastery, and Chorten a Shrine)

in relation to Italians, French and German interests. Central Asian influences (of mountain pastoralism and Islam) here overlap those of India (cereal farming and Hinduism) and of West Pakistan, the two latter countries being concerned with Kashmir as the source of rivers vital to irrigation and hydro-electric power to the Punjab. Since Kashmir includes tropical foothills as well as permanently snow-capped mountains, its agricultural range is wide, though farming is only in scattered valleys. Fruits, nuts and wool are produced for commerce, much wool entering trade as cottage-woven textiles and carpets. The lakes near Srinagar were major summer tourist centres for plains-people.

During the last 150 years commercial tourism became prominent in the Himalayas following the establishment of hill stations for respite from the great midsummer heat of the plains. Summer capitals were established at Simla, Mussori and Darjeeling, giving rise to annual administrative migrations to and from Delhi, Lahore and Calcutta, respectively. The mountain resorts have makeshift appearance, and are the dead-ends of mountain roads and hill railways. The custom of transferring the administration to such hill stations has ceased. Climbing the peaks draws attention to the Himalayas from time to time, but has little economic consequence.

III. The *Eastern Mountains* consist of all the roughly north–south extensions of the Arakan Yoma and the Assam–Burma Ranges inland to the extreme northeast, where they abut the Himalayas and enclose the

228

Brahmaputra lowland; adjoining these damp, tree-covered and tightly compacted folds is the Shillong Plateau arranged on east–west lines, a block outlier of the Deccan. The western ranges average about 7,000 feet high (peaks reach to 18,000 feet) mostly well below the snowline and thick with forest and extensive stretches of giant bamboo. The Assam–Burma Ranges have acted to isolate the continent from Southeast Asia and continue to be a major impediment. In them tribes of Mongoloid stock continue a primitive, largely subsistence economy, the more sedentary groups growing rice and maize (without irrigation) in patches along the malaria-infested valley floors, the more mobile groups on the upper levels, where shifting cultivation and "forest collecting" go on in a manner illustrating how communities from Eastern Tibet have slowly shifted southwards. While the Digboi oilfield to the far north indicates a potential which may prove more extensive, the ranges play little part in the economy of either India or Burma; the Ledo Road across them from Dibrugarh to the Hukawng Valley was a "backdoor" wartime route to Burma, but is no longer practical. Even the airlines are arranged round rather than across the ranges. The Barial Ranges, short replicas of the Arakan folds, stand between the Yoma and the Shillong Plateau to provide a lower route traversed by a railway linking Chittagong to the southern side of the Brahmaputra Valley with terminal points at Gauhati at one end and Sylhet at the other, a major outlet for tea from Inner Assam (see Fig. 74).

The Shillong Plateau, of much older rocks and structures than the Assam–Burma Ranges and rising abruptly from the plains northwest and south of it, maintain extensive altitudes over 4,000 feet. Its position in relation to winds cause it to be one of the rainiest localities in the world (Cherrapungi has 428 inches per annum) with a prolonged and dense cloud cover. Forest stands upon most of its heavily laterised surface, and consists of an almost equatorial vegetation, modified, however, after centuries of shifting cultivation by the Mongoloid tribes of Garo, Khasi and Gantia who maintain their primitive jungle economy here. Shillong attracts a little commerce to the plateau since it is the permanent administrative capital of Assam as well as a hill station, but it suffers from isolation, aggravated by boundaries. It is about 45 miles from the nearest railway, but stands midway along the trans-plateau road linking Sylhet to Gauhati (75,000 people), the junction of rail and river routes on the Brahmaputra.

The Arakan Ranges and the Shillong Plateau together probably support three-quarters of a million people, mostly tribesmen, so that this is one of the least developed and least accessible parts of the Subcontinent. It resembles the continental Southeast Asian environment rather than that of India.

CHAPTER EIGHTEEN

The Northern Plains

PHYSICAL ENVIRONMENT

THE NORTHERN PLAINS of "Pak–Ind" constitute one of the world's major features, distinctive physically and demographically. Surface of the huge, alluvium-filled foredeep or trench between the plateaux of Tibet and the Deccan, the plains are arranged like an inverted V whose southern ends reach the Tropic of Cancer, so that they lie almost entirely outside the mathematical Tropics. One arm, with axis roughly from Lahore to Karachi, is about 700 miles long, the other, on an axis from Lahore to the Ganges mouth, at least 1,200 miles long. While, therefore, physiographically the plain resembles the Lombardy Plain and Mesopotamia, it dwarfs them and is far larger than any of the alluvial plains in Eastern Asia. Forming about one-fifth of the Southern Subcontinent, the tract contains nearly half its total population. More significantly, it has a population considerably greater than that of the United States packed into a tenth as much land. The plain supports, in an out-dated agricultural way of life, an average density comparable to that of industrialised Britain.

Almost entirely built of debris from Himalayan streams, the Indo–Gangetic plains have soils varying in texture across the surface and also in vertical distribution, these variations reflecting the fluctuation and changes of the streams which laid the deposits and modelled them and in turn reflected by differing agricultural potential. Large-scale alluvial fans create many slight changes of surface relief not easily evident on the topographic map and on the ground, but the plains reach 700 feet above sea-level west of Delhi. The doabs are large but not high above their surroundings, critical though that height of 20 feet or so is in the control of water. The "land of the five rivers" (the Punjab) is itself a series of doabs, "mesopotamia" or interfluves related to similar forms of Ganges tributaries through Uttar Pradesh and Bengal. More striking than these variations of landform and soils is the dramatic rise of mountains north of the Indo–Gangetic Plain and of discontinuous hills on its south. The edges of the Deccan Plateau are distinctive and emphatic to the east, dipping gently northwest beneath the sands of Thar which there forms the southern physiographic boundary.

TABLE 3

CLIMATIC DATA FOR THE NORTHERN PLAINS

	Karachi	Peshawar	Lahore	Delhi	Allahabad	Calcutta	Dacca
Temperature (mean F. Jan.)	65	50	53	58	60	65	62
Rainfall (inches p.a.) . .	8	14	18	26	38	59	74
% in months June to Sept.	77	33	74	77	80	76	66
No. of months each less than 1 inch.	10	5	7	7	7	3	3

The plains are subject to the "monsoon" cycle of rains. The three or four months from June arc rainy, the rest of the year dry, while at the same time mild enough for temperatures to be above freezing-point for almost all the year everywhere. This régime comes from an alternation of winds from southerly points and others from the north.

Shallow cyclones from the Mediterranean during winter penetrate the Punjab to bring light rains highly valued there for winter wheat. The most distinctive difference between parts of the plain is the amount of annual rainfall (see Table 3). Dacca in the extreme east receives about 74 inches, Delhi 26 inches, Lahore 18 inches and Karachi, in the extreme west, less than 8 inches. About three-quarters of this rain in each case falls in the June–September months; and the balance in the rest of the year is lessened in effectiveness by the high temperatures and desiccating winds. Thus there is a wetter monsoon climate in Bengal, where rainfall exceeds evaporation by about 30 inches a year, an increasingly drier monsoon climate through the Ganges Valley as far as Lahore, and some arid steppe or desert climate in the southern Indus plains where the rate of evaporation exceeds rainfall by some 100 inches a year. The average number of rainy days during the wet season varies similarly along the plain: Calcutta has 63, Allahabad 41, Delhi 27, Multan 11 and Karachi 7 for June–September.

All streams moving into the plains have special significance as means for countering the prolonged dry season. Since they derive exclusively from the Himalayas, the rivers have least water in the second half of winter when the headwaters are frozen; snowmelt releases water into them steadily from early spring onwards, continuing through the arid summer and rising to a peak when the monsoon rains fall in the hills. Thus the water-level in streams fluctuates considerably, but has a cycle not geared solely to that of the rains. Their beds are very broad and contain great banks of

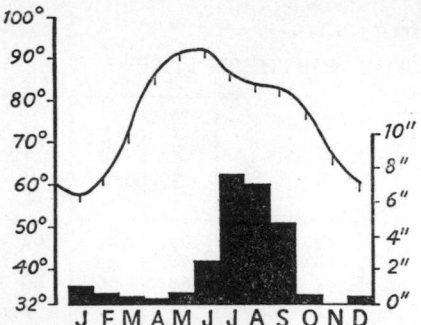

FIG. 71—Monsoon rain and temperature régimes at Delhi. The temperature drops when the rains set in

sand and silt, among which water moves in braids for much of the year. The banks change position after each rainy season, a fact which, combined with the enormous loss of river water by evaporation and seepage during the dry season, deters water transport.

The two major river systems show important contrasts. While its tributaries have a régime like that of the Ganges, the Indus passes for hundreds of miles through arid Sind, without tributaries and steadily losing water in a Nilotic setting. On the other hand, the Ganges receives tributaries all the way to Bengal, including the great Brahmaputra and Tista at its delta. This confluence in Bengal, together with heavy local rains, causes much of the delta to be a great sheet of water in August and September when the middle Brahmaputra becomes a huge lake.

Throughout the year temperatures permit plant growth, and the plains are protected by the mountains from those bitterly cold winds from Central Asia to which the North China plain is subject. Some dry föhn effects occur close to the ranges. In the Punjab winter cloud-free skies induce a great range between day and night temperatures; a slight night frost may occur in the northern plain, yet this is not damaging to crops. The cool season makes high rain effectiveness, an important point in the Punjab where rainfall exceeds evaporation only in two months of the year. Summer temperatures become extremely high everywhere in May and June; the June average in Lahore is 108° F.; the warmest month in Calcutta is May with a 95° mean.

Thus, the dominant physical factor for agriculture on the plains is the water supply. All parts are dry some months of the year. Towards the west drought is chronic, but towards the east water shortage is only seasonal. Because the cycle of water is so critical for farming, the régime peculiar to these northern plains has been much described. It involves a season of heavy rains three or four months after mid-year, followed and preceded by dry seasons, a hot one in early summer and a cool one in winter. While this cycle of three seasons is linked to Central Asia's continental winds, the mechanism of rainfall in the northern plains is thought to be largely internal; that is, chiefly consequent to features of the plains themselves. The Thar Desert gradually develops a low-pressure system due to intense insulation as summer advances, finally inducing an inflow from the Bay of Bengal of warm, moist air diverted from the southwesterlies.

The diverted air moving along the Gangetic plains from the southeast brings thunderstorms and violent rains first to Calcutta, then to the middle Ganges and finally to the Punjab. Calcutta rains begin in early May, those of Delhi in June and of Lahore in July. The rains are heaviest where coupled with relief effects, as in the eastern Himalayas and in funnel-like valleys of Assam. The rains do not move along the plains with the same timing each year.

When the rains come they dramatically change the countrysides. The plains until then have been parched, glaring, withered, dusty and over-poweringly hot. With the rains, clouds conceal the sun, the temperature falls, rivers rise, green leaves are thrust forth, tropical fruits swell and ripen and insects swarm. Human life at this time moves indoors, and health risks increase due to mosquitoes and flies, chills and waterborne fevers.

WATER CONTROL

Water control has evolved here consequent to result of the prolonged struggle of people to sustain themselves despite a direct rainfall which in varying degrees is low, unreliable or confined to a short season. Many ways were devised to overcome these natural difficulties, and those in use reflect the several traditions which have converged here. In the Ganges Delta, at the wettest end of the plain, only 2% of the fields are irrigated, the method used being small ponds or tanks intended to lengthen the period of inundation, with wet-farming for rice-growing and, later, for jute cultivation. Assam has about a fifth of its cultivable area irrigated, chiefly in the Myrmensingh region, which is slightly higher (and therefore less well-watered) than the delta proper. In the Bihar portion of the plain immediately outside the Ganges Delta but still rainy and low-lying, nearly 30% of fields are irrigated, some by modern canals to extend the area of wet-farming, some by tanks to prolong the season of wet fields rather than to extend the area. Farther inland still, in Uttar Pradesh where doabs of great size extend between the rivers Jumna, Ganges, Gumti, Gogra, Rapli and Gondak, an even greater percentage of cultivable land is irrigated, the devices used including engineered canals on the doabs, but the feature is irrigation from wells, an earlier method devised by peasants. The wells are related to underground lenses of clay (kankar), which maintain the sub-surface water-table at a level high enough to be easily accessible by shallow wells, the only kind peasants can construct with their simple tools. Fields here are serviced from the wells by various lifting devices; the endless belt of pots is used as well as a hide bag (known as mhote) at the end of a rope, motive power being an ox. For the belt of pots the ox walks round and round; for the mhote, the ox walks to and fro along a ramp. Shallowest wells are served by a small bucket hanging on the end of a long pole with a counterweight, a device (called the piccotah) looking like a large stork standing beside the fields. These devices suit subsistence farmers because they can be made and repaired easily; that none provide a very large supply from any one well limits the area serviced, a drawback which conserves the local supply and does not imperil the level of the water-table or induce saline inflows. Motorised pumps are rarely used, not only because of their cost but also because they quickly exhaust the supply.

Farther inland, three out of four cultivated acres of Western Punjab are irrigated, chiefly by canals. The older canals are short and without dams, keeping to the lower levels immediately adjoining the rivers; the latter ones have dams and large canals to tap the foothill reaches of the rivers. These doab-canal systems of West Pakistan invert the natural drainage pattern: the original river-beds have become drains or sumps for their own water which now runs along the higher levels of the countryside rather than, as nature arranged, at its lowest levels. In many districts between the Jhelum and Sutlej rivers, the cultivated area is all irrigated. Well irrigation is commoner to the north, where proximity to the mountains means a high water-table in the piedmont fans which were the earliest areas of development. In the lower reaches of "the Five Rivers" there runs only a small proportion of the original water; the rest has gone to the fields and been lost by evaporation or absorption.

Where the Lower Indus is Nilotic, as it passes through the deserts and steppes of Sind, irrigation has only been possible by the Nilotic device of building a barrage across it so as to provide a "head" from which canals lead off at high level to supply belts flanking the river. On one side of these canals lies desert, on the other is fertile, highly productive, commercial farming in modern "colonies". The great barrage at Sukkur provides the only means for cultivating in Sind whose farmland is entirely irrigated and only came into existence during the last thirty years or so, when modern engineering made the barrage possible. Most of the huge area irrigated on the doabs of the Indus tributaries, of the Ganges tributaries and in Sind is less than 100 years old, and has necessitated large-scale hydraulic engineering, making possible great expansions of production and population.

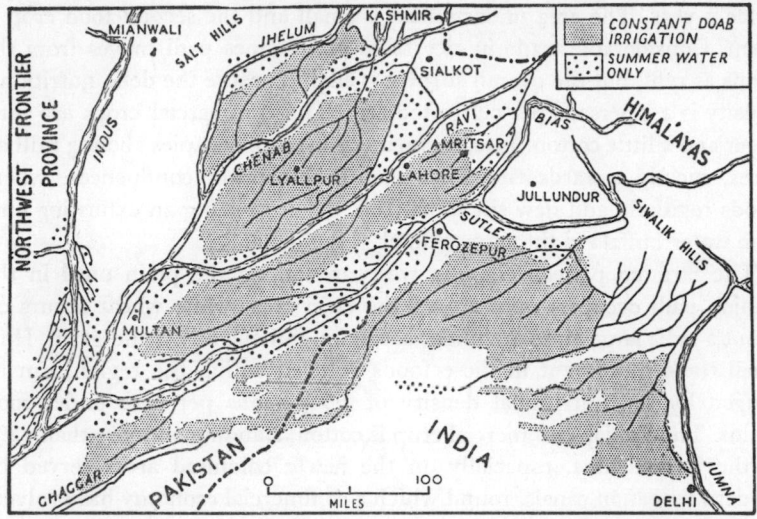

FIG. 72—The Punjab, showing the international boundary and the pattern of doab irrigation canals. The headwaters of the Chenab, Bias and Sutlej are in India but their waters have also been used for irrigation in Pakistan

Continuous cultivation does not always result from irrigation, mild though the winters are. Thus, while Assam has about 22% of its sown area irrigated, only about half the fields serviced are double-cropped. In East Pakistan (the Ganges Delta), double-cropping occurs on a quarter of the fields, though only 2% of them are irrigated; double-cropping there means harvesting a wet-field crop before the rains end and replanting at once with a "dry crop" before the fields dry out. Shallow depressions on the delta retain sufficient water for a second crop of padi. In Bihar the area double-cropped is practically the same as the area irrigated. At the other end of the plain, West Punjab has only 14% of its fields double-cropped, these being serviced by winter showers at a time when river levels are at their lowest, due to snow and ice in their headstreams. Only 15% of the Sind irrigated area is double-cropped for similar reasons. A further deterrent to continuous cropping, is the absence of a manuring tradition, animal manure here being reserved for fuel.

CEREAL FARMING

At the eastern end of the plain, high rainfalls and deltaic floods have led to an agriculture concentrating on rice which in places can be harvested twice a year. The area under wheat is small and the second food crop is gram. Considerable trade in rice takes place, since padi moves from the farms as rent, but the overall surplus is slight because the delta nutritional density is 2·5 persons per cultivated acre. The commercial crops are jute, sugar and a little cotton. Jute, the main cash-crop, occupies about 3 million acres, mostly towards the Tista and Brahmaputra confluences, where floods regularly add new silt to the soil, the crop being an exhusting one. The water buffalo is the farm animal of the delta.

The farming pattern changes westwards along the plain until in the Punjab padi occupies only 2% of the farm area, while wheat occurs on about a half; large areas are under sorghum, millets, maize and gram. How small trade movement in these foods is, even within the region, can be gauged by the nutritional density of 1·7 persons per acre under food grains. The Punjab commercial crop is cotton, standing on more than 12% of the farmed area, especially on the newly colonised areas served by modern irrigation canals, round which a commercial economy has evolved. Sugar, another cash-crop, occupies in the Punjab as large an area as it does in East Pakistan. The Punjabi farm chiefly with cattle, but the camel is often used for transport.

In Sind the agricultural pattern is different again. Outside the new colonisations along the Sukkur canals, the steppe and desert terrain provides only poor occasional grazing for sheep, goats and camels. The irrigated area has about 1·3 persons per acre of food-crops, and the emphasis is on commercial farming. A third of the area is used for cash-crops of rice, a slightly smaller area for wheat and a sixth for cotton; in no other region of India is cotton so prominent in the farming system or produced under such modern conditions, with the result that its yield here is nearly double the subcontinental average. Thus the Indus plains are identified both to the north and to the south with producing cotton.

The dual interest of farmers in rice and wheat at first appears anomalous to those who associate these major cereals with contrasting climatic conditions. The explanation turns on the seasonal contrast of the monsoon climate which, while almost equatorial for one season, is virtually that of the steppes at others. Further, on the plains there can be great differences in potential between fields standing side by side; one may enjoy some special water advantage during the dry season and therefore permits rice-growing which has exacting water requirements; while another nearby, depending solely on direct rainfall or being porous, may only permit a dry crop like wheat or millet. Locally great distinction is drawn between the seasonal crops. "Kharif" crops are sown as soon as the rains begin and harvested at their end; they include rice, sorghum, millets, maize, sessamum and jute. (Cotton is often described as a kharif crop, though it remains longer in the ground than one rainy season.) "Rabi" crops are sown after the rain ends, depending on such moisture as it has left in the ground, growing through the cool season to be harvested in spring; they include wheat, barley, gram, linseed, rape and mustard. To some extent these crops can be classified as either wet or dry. A crop in kharif and in rabi may be taken from the same field, but in general the rabi crops dominate on dryer upper levels, while the kharif are associated with lower levels, the flood-plains and fields serviced from tanks.

While traditionally the eastern plainsmen eat rice and the western wheat, the Sind padi area indicates a preference for rice even in the Indus Plains, whose traditional food is the unleavened pancake (chapati); this is partly because the older rice-growing areas are static, but are increasing in population so that rice continues to be in short supply and at a good price.

Padi-farming is thought to have evolved towards Bengal. More land is under padi in the Indo-Gangetic plain than in the whole of China; the Ganges delta alone has four times as much padi-land as Japan, though the yield is scarcely a third that of the Japanese. Wheat, the highly valued cereal towards the west, occupies only a third of the area under rice, but totals more than half the wheatlands of Australia and eight times those of Britain. Wheat yields on the plains are low, a third of the British average.

Outside Bengal, a feature is the large crops of sorghum, millets and similar coarse, tropical cereals (local names are bajra and jowrah) here used for human food (as contrasted with similar U.S. crops for fodder) and having the advantage of tolerating low rainfall and high temperature better than either rice or wheat, which makes them useful "insurance" crops as well as typical rabi crops. They show greatest prominence in Uttar Pradesh, which has a climate between the extremes of the Punjab and Bengal; two-thirds of the Uttar Pradesh grain-growing area is under these crops. Sugar-cane, physically resembling the giant tropical cereals, is a key commercial crop in Uttar Pradesh, occupying an area greater than padi and wheat combined, located on the great doabs serviced by modern irrigation and amounting to three-quarters of the total "Pak–Ind" sugar acreage.

Prejudiced against using on their fields manure from their cattle, farmers on the northern plains have countered the low yields inevitable under continuous cropping by including legumes in their rotation, particularly as quick-maturing rabi crops. Gram, sesame, groundnuts, rape and mustard are cropped everywhere, though least in the Ganges Delta. These beans and the oil produced from some of them are vital as the chief protein in local diet, which is vegetarian. The groundnut, a recent innovation, is more extensive in Uttar Pradesh than elsewhere. Commercial vegetable oils are also produced from flax, here grown for its "linseed", and from castor nuts. Coconut is a minor interest on the Bengal coast, but other palms appear along the delta—dates to the west and areca (for betel chewing) to the east. Tree crops are on a very small scale; some orchards of mangoes occur in the east, and citrus fruits, apricots and almonds in the Punjab. The older and more intensive agriculture is on the Himalayan or northern side of the plains, the middle and southern sides being everywhere later developments, mostly related to engineered canals.

ANIMAL FARMING

Much of the plain was probably natural grassland—savannah to the east, steppe to the west. Cattle-farming is now of only secondary interest to the farming community. Relic of an ancient cattle-farming tradition continues in the Hindu reverence for cattle, but finds no reflection in large-scale commercial breeding or herding, or commercial use of cattle products. Uttar Pradesh, whose broadly based and complex farming system combines features of those in the Punjab and Bengal, employs an average of nearly one ox per acre, which is far higher than for India as a whole. The plains support a density of cattle astonishingly high by comparison with anything in China; at least one-eighth of the total of the world's cattle population is thought to live on these Indo-Gangetic plains. Many of these animals are almost useless by reason of age and disease. Herds of sheep are still evident in the west, though increasingly relegated to the semi-deserts or to the hills, away from the irrigable lowlands. In the west there is no religious deterrent to eating mutton, beef or goatflesh. A wool trade continues in the Indus plains, and there is a steady trade in hides. An enormous goat population, scavenging for fodder, is spread evenly through the plain, of interest as supplying milk to smallholders and for sacrifices. Nothing is cultivated for feeding animals, which accounts for their poor quality.

POPULATION

Throughout the plains from the Punjab to the Ganges Delta, states commonly have densities greater than 500 persons per square mile, but those

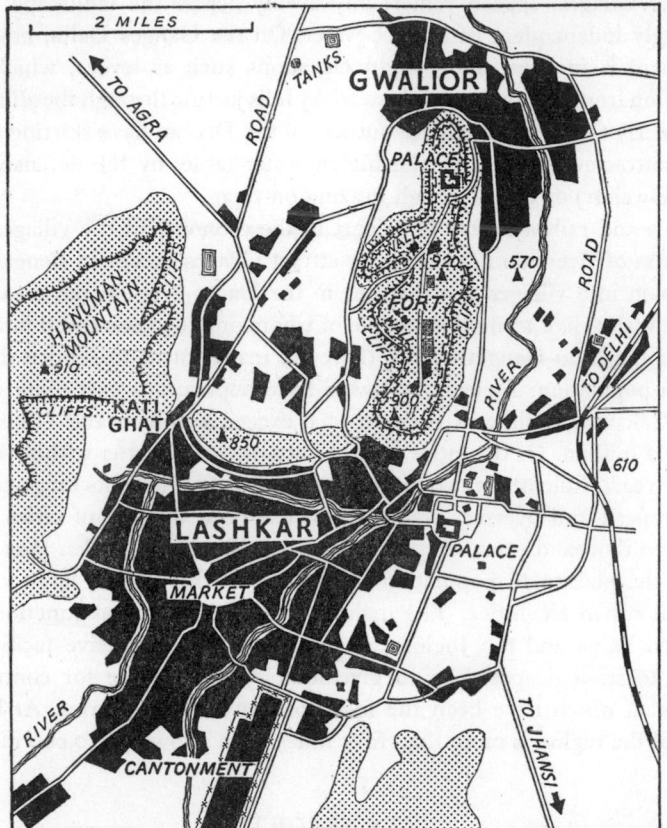

FIG. 73—Gwalior and Lashkar—the shaded areas represent land higher than 500 ft., whilst those in black denote houses etc. Gwalior has a historic fort overlooking the Ganges plain from a spur of the Deccan

along the lower Indus have densities below 250 per square mile. Excluding Delhi and Calcutta, large areas north of Patna, on the Ganges Delta and the Punjab are far denser, commonly exceeding 1,000 per square mile. The Brahmaputra Valley, still a pioneering area, has only 250 people per square mile. The Punjab has experienced great increases this century consequent to the great extensions of modern canals. North of the Lahore–Calcutta axis access to water is easier and rainfalls higher, so that it has been settled longer than the southern side, which has less rainfall, a lower water-table and more erratic streams.

The plainsmen, being four-fifths agriculturists, are distributed in small, compact villages, spaced remarkably evenly across the landscape, often seemingly independent of surface water. On the Ganges Delta, however, settlement is in lines along slight elevations such as levees, which give protection from seasonal flood. Low rocky hills jutting through the alluvium, particularly to the south, where outliers of the Deccan have skirting settlements attracted to them by the higher water-table, by the defensive site (as at Gwalior) or by the rough grazing on them.

Roads and railways play little part in the economy of the villages, and the banks of rivers do not markedly attract villages except in Bengal. The dispersion into villages is a feature; in the Dacca division (an area twice that of Wales) live 17 million people of whom only 670,000 dwell in towns.

Over the Indo-Gangetic plain there are many towns to service the 190 million population. At least 65 towns have populations exceeding 50,000 each; Calcutta, Delhi and Karachi each exceed a million and Lahore has almost a million. Of the cities Karachi attained this status within the last twenty years. Calcutta is two or three centuries old, owing its long standing to European and overseas trade. Delhi has been the site of cities for at least two thousand years. But the towns contain altogether *less than one in ten* of the plainsmen population. Many are market towns, large villages without urban amenities. The major urban clusters are at junction sites between Patna and the Jhelum, at points where a defensive facility has added to strategic positions to give military significance for controlling the plains which have been the focus of power for centuries. At least a third of the region is more than fifty miles from a town of 50,000 rank.

TRANSPORT

Ancient ways and tracks which formed lines of the pressure upon the Punjab and thence to the Ganges Delta have left their mark not only in the strings of fortified towns spread from Peshawar to Calcutta, but also in the network of roads and railways, here the densest in Pak–Ind. From Agra to Lahore runs the first great trunk road built by the East India Company, leading to extensive development there. The physical asset of uniformity over the plain has made it easy to construct modern roads and railways, but the tradition of self-sufficiency and subsistence farming means that there is little commerce in the farm produce, huge though it grosses. The railway, usually single track, is the dominant means of transport because outside the towns all-season metalled roads are few and narrow so that there is scarcely any medium or long-distance road traffic. Road services, erratic and short though they be, serve as lines of contact rather than of commodity movement. Cattle carts in the north and east and the camel cart in the southwest still move the local farm-stuffs, even cotton and jute. The Ganges Delta waterways are locally used, but the main streams carry little traffic. In conjunction with commercialised irrigation, roads and railways have been constructed in Sind, but otherwise the communication pattern of the middle and lower Indus is very open and slight. River and canal transport is negligible, largely due to long seasons of low water. On the Bengal distributaries there is a little waterborne movement of bulky rice and jute.

INDUSTRY

The young alluvial materials of the Indo-Gangetic plains imply no significant local mineral or power resources. The electric power generated in the towns is derived from steam coal railed inland from the Deccan edge near Calcutta. The plain lacks the usual bases for heavy industry; Calcutta and Hooghly-side have engineering factories drawing materials from the Jamshedpur–Asansol region (outside the plain) and they service the railway and local shipping. There are scattered mills and factories processing local farm-stuffs. Small engineering trades have been established at Lahore and Amritsar, where there are cotton cloth mills, hosiery and knitwear factories making use of local wool.

Cotton spinning and weaving go on at scattered points in response to the heavy production of cotton and to the enormous market for coarse cloth among the peasants, for whom cotton shirts and dhoties are staple needs. At Calcutta, Cawnpore, Agra, Delhi and Lahore are located numerous cotton mills, typically small-scale and little specialised. The Ganges Delta, which virtually monopolises jute cultivation, has mills for hessian and gunny-bags. At one time the mills concentrated on the Hooghly banks, but new ones have now been established in East Pakistan, round Dacca and Chittagong on the other side of the delta. Leather goods (chiefly shoes) based on the local supply of hides are made in Calcutta, Cawnpore and Lahore, the hides being tanned chemically now that the supply of tannin bark has declined. Sugar refineries are numerous, particularly through Uttar Pradesh, the chief cane-producing section, yet most local sugar is produced on a cottage basis as the fudge-like gur or jaggery. Towards the hilly margins of the Punjab and of southern Uttar Pradesh, cement works and small glass factories operate.

New factories for a miscellany of light-processed goods using local materials and serving local markets have sprung up since 1947, consequent to the shift of millions of people and their savings across the new borders.

SOCIAL GEOGRAPHY

Because the highly productive Indo-Gangetic plain has attracted people of many backgrounds, characteristics of many cultures and civilisations appear. Mongolian physical features can be seen among people of the eastern plains and Caucasian features among the western. Dark-skinned people predominate in the east and lighter skins in the west. Cultural differences have been perpetuated by self-contained farming, by lack of communications, as well as by the caste tradition. Religious differences proved to have such command over people's actions as to lead to political partition on a theocratic basis in 1947. Gaya near Benares is identified with Buddha and the religion he inspired. Amritsar in the northwest is the centre of Sikhism. Most plainsmen are either Muslim or Hindu, Muslims predominating in the west (arising from proximity to the Middle East, whence Islam spread overland) and on the Ganges Delta (spread by water-borne traders from the Middle East). Hindus are dominant elsewhere, especially in Uttar Pradesh, where they form 85% of the population. The overlap of these major faiths was around Delhi, where neither commanded a clear majority. Muslim and Hindu communities profoundly differ in their way of life, though in some places blurred by long association. Muslims to the west eat wheat and meat, rear animals (horses, cattle and sheep) and are militant; while the Hindus are often rice-eating, vegetarian, unin-terested in cattle economically except as beasts of burden, and follow the caste tradition. During British administration, these religious communities existed side by side without territorial restriction. Since the creation of Pakistan as the political organisation of Muslims, religious distinctions have become intensified. A movement of many millions of religious refugees took place so that the new boundaries more sharply divide the cultures than when originally drawn. The migration from one side to the other after 1947 was accompanied by much social stress and civil disturbances. The Plain now has major political subdivisions. Pakistan, the Muslim state, has two parts, one in the west (the Indus Plains), the other in the east, including most of the Ganges Delta, but not reaching to Himalayas. The Indian Union of Hindus stretches through the Ganges Plain, separat-ing the two Pakistans and extending along the Brahmaputra. The economic strains arising from these divisions based on religion were considerable. Both countries still contain religious minorities.

To complicate the social geography, there are wide differences of speech and of alphabet among these 190 million plainsmen. Bengali, the language of the east, is distinct from the Assamese spoken along the Brahmaputra Valley, and from Hindi which runs in Uttar Pradesh. Punjabi, which is different again in speech and alphabet, dominates the "five rivers", while yet another language, Sindi, runs through the Lower Indus. The herding communities between the Indus and Jumna speak Rajasthani. Hence English has wide use as the inter-communal language.

CHAPTER NINETEEN

Regions of the Northern Plains

THE NORTHERN plains consist of the following regions:
1. The Brahmaputra Valley,
2. Bengal, compounded of the Ganges, Tista, Brahmaputra and Surmi deltas,
3. The Ganges Plain and the great doabs,
4. The Marchland of the Indo-Gangetic watershed in East Punjab, and of the Indus as far south as Baharwalpur,
5. The Punjab,
6. The lower Indus plains of Sind.

THE BRAHMAPUTRA VALLEY

The Brahmaputra Valley is some 400 by 60 miles of flood-plain almost enclosed by mountains rising steeply to north and south, whose effects on the monsoon rains make it far wetter than any other northern lowland. The river braids and twists confusingly, and may rise 10 feet in few hours during the rain, deterring bankside settlements and impeding trade movements. Flood is the major physical problem, so that irrigation is negligible. Huge areas of the lowland continue in deciduous forest and reeds. Villages are smaller than the Indian average and located to avoid floods, on levees or to the sides. Four-fifths of the sown area (see Table 4) is in rice with average holdings of about five acres, a sign that this is a new pioneering zone. Cottage-spinning and weaving of cotton is very common, facilitated by the isolation of self-contained farms.

A few steamers use the broad Brahmaputra, chiefly to Gauhati which is also a ferry-link for a devious northside railway to Calcutta and a southside line to Sadiya and Dibrugarh. No lengthwise all-season road exists, and only tracks lead south to Burma by way of Manipur and the Ledo Valley. Ways into Tibet are here specially difficult.

Oil is now being obtained near Digboi but faces transport difficulties which are being met by a pipeline. Tea plantations stand closer to the hills but principally outside the flood-plain and towards Shillong. A steady immigration has gone on this century by people moving from overcrowded

TABLE 4

FARMING ON THE NORTHERN PLAINS, 1952
(Data on a state basis includes small areas outside the Indo-Gangetic
Plains)

	Assam	Eastern Pakistan	Western Bengal	Bihar	Uttar Pradesh	Delhi	Western Punjab (W. Pak.)	Sind (W. Pak.)
Net sown area (million acres)	5.4	19.9	9.6	17.5	37.4	0.2	17.0	5·5
% irrigated	22.0	2·0	19·0	29·0	30·0	25·0	74·0	100·0
% double sown	13·0	28·0	10·0	31·0	23·0	40·0	14·0	15·0
Rice (mill. acres)	4.0	20·4	8·0	9·7	7·0	—	0·4	1·4
Wheat (mill. acres)	—	0·1	0·1	1·2	8·0	0·1	7·3	1·3
Other Foods (mill. acres).	1·3	0·2	0·9	9·0	25·7	0·2	5·0	1·6
Sugar (mill. acres)	0·1	0·3	0·1	0·4	1·8	—	0·3	—
Cotton (mill. acres)	1·0	0·1	—	—	0·2	—	1·9	0·8
Jute (mill. acres)	—	1·2	1·6	—	—	—	—	—
Pop. per net sown acre 1951–2	2·3	2·9	3·1	2·7	2·2	10·0	1·7	1·3

Bengal, seeking new rice lands along the valley or moving to the tea plantations which have suffered local labour scarcity. Logging and rice-milling
are done on a small scale. The valley has a density of 250 persons per square
mile, and the junction town of Gauhati is the only one which exceeds 50,000
people. Out-going trade from the valley is chiefly tea.

BENGAL

Built of "old mud, new mud and marsh" by the Ganges, Tista, Brahmaputra and Sarma rivers, Bengal is a huge deltaic area sustaining about
26 million people whose way of life turns upon exploiting low-lying soils
to grow rice for subsistence and jute for cash. The forested mountains of
the Himalayas to the north and the forested hills at Garo, Khasi and Lushai
to the east rise almost abruptly from the flat alluvium, but the Deccan
forms a gentler western margin of dry scrubland.

Though the Ganges and Brahmaputra approach this region almost head
on, the old lateritic alluvials of Barind and the Tista piedmont fan deviate
both rivers southward so that they meet at an acute angle well to the east
which is the newer deltaic section where the meanders are mobile, floods
are prolonged and vast silt-banks continuously re-form. The Tista and

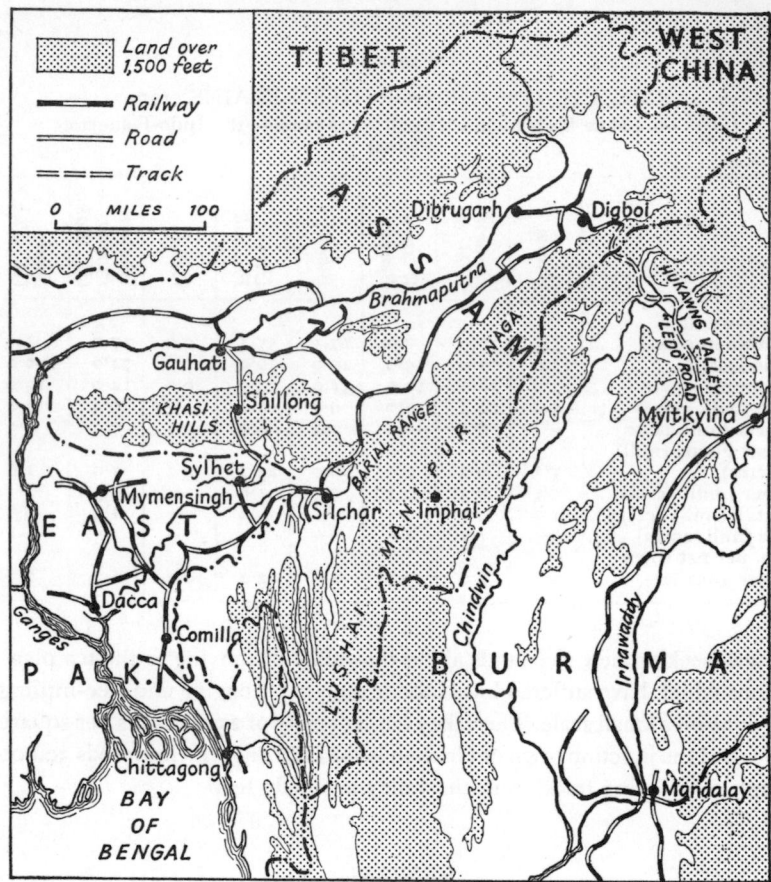

FIG. 74—The Brahmaputra Valley, Arakan Yoma and Northern Burma

Sarma régimes are more extreme (often catastrophically devastating) than those of the Ganges and Brahmaputra which, having large catchment basins, deliver a more even flow at the delta. The western delta is largely moribund, the Ganges distributaries there having silted so much that they carry only a small part of the discharge and have reached static positions for the time being, the main discharge being farther east. The Hooghly, chief Ganges distributary in the seventeenth century, now carries most water from the short, erratic streams descending from the Deccan hills of West Bengal. The dryer west farms wheat, maize and mulberries for a little silk. At its seaward edge the delta has lobate mangrove swamps—the Sundar-

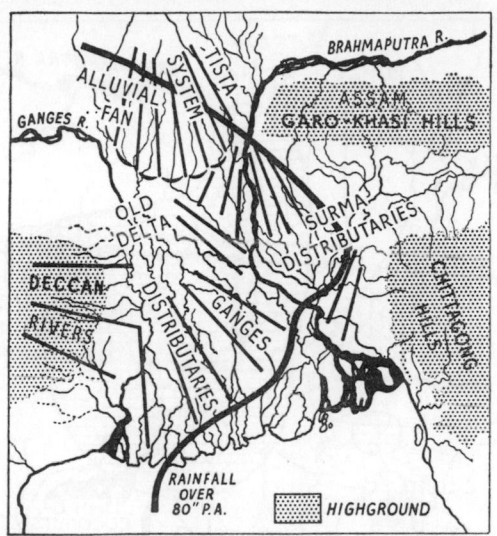

FIG. 75—The Deltas of Bengal. West of the bold line rainfalls
average less than 80 in. per annum

bans—which are fairly static to the west and rapidly extending and
changing to the east; pioneer cultivation for padi steadily penetrates the
Sundarbans as the pressure of people increases.

In detail, the delta surface has considerable relief of levees, lagoons, old
wave-built spits and abandoned river-beds (bhils). The tide often rises and
falls 12 feet or so, causing a daily ebb and flow of such strength that there
is a continuous scour and modelling process 10 to 12 miles inland.

The annual rainfall over much of the delta is below 80 inches; much
heavier falls occur to the north and east, where on-shore air movements
meet the abrupt relief to produce violent and very heavy rain-storms. The
same side of the delta also experiences cool-season rains from cyclones
coming from the northwest and converging on the eastern hills. These cool-
season showers assist double-cropping.

The greater part of the delta is now "East Pakistan" consequent to
Muslim predominance. Hooghly-side and most of the dryer western delta
round Calcutta forms West Bengal and has a Hindu majority. The delta
is thus traversed by a political boundary which often runs athwart old-
established lines of trade and communication. Sharp differences of policy
on the border have led to Dacca and Chittagong developing over the last
decade as economic and political centres for the productive newer delta in
East Pakistan, and there has been much migration across the borders.

247

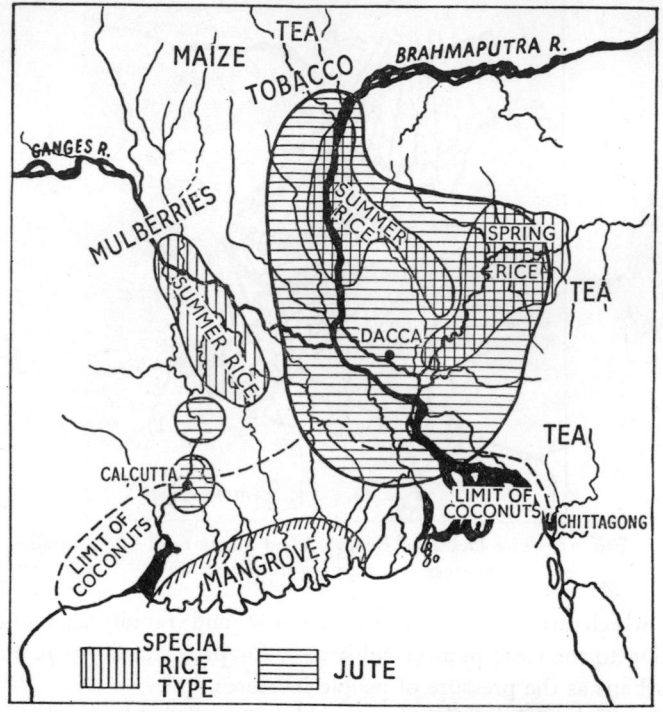

FIG. 76—Agriculture in Bengal and East Pakistan. The special rice is
additional to the normal kharif crop of rice

THE GANGES PLAIN

Shortly before it debouches into Bengal, the Ganges moves through the
narrowest part of its plain. Near Monghya, the plain occupies only about
a hundred miles between Duar foothills of the Himalayas and the Rajmahal
Hills, northern fringe of the Deccan. The Ganges Plain stretches 700
miles from here to the Jumna, broadening to 250 miles at Cawnpore. While
uniformly low, the plain has variations of shape, texture, water supply
and climate, which lead to several types of farming. Large piedmont fans
constitute a belt about 20 miles broad along its northern edge, succeeded
southwards by great doabs, now much engineered for irrigation, and by
old river-beds and stretches of coarse gravels (balbar). On the south appear
some low Deccan hills and confluence plains, where a few Deccan tributaries add their intermittent run-off to the Ganges. East of a line from
Allahabad to where the Gogra leaves the Himalaya, the *Middle Ganges*

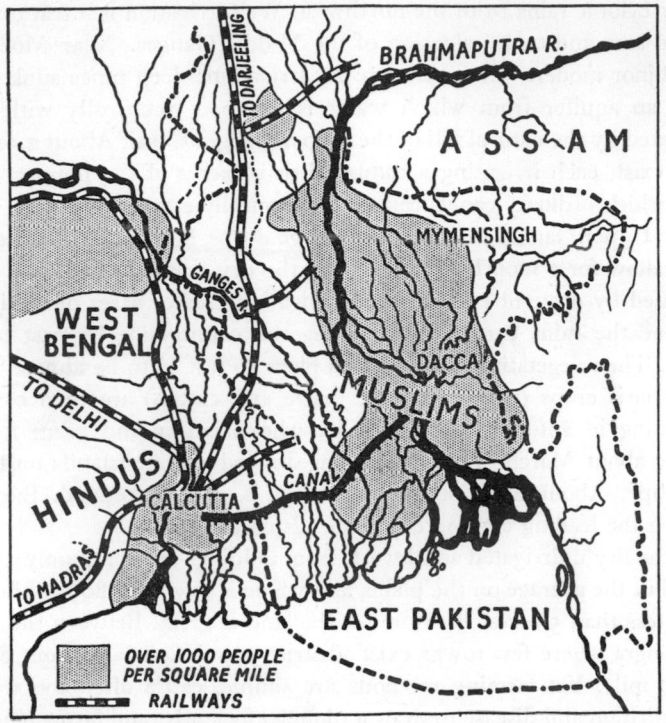

FIG. 77—Bengal: Population, political boundary, religion and transport

Plains have higher rainfalls and a longer rainy season than to the west, where stretch the *Upper Ganges Plains*. Evaporation gradually becomes greater than rainfall in the west. Both isohyets and doabs have skew patterns roughly N.W.–S.E. across the plains, reflected both in agricultural and population patterns, in turn complicated by the drainage asymmetry consequent to the Himalayan streams pressing well south across the plains.

In the Middle Ganges more plentiful rains make possible padi-farming, sugar growing and some jute; trees are fairly common. The Upper Ganges has a little padi-growing but the emphasis is on wheat, supplemented by sorghum, millet and gram as food crops; sugar and cotton are the commerical crops, and trees are less common and more noticeably deciduous; acacia trees are common and the eucalyptus is being introduced. Large-scale irrigation is now a feature of the Upper Ganges, but the large unirrigated wheat area towards Saharanpur is consequent to an inch or so of

249

winter cylonic rains from the northwest. Well irrigation is a feature of the central area and tank irrigation of the Middle Ganges. Near Moradabad and Bijnor modern tube wells are for irrigation; deep pipes sunk 50 feet reach an aquifer from which water is pumped electrically with power generated by the natural fall of the Upper Ganges Canal. About 2,500 such wells exist, each irrigating a thousand or so acres of the porous "bhur" soils, which ordinary canals cannot economically serve.

The Upper Ganges Plains, mainly large doabs, are much cultivated, and only fallow for a month or two late in the dry season, when they appear desolated by drought except where irrigation creates oases of cultivation. In June the rains come, transforming the countryside by east to west stages. Then vegetative growth takes place so fast as to be almost visible. The kharif crops (rice, sorghum, maize and cotton) are then sown for harvesting in autumn; succeeded by wheat, barley and gram for harvesting about March. Trees and villages stand up like islands on the flat landscape. About 20% of the field area is double-cropped. Sugar has become the leading commercial crop, displacing cotton.

In the dry unirrigated southwest, farm holdings are commonly 13 acres each, but the average on the plains as a whole is low, over 80% of holdings being less than 5 acres. Pressure on the land is great. Between the Jumna and Gogra where few towns exist, district populations are about 800 per square mile. Yet farming methods are simple, cattle often too weak by malnutirition and disease to draw a plough efficiently, and farms have little storage facility. Inadequate marketing and difficulties with landlords have worsened the rural situation. Villages are often as densely peopled as the worst nineteenth century industrial slums in Europe, isolated and crudely built, possibly with only one brick-built house to each village. The villages make an equidistant pattern on the map. Little fort towns and market towns (commonly located at mid-doabs) are numerous. Variable and erratic though their waters are, few small shallow, country craft use them to move the bulky farm-stuffs to market, but steam navigation has never been significant despite the lack of other alternatives than the rough track. Here only 1 mile of surfaced road exists for each 13 square miles and each 7,000 people. Industries are few, chiefly sugar milling and cotton mills, all very seasonal. Village crafts continue, and brassware, carved ivory, gold and silver embroidery and jewellery, now luxury goods, continue to be made in cottages.

While the Middle Ganges Plain has higher agricultural potential than the Upper, having greater and more reliable rains, it has a higher flood risk. Because its level is so low, wide stretches are flooded by the Ganges

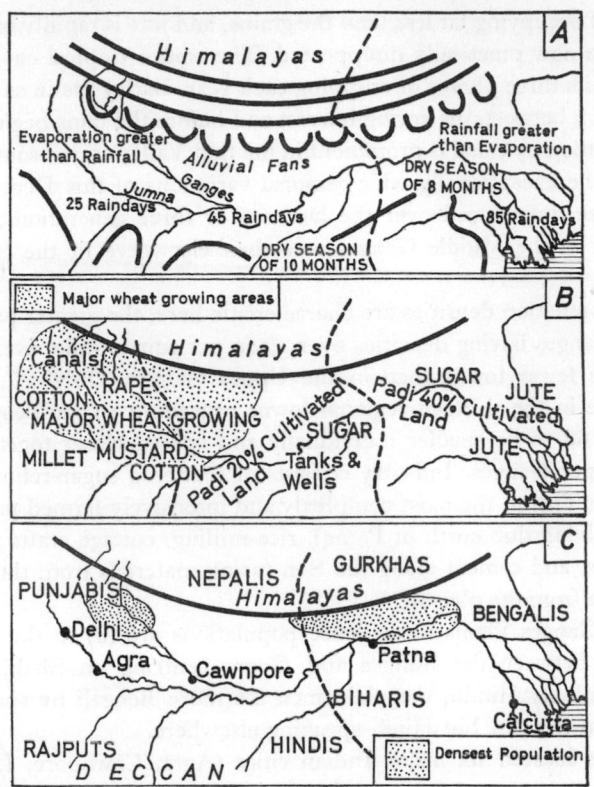

F<small>IG</small>. 78—Sketch-maps of the Ganges Plain: A. physical features, B. agriculture, C. population, races and cities

and its greater tributaries, which have changed position considerably through the centuries. Certain Himalayan tributaries, like the Kosi, respond violently to monsoon rains in the mountains and change level rapidly. The Kosi has been known to rise 30 feet in a day even well out on the plains. Control is being established both to protect the plains from Kosi floods, to irrigate the coarser soils of its northern alluvials and to provide rural power. Abandoned beds and cutoff loops are common everywhere, adding the malarial incidence. The Ganges leveés have been built up to such an extent that they obstruct tributaries and cause flooding near confluence points; in the same way, railway and road embankments have induced local floods.

Rice dominates the Middle Ganges food crops, followed in area by wheat, barley, maize and gram. Cotton is a declining interest, sugar widespread but occupying far less than the grains, and jute is rapidly increasing. Indigo has now practically disappeared. The wetter tropical environment here permits three phases of cropping each year. Barley fits in as the third grain grown between the spring harvest and before the rains begin. Large-scale irrigation by canal is prominent in the Son Valley on the south, where it offsets the exceptionally wide seasonal variations of this Deccan tributary. Maize, introduced over the last two or three generations, is more prominent in the Middle Ganges area than elsewhere in the Subcontinent.

High population densities are characteristic here, the greater part of the Middle Ganges having densities over 1,100 per square mile, even though it contains fewer towns than in the Upper Ganges. Only 2% of local people live in the thirteen regional towns exceeding 10,000 people each. Villages tend to be smaller individually and spaced closer together than in the Upper Ganges. Industry consists of scattered sugar-refining (particularly in Tirhut, the most complexly and intensively farmed part of the plain and lying due north of Patna), rice-milling, cottage crafts for brass and fabrics, and cement along the Son (using materials from the Deccan rather than from the plains).

In the Ganges Plains most dense populations are (a) to the north of Patna, (b) between the Ganges and Gogra centring on Shahjahanpur. Overwhelmingly Hindu, the plainsmen are more Bengali by speech and physique to the east but Hindi-speaking elsewhere.

Here are located six major Indian cities (Agra, Cawnpore, Lucknow, Allahabad, Benares and Patna, each exceeding 250,000) and six lesser ones (Saharanpur, Meerut, Moradabad, Aligarh, Bareli, Shahjahanpur, each between a 100,000 and 250,000). The major cities have riverside locations, most of the lesser are central to doabs and "large-market" in type. The towns are as much as 15% Muslim in their population, though rural people are almost exclusively Hindu (Aligarh was for a long time Pak–Ind's chief Muslim university). Urban centres are nodes in the network of railways; all the major cities except Lucknow are junctions for trans-Deccan lines, linking the plains to the ports of Bombay and Calcutta respectively. The core zone of several cities has changed position several times. The historical variation of Indian towns has arisen from an interplay of catastrophic floods, decimating epidemics and the whims of conquerors. The five cities show significant contrasts indicating the varied interests and traditions present. *Benares* (about 400,000), also known as Kasi, is an ancient centre of both Buddhist and Hindu religions, full of shrines and temples, attracting tourists by the myths and sagas of its past, labyrinthine in street pattern, continuing cottage silk-weaving, embroidery and brass-ware. Few cities of Asia today are as "medievally oriental" as Benares.

Allahabad (about 300,000) is a modern city, though it has a long history stemming from its site at the confluence of the Jumna and Ganges. Its great fort is Muslim, by origin and population it is Hindu. Now an administrative and legal centre, it attracts large numbers to its annual agricultural fair.

Agra (400,000) is the ruin of a capital established when the Muslim Moguls controlled all Northern India. Its design is military, its fort huge, its architecture dominated by the tombs and minarets of Islam, its atmosphere remarkably "Arabian Nights". Today the cramped city has small cotton mills and is a great market for hides and wool, the latter drawn from Rajasthan to serve a carpet industry largely on a cottage basis. Its strategic position on the major route from the plains into Malwa and across the Deccan is underlined by the convergance on it of several railways.

Lucknow (500,000) was a late Muslim foundation, located to exploit the highly productive plains of Oudh. Brick and stucco built, it is distinctively a plainsmen's city (in contrast to the stone and marble of Agra and Allahabad, where Deccan materials are prominent). Its regional market character has limited its size, but the development of processing industries has led to expansion based on abundant local commodities and cheap labour. Today it is an important inland servicing centre for railways, has paper and cotton-mills, sugar refineries and small factories for a range of local consumer goods.

Cawnpore (750,000) was until 1800 only a village. It then grew rapidly as a chief inland location of Western-style industries in large factories, particularly for producing cotton goods based on the local crop. It exemplifies how a town originally buying cotton for overseas manufactures became itself a manufacturing centre of cotton goods as industry gravitated towards sources of raw material. Today Cawnpore is a mixture of nineteenth- and twentieth-century factory and urban industrial patterns, and the second greatest industrial city of India. No longer so exclusively related to cotton, it is India's greatest wool and leather centre, has large flour and vegetable oil mills, sugar refineries and chemical factories.

Patna (300,000), the capital of the Middle Ganges Plain, is smaller than Benares, but has a similar link with ancient Hindu kingdoms. It has given its name to a high-grade rice, indicating its function as a market town now extended as major regional administrative centre. A few rice, oil and cotton mills handle local commodities. It has been by-passed to some extent because several major railway lines from the plain bear south to make a short-cut across the Deccan to Calcutta by way of the Damodar Valley.

THE INDO-GANGETIC MARCHLAND

Between the Jumna and Sutlej, the Indo-Gangetic Plains reach the 600-foot level, are uncrossed by rivers with long head-streams in the Himalayas and form a transitional divide between the Ganges and the Indus.

This borderland is so much drier than the Upper Ganges Plains that agriculture cannot be done regularly unless irrigated. It is more "monsoon" in its rainfall régime than the West Punjab and lacks cool-season rains. It separates streams and doabs leading westwards and eastwards, and is the home of Sikhism. It roughly divides the Muslim realm from the Hindu, and the wheat-herdsmen people from the rice-sorghum vegetarians.

Deforestation has caused the rough gravels of the Siwalik foothills northward to become heavily eroded in gullies and "badlands". The intermittent short streams issuing from them are most erratic; any water they contain moves across the level country like a sheet flood, and then quickly disappears southward into the very sandy subsoil. The eastern flank of the Sutlej has native ribbon irrigation, but elsewhere short, dead-end doab canals without modern headworks have been the basis of cultivation. The wadi-like rivers (known here as chos) are avoided by farmers owing to the danger of "wash out". Wells are uncommon, ground-water lying too deep to be accessible except by pumping and tubes. A new dam across the upper Sutlej at Bhakra Nangal is to provide steady irrigation for 4 million acres and some rural electricity. At Harike, Sutlej water is being dammed exclusively into Indian irrigation canals via the Talwara Jeel and away from Pakistani users below the Bias–Sutlej confluence.

Farming (for winter wheat and summer millet) and settlements are located to the north, decreasing southwards in transition to the Thar Desert. At Delhi a low ridge from the Aravallis indicates that this is a marchland for the Deccan as well. Because farming is more precarious here, rural population density is low. Villages are nucleated and average farther apart than in Uttar Pradesh. One or two districts have densities of the order of 600 per square mile, but most are less than 200 per square mile. Settlements and towns show signs of a long history of military action. Forts and strategic sites are common, and the territory remained divided for a long time into militarised principalities and chieftaincies. Many critical battles took place here because the marchland controls the ways from east to west through the plains and from the northwest into the

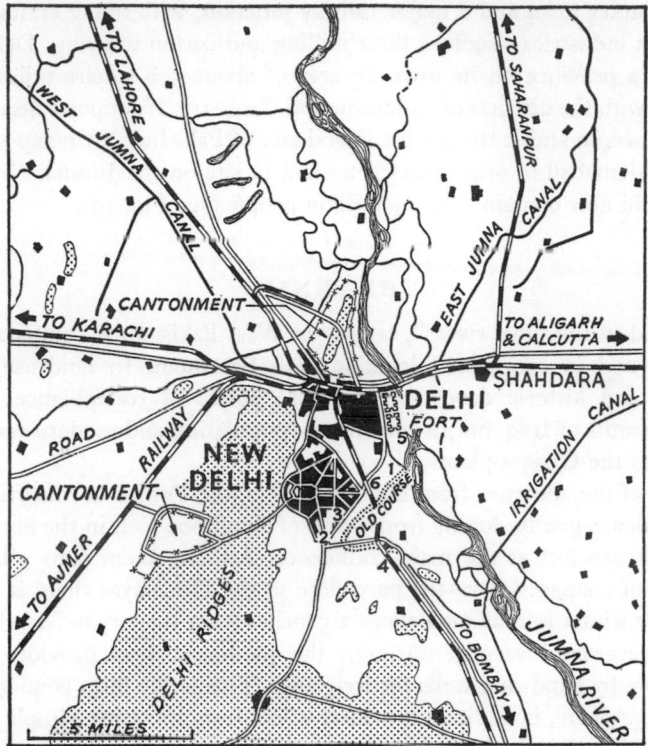

FIG. 79—Delhi, the historic point of control of the Northern Plains on a ridge extension of the Aravallis. The numbers mark sites of ruins of cities other than the present Delhi and New Delhi; the former is still a congested, walled oriental city; the latter is the modern administrative capital, planned in the tradition of Paris, Canberra and Washington

Deccan, and is now traversed by the modern India–Pakistan boundary.

Delhi has been a node of routes and centre of control for millennia, justifying its title as "the Rome of India". Seven old citadels have their ruins within a few miles of the present capital, New Delhi, modern creation of the British imperial period. The earlier cities have walls and acted as forts. What is now called Old Delhi was the walled Muslim-style capital of the Mogul, Shah Jahan (mid-seventeenth century). New Delhi has the geometric form of planned modern capitals, like Washington and Canberra. It is cosmopolitan in character, but strongly Hindu. The new city is an administrative one: the Shah Jahan city is tortuously "Oriental", a dusty market town and a major railway junction, with many crafts and a few light industries—such as flour milling and cotton weaving. Delhi has become a province on its own, an area of about 570 square miles comparable with the districts of Columbia and Canberra. It supports nearly two million people and is the largest inland city of Pak–Ind. In many ways it recalls Allahabad in origin, character and in site on the Jumna. New and Old Delhi now contain over $1\frac{1}{4}$ million people (see Fig. 79).

THE PUNJAB

The land of the "five rivers", largely in West Pakistan, is comparable in latitude and in continental location with Szechuan. In land use, farm pattern and historic development it has points of resemblance to the Mesopotamia of Iraq, but in land-forms, population and modern economy relates to the Ganges plains.

Built of the alluvium from five long rivers, the Punjab is constituted of several doabs gently sloping from levels of about 600 feet, in the northeast, to about 250 feet at the main confluence. Athwart them runs a banded pattern of change: (a) In the part close to the Himalayas there is a considerable winter rainfall (at Lahore 2·5 inches from January to March), and the underground seepage through the piedmont fans provides water accessible by hand-dug wells for irrigation. This is the farm zone of great antiquity, where, in addition to winter wheat from the rains, simple irrigation could exploit the large Himalayan streams which rise with snow-melt in spring to facilitate summer cultivation. Holdings are much divided and field patterns irregular within a fan of old tracks radiating from each village. (b) At slightly lower levels farther south are the main doabs, where in the last hundred years large canals have been constructed for irrigation by colonies of settlers who came in such numbers from the old, over-crowded rural areas farther north that the population pattern radically changed. The doabs from the Jhelum to the Sutlej have by now become fully developed on modern lines, the western Thal doab between the Jhelum and the Indus is the last to reach that stage. The main doabs have dead-end canals, as Fig. 72 indicates, and produce wheat and cotton on a commercial basis from holdings laid out in the planned squareness of new colonies, larger than those in the Ganges Plain, and set within the roughly rectangular pattern of canals. (c) Beside the Lower Sutlej and the Lower Chenab and Indus are many short inundation canals (i.e. without barrages), which never gave perennial water because the river levels were lowest when water was most needed. These areas now suffer from exceptionally low water consequent to great off-takes (as much as half) by upstream diversion. (d) Outside the Punjab doabs to the south, east and west are terrains varying from poor steppe to desert. The gravelly wadis are unusable for irrigation and left to poor grazing.

Steppe conditions now evident in (d) probably represent those general on the large doabs before they were irrigated. The whole region has seen much readjustment of levels and river positions, and much remodelling of river bluffs and sands consequent to the removal of natural vegetation, close to the mountains during the last two millennia. Large-scale water diversion has gone on during the last hundred years.

Both continental location and long cloud-free seasons mean that, while the Punjab is never cold for long, it regularly has frosts even as far south as Multan, and the temperature range between night and day, and between winter and summer, is wide. The monthly average temperature at Lahore varies from 55° F. (January) to 94° F. (June); but the mean January minimum is 35° and the mean June maximum is 115°. The high summer evaporation rate aggravates the loss of water by percolation through the more porous alluvials. Salt may be carried up and deposited on the surface, but by now most Punjab farmers have adjusted their methods to minimise this. The non-irrigated areas of the east, south and west have saline soils. Concern about loss by evaporation and seepage account for a complex local vocabulary of soils according to their water-holding capacity. Seepage and irrigation are both so great that rivers once dry for half the year now usually contain some water all the time by subsurface percolation. At least a fifth of the irrigated area is double-cropped.

While three-quarters of its cultivated area is irrigated, the proportion differs, being greatest between the Chenab and the Sutlej. On each major doab, the northern districts may be totally irrigated but half served by wells (as in Amritsar), and the southern districts almost entirely watered by canals (as in Lyallpur and Montgomery). The newest irrigation colony is in Thal on the Indus–Chenab doab, where over 300,000 acres are now being cultivated by 23,000 settlers.

The Punjab was always a wheat-growing region even in the older northern belt, and the crop dominates in newer areas on the great doabs. About half the cultivated area is in wheat, a proportion unequalled anywhere else in the subcontinent. Before the First World War wheat formed a substantial export to the international market. Later the output was absorbed in trade within Pak–Ind. Since partition, even the movement of wheat to India has ceased, owing to domestic needs in Pakistan. Cotton, by far the most important commercial crop, is exclusively irrigated on about 2 million acres. Once grown for export, the high-grade, long-staple cotton is now being increasingly retained for spinning and weaving within Pakistan. The yardage of cotton cloth manufactured in 1957 was nearly five times that of 1951, a repercussion of the new boundaries separating Punjab cotton from Indian mills. Rice, while occupying only a small area, is produced as a commercial crop. Sheep rearing and wool production have declined as irrigation extended, but the region attracts wool from the surrounding hills and from the adjoining steppes. By necessity, substantial areas are under fodder to maintain the many draught cattle and horses prominent in Punjabi tradition.

Industrialisation is in small units, often on a cottage basis and always processing local materials. Modern cotton mills operate to Lahore, Amritsar, Lyallpur and Montgomery, and small cotton gins are widespread. Wool and silk (the latter from cottages in the Himalayan foothills) are similarly worked in Lahore, Amritsar and Multan; some wool for knitting and hosiery even being imported from Australia. Light metal goods are produced at Patiala, and Lahore has engineering workshops servicing the railway. The pattern of industry has been rapidly changing to avoid dependence on Indian supplies.

The Punjab is served by a closer net of railways and roads than most of the Northern Plains. The form of the doabs and the alignment of the Himalayas dominate their pattern. In the historic northern belt are many small towns, often fortified to command crossings, bridge points and marketing centres along the ancient way from the Northwest Frontier into the Ganges Plain. Lahore and Amritzar are the largest modern towns evolved from this old string of settlements. Multan (about 200,000) began as a medieval fort commanding the riverine approaches to the Punjab from the south and caravan routes through Afghanistan. It has increased in size and importance this century as agriculture and population gravitated southward. That shift led to the growth of new marketing centres, of which Lyallpur and Montgomery (about 180,000 each and surrounded by districts with a combined farming population of over 4 millions) are typical, but there are many others among the new doab colonies.

Sialkot, Lahore and Amritsar are all major towns in the older piedmont-fan agricultural areas. *Sialkot* (150,000), close to the foothills, is least important now, partly because it is a dead-end. *Amritsar* (about 350,000) is central to one of the most complexly irrigated of those older fans largely built by the Bias River running through India. Amritsar functions as market not only for the large local production but also for the Himalayan valleys. A major fort on the Peshawar-Delhi highway, it had great significance as the home of Sikhism. Today Amritsar, despite the disruption of partition and the new boundary which separates it from the Punjab, continues to make woollen goods, carpets, silks and embroideries and to service the densely populated countryside round it. *Lahore* remains the capital of the Punjab, a "million" city and second largest inland town of the Subcontinent. It has maintained its standing for centuries under Muslim, Sikh and British régimes. Its fort is skirted by dense, tortuous streets and bazaars, with an outer modern residential area and a large military cantonment. It acts as a regional focus of roads, railways, administration, commercial distribution and collection. Lahore is about as far inside West Pakistan as Amritsar is outside, and at the partition received a flood of refugee Muslims and witnessed the flight of Hindus. In 1959, Rawalpindi, a small military training town and free from provincial tension, became capital of the Pakistan central government.

THE PLAINS OF SIND

From the confluence of the "five rivers", the combined Indus is known locally as the Panjnab and assumes a Nilotic character, flowing through Sind as a braided misfit stream within its levees, amid a deserted, dry and often sandy landscape. No new tributaries join it for hundreds of miles. The Panjnab swings west to the ranges and mountain deserts of Baluchistan and Afghanistan. These arid plains of Sind, where the earliest Arabs and Muslims infiltrated into the subcontinent, merge into the Thar Desert eastwards, beyond sandy bluffs, but to the west more sharply terminate in high relief. The clay desert of Pat extends the Sind plains westwards into a large embayment between the Kirthar and the Sulaiman Ranges, a region notorious for holding the Pak–Ind record high temperatures (126°). Wadi-like scars and old river channels show repeatedly on the Sind landscape, and may occasionally be the scene of a flash flood coming from violent convectional storms at long intervals.

The Indus contains most water about early September and least in February. Its load is heavy, its rate of deposition rapid so that meandering and forming and re-forming of the levees is continuous. At Sukkur is a low limestone outcrop through which the main river has worked a channel that has remained a fixed point in the river system for millennia. This firm rock provides foundation for the mile-long barrage across the river, a structure which enables some 36,000 miles of channels and distributaries to irrigate what is in effect a vast oasis area south of Sukkur which is becoming greater than the total cultivated area of Egypt. Outside the green zone served by the barrage, Sind is without economic development, the

259

FIG. 80—West Pakistan and the Indus Plain; the towns are: Hyd. Hyderabad, in Sind; L. Lahore; M. Multan

nomadic pastoralists of its steppes having diminished since canalisation brought sheep and cattle runs under the plough.

The Western Nara and Eastern Nara are old Indus distributaries now canalized by the Barrage. The doabs between them and the main Indus constitute the new farm area of Sind. Outside the range of irrigation the delta merges into the "bad-lands" of the Rann of Cutch; it contains the silted creeks and ruins of ports, is lined with strips of mangrove and wave-built sandspits, and scattered with thickets of thorn or tall marsh grasses or salty waste.

The perennial irrigated area which was opened in 1932 is laid out in large holdings geometrically shaped and with nucleated settlements in a total cultivated area of about 5 million acres. Double-cropping is done on much of the new land but fallowing and rotation are standard practices. Rice and wheat occupy similar acreages. Commercial farming is the standard practice and three-quarters of the irrigated area is under cereals. About one-fifth of it is under high-grade cotton, the dominant export commodity. Date palms are scattered in large numbers through the oasis and form a considerable trade. Camels, buffaloes, sheep and goats are numerous, evidence of an older tradition, and of the need for many draught animals.

About 4·5 million people live in the Sind plains, most of them being irrigation farmers. *Hyderabad*, an old caravanserai (about 250,000), has rapidly expanded since irrigation revolutionised the countryside round it and amplified its function as capital to Sind. Cotton processing, glasswork and leather work are done there, mostly in factories set up since Pakistan was created. *Sukkur* is now a fairly large country town, but not much more than a quarter the size of Hyderabad.

Equally spectacular has been the growth of *Karachi*, recently capital of Pakistan as a whole and of the largest Muslim nation. It now contains about 1½ million people, as compared with 350,000 in 1941. A large sandspit and island shelter it from strong east-moving seas which in turn lead away from Karachi harbour the silt-laden discharges of the Indus. Largely a man-made harbour surrounded by semi-desert, a long mole has been necessary owing to the shallow approaches. Karachi has grown in response to trade with its newly developed hinterland, and it has benefitted by the cotton and wheat booms which have recurred in the war periods. Cotton, wheat, hides, oil seeds and wool are the basis of its exports, and piece goods, petroleum and capital equipment of its imports. During the Second World War it was a major entry for war materials intended to make India a bastion, and it acted as military entrepôt for the Middle East as far as Suez. Muslim industrialists, refugees from India, have set up many small factories here since 1947. Its function has been augmented by world airways; Karachi is the most important airport of the Subcontinent largely because of its position in relation to the very long and still occasionally hazardous air routes over the deserts and mountains between "Pak–Ind" and the Mediterranean. The location is a difficult one for a large city because domestic water must come from far or by way of expensive, deep modern wells. Some water reaches Karachi by a 90-mile conduit from the Indus. Water is a continuing problem worsened by the sanitary needs of thousands of homeless refugees who squatted there after 1947. Its function as national capital led to much rapid building and make-shift city services, but in 1959 government transferred to Rawalpindi in the Punjab.

A single main road and railway connect Karachi inland. Between Hyderabad and Sukkur lines and roads run each side of the Indus and there are branches across the Pat Desert towards Quetta, a direct road link west of the Indus to Peshawar, as well as road and railway links to the "inland capital" at Lahore. Hyderabad, a major railway junction, is linked across the Thar to the Deccan and to the Ganges Plain.

CHAPTER TWENTY

Peninsular India

THE DECCAN

SOUTH OF THE Indo-Gangetic Plain stretches by far the larger part of the Subcontinent. Called "Deccan India" or "Peninsular India", it is peninsular only to the south. Approached from the northern plains, Deccan India rises gradually; a third of it never rises above the level of the Indo-Gangetic Marchland. For thousands of square miles, its climate differs little from that of the northern plain, and changes only gradually over the Deccan. There is more difference between one part and another of the Deccan, and between the Deccan and its coastal fringes than between the Deccan and the Northern Plains. In a sense the Deccan is a vast marchland between the racial groups of the northern plains and of the coastal plains along Malabar and Coromandel. Its size induces variations: the Deccan quadrilateral from the Thar Desert to East Bengal and to Cape Comorin has proportions comparable to one between London, Warsaw, Odessa and Naples; two-thirds lie south of the tropic, but its northern corner reaches the latitude of Cairo and New Orleans.

Peninsular India is geologically very old and stable, a structural block multiple-faulted on all except its northern edges, and built chiefly of gneiss rock to the south and east and of much-metaphosed sedimentaries in the north. A quarter of the block is masked by a sheet of lava with the Tapti River as axis. The block is tilted from a high western edge down to the east, and there are subsidiary tilts from the Vindhya Ranges down towards the northwest. Exposed to tropical erosion through long geological periods, the surface has weathered to rounded outlines and rolling plains whose red and yellow soils have been laterised to a low agricultural potential, except on the Deccan Lava Plateau which, being of nearly horizontal basaltic layers, has flat-topped, square-cut mesa landscapes. The lava weathers to a dark or black clay soil called regur, whose mineral content makes for a fertility exceptional on the Deccan. Beyond the lavas stretch the gneiss or granite foundation, hidden at other places by fragments of old (Gondwana and Pre-Cambrian) sedimentaries, which include coal-bearing strata in Chota Nagpur to the northeast. The sharp outlines of the Aravalli

TABLE 5

CLIMATIC DATA FOR DECCAN INDIA

	Bikaner	*Jubbulpur*	*Nagpur*	*Poona*	*Hyderabad*	*Bangalore*
Temperature (mean F. Jan.)	48	46	55	55	58	57
Rainfall (inches p.a.)	12	56	50	28	31	36
% in months June to Sept.	80	90	86	75	75	55
Raindays in months June to Sept. . .	14	53	49	36	37	33
No. of months each less than 1 inch .	8	7	7	6	4	4
Net rain minus evap. (inches p.a.) . .	−132	−65	−60	−79	−61	−30

Valley and Thar landscapes to the northwest are of suchancient sedimentaries.

Rivers emphasise the structural differences. A southern group of streams (Kistna, Godavari, Mahanadi, Cauvery) flows eastwards, responding to the general tilt. A northern group parallels the faulted Aravalli–Vindhya ranges on N.E.–S.W. lines, with the Narbada–Mahi–Tapti rivers debouching west or southwestward, and the Chanbal–Betwa–Son group discharging northeast into the Ganges. Highest relief is in the Western Ghats, a continuous line of high fault scarps extending south with little break towards Cape Comorin. The Eastern Ghats are very much less distinct, less continuous and more broken by broad valleys. The fault lines of the Aravalli and Vindhya Ranges, bare, scarred and flanked by well-entrenched parallel rivers, appear mountainous though below 4,500 feet, the mean Deccan level being 2,800 feet. South of Mysore where the block breaks sharply, the narrowness of the peninsula, vigorous water erosion and the disappearance of eastern hills, change the landscape, so that Tamil-nad will be dealt with as part of the periphery of the coastal plains.

CLIMATE AND WATER SUPPLY

The monsoon régime is characteristic of the Deccan. But the summer inflow of air towards Thar involves one stream blowing directly over the Arabian Sea across the Deccan country from the southwest, and another from more southerly points almost paralleling the Coromandel coast before curving inland over Bengal. From the Arabian Sea winds the abrupt Western Ghats derive relief rains, but farther east the Deccan suffers from "rainshadow" effects. The Aravalli and Vindhya are edgewise to the air movements, the former roughly delimiting the dryest (less than 20 inches per annum) part of the Deccan–Rajasthan. East of about lat. 80° the rainfall is slightly higher from the effects of Bay of Bengal winds and local relief athwart them. Concentration of rain into the June–September period is most pronounced except along the southeastern edges which are anomalous; south of the Kistna the Deccan has peak rains in September. The rain is everywhere intense when it comes, averaging about $\frac{3}{4}$ inches per rain day in the wet season and with correspondingly greater scour. Immediately before the rains, temperatures exceed means of 95°, relief being insufficient to cause significant local reductions. Prolonged drought is a feature, and the annual rate of evaporation is commonly several times greater than annual rainfall, the effects being worsened by great irregularity. Much of the Deccan has weather like that round Delhi. The weather and climate to the south from the Punjab–Uttar Pradesh axis changes little for thousands of square miles, making for continuity in the crop and vegetation types and the problem of water supply. Owing to the small areas of farmable lowlands, natural vegetation continues to be more apparent on the Deccan than in the Indo–Gangetic Plains. North of the Vindhyas and in the rain-shadow of the Western Ghats are large stretches of thorn forest and open vegetation stunted by drought; acacias and euphorbias occur but thorny plants are commonest by surviving the browsing cattle and goats. Over the central and northern plateau stretches a dry deciduous forest with a wetter variety covering the eastern corner. In the hot, dry season vegetation seems so burnt and shrivelled that its survival seems impossible, and its quick change of colour and leaf when the rains come has attracted comment from all travellers. Bamboo is not widespread except in the east, where the sal tree (*Shorea robusta*) also appears and is much used domestically. Only the Western Ghats has lumbering. For long seasons the Deccan appears less covered than it is, owing to plants shrivelling in drought. Only marginally, in the Western Ghats and in the Orissa coastal mountains, does the forest continue green through the year.

Great variation in water content is a feature of Deccan rivers whose large catchments have little natural storage such as snowfields or trees provide. Many rivers by the end of May are strings of discontinuous ponds if water be present at all; others are little more than wadis. This condition coupled with low rainfall makes irrigation essential but most difficult. Inundation canals cannot be used much, and only in the Malwa area can rock wells be

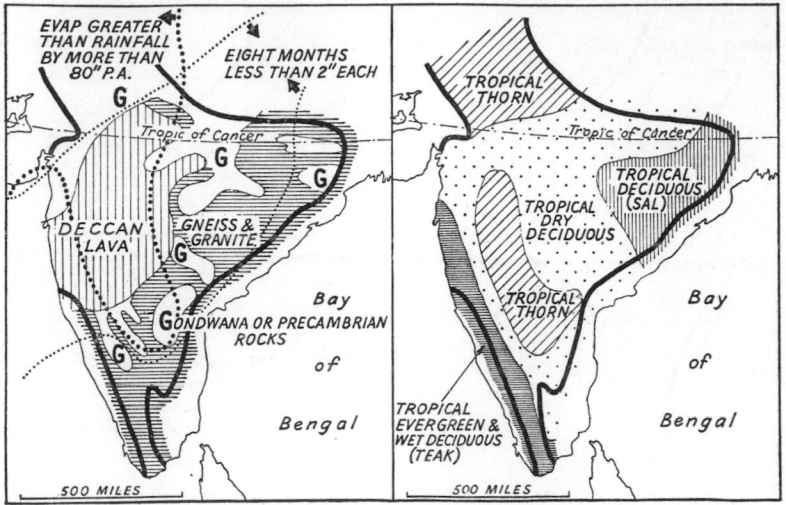

FIG. 81—Peninsular India: physiography and vegetation
The heavy line encloses the Deccan block

used. Tank irrigation is done in the south. Modern irrigation works exist east of the Ghats in Bombay and at Chattisgarh on the Mahanadi, and development plans include irrigation dams at Kakrapura on the Upper Tapti, at Hirakud on the Tungabhadra tributary of the Kistna in Hyderabad, at Tikarpara and Naraj on the Mahanadi, and new works on the Damodar. Most new projects are for power as well as irrigation. The broad rolling valley form renders doab canalisation impractical and most irrigation barrages are of necessity long and low, creating reservoirs of great area, shallow depth and high evaporation loss.

DECCAN AGRICULTURE

Deccan farmers, facing greater difficulties than their counterparts on the Indo–Gangetic Plain, depend almost entirely on unreliable direct rainfalls. Coarse Indian millets and sorghums dominate the farming and large areas remain unused or in bush. The bareness of the landscape is emphasised by the absence of fences and disinterest in animal farming. A line roughly along 80° E. is the western limit of districts where at least 20% of the cropped land is under padi. In Madhya Pradesh (Central Province) millets occupy a quarter of the farmed area. Wheat is a major food crop to the

265

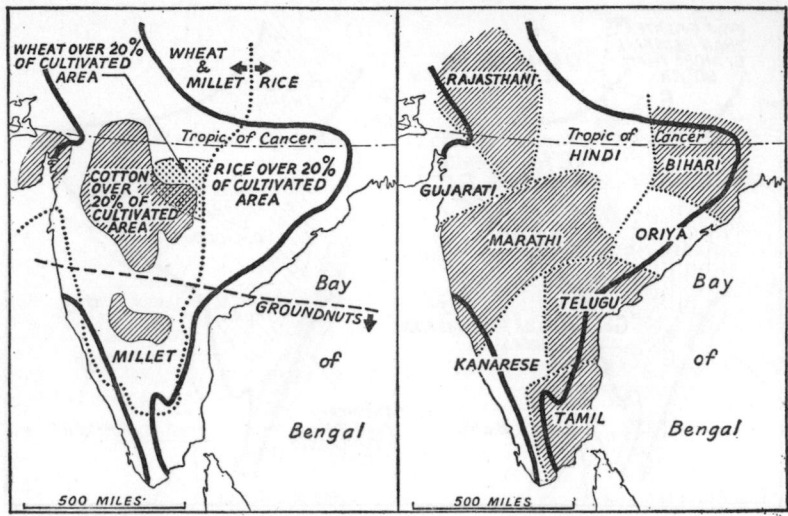

FIG. 82—Peninsular India: agriculture and languages

north and west but in only a few districts round Jubbulpore does it occupy as much as a fifth of the farmland. In Hyderabad and Mysore the groundnut is prominent as an oil crop, but to the north rape, sesame and mustard are more common. Great areas are under cotton, the dominant crop on the regur clays both *in situ* and where redistributed in valleys. In Malwa, Western Madhya Pradesh, Northern Hyderabad and the Tungabhadra valley many districts have over 20% of their farmland under cotton. Crops vary in nature and in yield year by year according to the local rainfall. Over most of the plateau a precarious subsistence farming goes on. All yields here are low; even cotton, the Deccan's chief cash crop, yields less than half that in Sind and a quarter that in the U.S.A.

The Deccan population is therefore scanty. From the south Mysore boundary the Deccan everywhere has so harsh and forbidding an environment that it has a lower density than the national average. Of the major Indian provinces, Madhya Pradesh averages least people to the cultivated acre (1·2 persons per acre) and least to the square mile (171 in 1956), the latter being almost half the national average. Over considerable areas its density is less than 60 to the square mile. Cotton-growing districts have the highest densities. The scanty Deccan population is in contrast to the low plains surrounding it, and virtually coincides with the structural limits. That water difficulties are so acute implies emphatic nucleation of people

266

into villages, which are here more widely separated than elsewhere in India and located round a rock well, at a water-conserving fissure in the rock, near a stream bed where some subsurface water will remain for long periods, or beside a shallow tank. Villages are frequently set centrally to shallow "saucers" of soil collected within a slight depression of parent rock. Towns are few and widely separated. About two-thirds of the plateau is over 50 miles from any town of 50,000 or more people, a low degree of urbanisation comparable only to that of Siberia. Rock and stone are used for houses and for forts or castles on rocky knobs or bluffs commanding historic routes.

ROUTES AND CONTACTS

Because the plateau separates the highly productive and densely peopled plains around it (the Indo–Gangetic Plains, the Coromandel, Golconda and Malabar coasts and Tamilnad in the extreme south), ways across the Deccan were for long periods more important than production upon it. Many of these ways have by now become fixed by the patterns of nineteenth-century railways (focusing on Nagpur) and by a few modern roads. From the Gulf of Cambay, the Tapti, Narbada and Maha valleys and rifts provide low-level routes over the Deccan to the Ganges Plain. The Godavari and Kistna similarly provide ways from the Coromandel coast to Cambay and to the Middle Ganges. The western foothill zone to the Aravallis, providing the shortest routes from Ahmadabad to Delhi, was a horse-and-bullock-cart trade route through the steppes as well as the first line of defence against the people infiltrating from the northwest towards the Deccan. Because the south is Hindu whereas people to the northwest are largely Muslim, the Aravalli, Vindhya and the Narbada valleys for centuries were the uneasy borderland between two cultures. Hence the many forts, the military landscape of defence and the

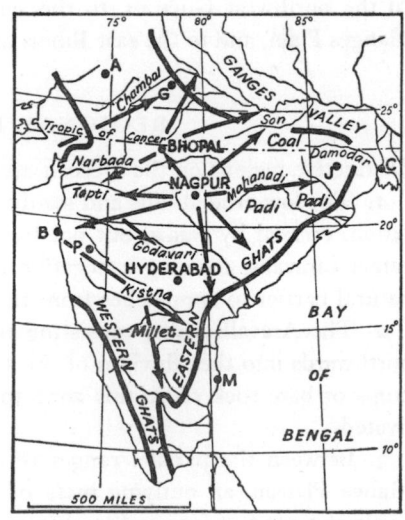

FIG. 83—Peninsular India: lines of movement and sites of cities

military tradition of Jodhpur, Bikaner, Ajmer, Jaipur and Bhopal. There have also been prolonged pressures from the northern plains against the darker Dravidian peoples of Sanskrit languages now prominent on the Coromandel and Malabar coasts. This southward pressure left its mark on places farther south, in the forts of the Marathis, the military centre in Poona and the militant Muslim Nizams of Hyderabad. Much less pressure of this kind played across the eastern horn of the Deccan where the isolation of Chota Nagpur shows even today in little touched areas of forest and considerable populations of primitive forest tribes whose numbers in some east Deccan districts exceed those of the Hindus.

The cultural borderland arising from its position accounts for two features of Deccan human geography. While largely Hindu, the populations everywhere include substantial Muslim groups partly consequent to military invasion from the north, partly to penetration by Muslim traders moving inland from Malabar and Coromandel which they reached from overseas. Hence numerous Hindu temples and shrines stand up on the landscape, but there are many mosques. The second characteristic is linguistic: large wedges of languages radically different in sound and in caligraphy, sprawl across the plateau, a sign of the many cultures which have pressed over it from time to time, and of the long-standing spatial isolation of the groups living in this thinly peopled region. To the south are the Kanaras, Telegu and Tamil languages, centrally the Marathi language, to the northwest Gujarati, to the north Rajasthani and Hindi from the Ganges Plain, and to the east Bihari and Oriya varieties of Bengali.

REGIONAL DIVISIONS

Distinctive regions on the Deccan are:

1. The low eroded hills and sandy wastes of Thar or semi-desert vegetation, crossed by wadis, but not by communications more modern than camel caravans, forming a negative area for people and farming, and a natural barrier to approaches from the northwest.

2. The Aravalli Hills, consisting of Gondwana sedimentaries dipping northwards into the alluvium of the Ganges Plain near Delhi. Large outcrops of bare rock cause this zone to be sparsely peopled and little cultivated.

3. Between the parallel ranges of Aravalli and Vindhya stretches the Malwa Plateau, an outlying mass of flat-topped Deccan lava sustaining levels of 2,000 feet for considerable areas. The rugged, harsh, dry Vindhya forms the southern edge of this plateau, where lie exposed sandstones from

underneath the lava. Both the lava and sandstone cause the Narbada and similar streams to have deep, narrow and steep-sided valleys. The Vindhya are properly an eroded scarp, in a complexly folded and fractured anti-clinal belt which includes fertile valleys running right across the Deccan separating Malwa from the main Deccan lava sheet. Along this furrow drained westwards by the Narbada (which ranks in holiness second only to the Ganges) and east by the Son, run routes (Bombay–Allahabad–Calcutta) of major significance historically and commercially. The Son section of the furrow has never played a role as important as the Narbada, not least because the Son has only slightly ameliorated the countryside near it.

4. The Satpura Range, rising abruptly to 2,500 feet south of the Nar-bada, is the northern edge of the Deccan Lava Plateau, constituting a major divide both of drainage and of cultural traditions (Aryan to the north and Dravidian to the south).

5. The Deccan Lava Plateau is distinctively terraced with wide undu-lating plains and mesa hills. Rising slightly to the Western Ghats, the step-like profiles continue to the west coast, which is rocky, forbidding and thickly forested.

Identified with the Marathi State (Maharashtra) this has been one of the most productive regions of the Deccan, chiefly owing to the qualities of its regur. While great areas of level ground tilt gently to the east, long tongues of higher land stretch across from west to east as level-topped interfluves. Most streams across the lava are only slightly incised, except at the lava edges or near the Tapti fault trough. Rain-shadow effects cause much of the landscape to be dry, particularly in a 60-mile N.–S. belt well to the west. The 30-inch isohyet halves the region, the eastern part being the wetter, the western being in rain-shadow. The whole economy turns upon the dark regur which not only has the capacity to retain moisture despite the heat but also is self-aerating. By frequently cracking in the heat, the regur induces fairly deep oxidation, the cracking and closing process serving almost the purpose of deep ploughing. Weathered *in situ* and remarkable for extending over so large an agricultural region without much variation, the regur differs in detail. Water-transported regur and soil-creep give the valleys deeper and better farming soils than on the higher interfluves and mesas, where the regur is either very thin or has laterised and lost quality. But almost two-thirds of the regur is continuously cultivated. Some of the higher, less fertile fields may lie fallow for several years at a time. Irrigation, only possible from wells, serves less than 2% of the total sown area, and is more common marginally than centrally to the lava. Operating

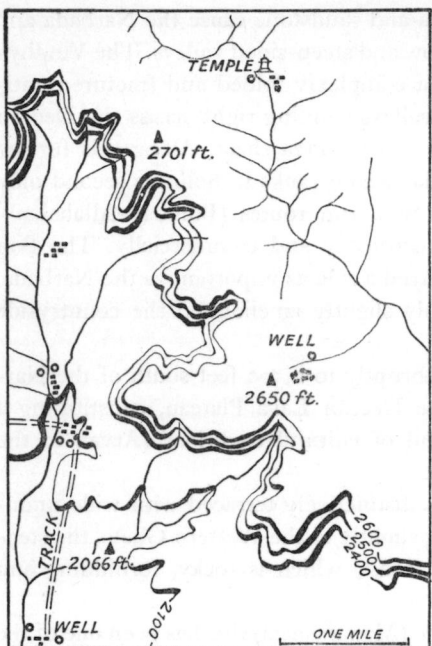

FIG. 84—Edge of a lava mesa on the Dec-[can, from a topographic map. The "step" is shown by varying the thickness of the contours to suggest shadow

against irrigation is the nature of the regur which, when wet, is too heavy and sticky for working by light, cattle-drawn native ploughs. Several crop associations occur correlating with the different types of regur along the rivers and interfluves. Very little rice is grown and chiefly near the Western Ghats. Over most of the regur, wheat is the cereal where irrigation is done, and millet the food crop elsewhere. In broad belts along the Tapti, Godavari and Kistna, millet, wheat, cotton, linseed and gram form close associations, growing side by side as well as in rotation. But the Pengarga, Bhima and Middle Monjura districts have a less complex crop association involving millet, cotton and gram. On the poorer regurs of upper levels only millets and pulses grow.

While cotton is king because of its commercial value, only about an eighth of the total farmland on the Lava Plateau carries it, and the last decade has seen a decrease in cotton acreage. Millets and sorghum occupy at least a third of the farmed area. Districts of richer regur may have as much as half the farmland under cotton, such specialisation occuring along the Tapti, the Upper Godavari and round Belgaum to the south, the latter producing the better-priced fibre of long staple in contrast with the short fibre grown elsewhere. A new native fibre from a 10-foot plant called mesta is coming into cultivation on the lava, traded as a substitute for jute. Sugar-cane is cropped on the extreme southern margins of the lava. The cotton is of special interest: planting takes place immediately after the onset of the rain (July), and remains in the ground for harvesting in February or March. Most cotton moves away from the Deccan for fabrication. Because the farming is remarkable for its commercialisation, communications have special importance, a close network of railways providing links with Bombay and Ahmadabad. Roads are no better developed than elsewhere in India, but cart tracks are numerous. Metalled highways cross the region from Bombay to Delhi and from Bombay to Madras. Towns here are mostly small marketing centres, and the larger ones are where routes converge. Nagpur, Poona and Sholapur are the only towns of between half and a quarter of a million people; the first is on the edge of the lava and focus of major trans-Deccan routes, and the last a new cotton-mill town within a productive cotton-growing locality.

6. South and east of the Deccan Lavas may be recognised the crystalline massifs of (a) Chota Nagpur (wild, little known, fairly rugged and a third of it still under forest, but with India's chief coalfields on its eastern margin); (b) the central section of the eroded Eastern Ghats, and (c) the South Deccan (Mysore and much of Hyderabad—a poor lateritic surface on a tilted block reaching 9,000-feet levels on its western edges). These massive bosses are part of one continuous structure, and are separated by several broad basins which take their names from the main river draining them and linking them to the eastern coastal lowlands by low necks. These basins are (a) the Mahanadi, (b) Godavari, (c) Kistna, and each consists of a depression where some Gondwana sedimentaries are preserved. The Mahanadi Basin contains the Chattisgarh irrigation area and is the chief rice-growing part of the Deccan; it contains some potential coalfields. The river has a gorge through the Eastern Ghats which lends itself to damming. The Godavari Basin has a more trench-like form owing to its foss structure, and it is followed by a major route to the north. The Kistna Basin is saucer shaped, its tributaries being almost radial. Within it isolated rocky knobs and tors, last stages of peneplainisations, provided spectacular sites for temples and forts. Like the other basins, it has only a slight irregular cover of much-leached soil of poor farming quality.

ECONOMIC MINERALS

Its crystalline and metamorphic rocks make the Deccan a highly mineralised structure, and its prolonged exposure to erosion renders its minerals reasonably accessible. In these respects it compares with the Laurentian Shield. The Lava Plateau conceals the gneiss and crystalline rocks, so that it is negative for metallic minerals.

Greatest exploitation of minerals is at the Chota Nagpur–Orissa margin near *Jamshedpur*, where power resources are developed on three pockets of Gondwana coal-bearing sedimentaries strung along the Damodar River

271

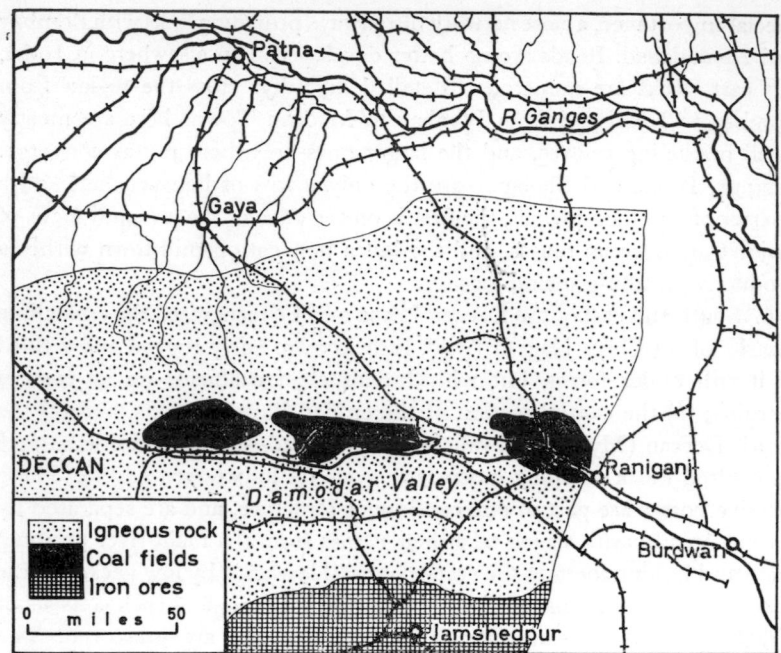

FIG. 85—The Damodar Valley Coalfield and Jamshedpur iron ores in relation to transport lines between the Ganges Valley and Calcutta, which lies southeast of Burdwan

which leads to the Hooghly and industrialised Calcutta. Coal in similar but little developed formations occurs also in the Lower Godavari and Mahanadi valleys (at Pench, Singaram and Tandur). Damodar coal is bituminous, easily worked, some 50 feet thick and little disturbed. Mining has mostly been organised till now in units too small for efficiency by modern standards, but reorganisation is going on and great changes in production and use are likely. On the northern flanks of the Orissa hills at *Singhbum* are high-grade (65%) iron ores in an "iron mountain" 40 miles long, a deposit larger than those which have made Lake Superior ores famous. The Singhbum deposit is only now becoming exploited on modern lines. Patches of the same ore extend to Chattisgarh and southern Madhya Pradesh. Ramgarij beside the Damodar has low-grade, little-used ironstone shales within the coal formations. *Jamshedpur* and *Asansol*, the chief smelting centres here, use only high-content ores. At Raipur along the Vizagapatam Railway in Madhya Pradesh, at Singhbum and Udaipur, manganese ores are worked. Chromite and vanadium ores are also worked

XXIII. Landscape of the Northwest Frontier. A flat-topped, tightly packed village huddles round a patch of wheat cultivation in a Malakand valley.

XXIV. A Karachi street. The lorry carries sacks of grain from Sind. A hawker is pushing fruit to market on a barrow fitted with bicycle wheels. Male dress is a western-style shirt with Middle Eastern loose cotton trousers of pyjama type, topped by a Muslim fez-like hat. Note the Middle East style of latticed verandah and the western lorry with sacks of grain.

XXV. Bombay is the most modernised, industrialised and wealthy trading port of India. The sweep of well-built residences by the sea typifies the westernised style to be seen in urban India. Not all Bombay is like this—it has an extensive oriental industrial slum sector as well.

XXVI. This squalid street scene in Calcutta exemplifies another aspect of urban India: the sacred cows—thin and neglected—side by side with sleek modern cars, the unhygienic food stalls, the coconut husks, the unclean streets and all the squalor which perpetuates fly- and flea-borne diseases.

in Singhbum. The Vindhya Hills have lead ores within their limestones and are mined open-cast at Udaipur. On the southern edge of the Deccan at Kolar in Mysore gold is mined. An 8-mile copper belt south of Jamshedpur is worked despite its low grade because it is one of the few major copper deposits in Pak–Ind. In the laterised surface occurs substantial low-grade, easily accessible iron ores which may prove workable in the future. Several minor metallic ores have begun to assume significance in the steel industry and for jet engines and atomic plant. Bauxite is worked in Madhya Pradesh and in Chota Nagpur for the new aluminium smelter at Muri near Jamshedpur. The Deccan is the world's main source of mica, which comes from Hazaribagh. The needs of atomic reactors give interest to beryllium ores found in Rajasthan and monazite (thorium ores) in the far south, but these are low-grade deposits, expensive to work, employ little labour and produce small quantities.

CHAPTER TWENTY-ONE

The Coastal Margins of Peninsular India

SURROUNDING THE Deccan to the west, south and east are varying widths of a coastal belt in which the environmental and human associations are distinct from those of the plateau. In this fringing zone maritime factors are at least as important as landward relations, inducing a line of development and cultural evolution quite different from that in Northern India where historic impulses have come from the continent.

Distinctive in the V pattern of the fringe is the country immediately south of the Mysore border, a line roughly northeastwards through the Nilgiri Hills marking the main Deccan limit. This distinct physical break is roughly parallel to and some 220 miles from the coast of the Gulf of Manar and the Palk Strait, giving this southernmost peninsula unit the form of a skew parallelogram from which the two coastal belts stretch on either side of the Deccan towards the north.

THE DRAVIDIAN PENINSULA

In the southern parallelogram about 50 million people live, and have preserved racial, linguistic and religious features unlike those of India because the cultural effects of the northern Aryan and Muslim empires had only slight and marginal effects due to remoteness from the Indo–Gangetic Plain. The dark-skinned Dravidian people of the deep south are physically unlike Indians farther north, and speak languages so different that South Indian speaks to North Indian more commonly in English.

Dravidian India has a complex and varied form in detail. While the Western Ghats come to an abrupt end at the small Nilgiri block, a similar relief feature may be traced beyond the Palghat Gap in the complex hills of Animalai, Cardamom and Palai and the N.–S. line of small blocks continues to Cape Comorin. Low-lying masses of gneiss underlie much of the landscape east of these hills and often show as large monadnocks. Well to the east of them are young Cretaceous and Triassic sedimentary rocks, including limestones and sandstones, eroded into cuestas and broken scarp hills, unlike any landscape on the Deccan. To the west and to the east lie belts of recent alluvial soils which are of critical importance for

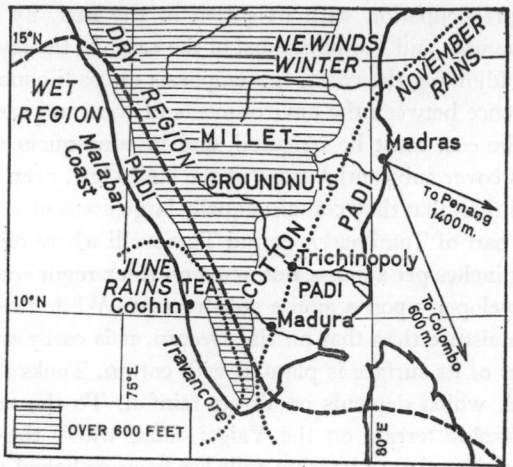

FIG. 86—The Dravidian South: relief, rainfalls and products

local farming; they are smallest to the west where the streams are short and greatest to the east where the rivers Cauvery, Vaijal and Ponnaiyar have built large deltas. Cape Comorin isolates these two alluvial belts. Complicating the surface are large areas of poor lateritic soil on low inland platforms rising above the alluvials. A few knobs of steep-sided rock jut through the coastal plain as near Madras.

The narrower west-coast belt, now known as Kerala (previously Travancore and Cochin), faces squarely the summer winds from the southwest, so that aspect and the relief of the Animalais induce heavy rainfalls (maximum in June), but form a rain-shadow during the northeasterlies. Relief and convectional rains occur at all seasons in the hills, so that they are forested and the west-flowing rivers are always well watered. East of these hills is *Tamilnad*, the greater southern part of the old Madras Presidency, lying in rain-shadow during the southwesterlies; local relief is so low and so aligned that during the northeasterlies rains are light and there are rain-shadow effects, especially round Salem beneath the Deccan scarp. In Tamilnad, the larger easterly part of the Dravidian parallelogram, rains are thus both light and come chiefly in November with northeasterly winds, establishing a special agricultural cycle and producing a prolonged drought which largely offsets the great area of farmable land. The contrast between Kerala and Tamilnad, the western and eastern coastal zones, has led to great contrast in the way of life indicated by considerable tea and rubber growing to the west and cotton and groundnuts to he east, by preoccupation with irrigation in the east, by the Malayali anguage to the west and Tamil in most of the east. In the low-lying plains (see Fig. 91) adjoining the coast, the emphasis on padi conceals the great natural difference between the environments of west and east, except that the padi to the east must be irrigated, and in consequence innumerable shallow tanks cover substantial areas of the landscape, even although it is only now and then that they contain equally large areas of water.

The driest part of Tamilnad is round Tinnevelli where rainfalls average only about 25 inches per annum, but occur on thick regur soil (here known as karisal) developed upon a gneiss substructure. While this regur is less retentive of moisture than that on the Deccan, it is easily worked, and at least a quarter of its surface is planted with cotton. Tanks are rarely seen on the karisal, which depends on direct rainfall. To the northeast is an equally remarkable terrain on the Valgai delta, where the flat drought-ridden countryside of poor lateritic soils has been reshaped manually over many generations into a fantastic number of saucer-like tanks which are also linked by small channels to the rivers, whose occasional storm-water they conserve. Very little run-off from the ground or from the rivers reaches the sea: the Valgai distributaries are almost dry. This region of innumerable tanks represents a probably unique degree of water control. In some localities tanks occupy an eighth of the land. Only by this strict control has it been possible with an unreliable rainfall averaging only 34 inches per annum and much reduced in efficiency by high evaporation, to maintain padi-farming (which occupies about a quarter of the cultivated area) and to grow cotton (on a fifth of the area), and by this means support from one annual crop over 1,300 people per square mile. Despite this effort, farmers have an exceptionally low standard of living.

The Cauvery Delta, supporting a similar high density of farmers with an equally long history of cultivation, is elaborately irrigated. Cauvery water below Trichinopoly is diverted to a fan of man-made distributaries stretching 75 miles from north to south. Without barrage or dam, old innundation canals lead overflow directly to the fields, but diversion to storage tanks is also done, so that water is available for most of the year as against the brief, occasional water in Valgai tanks. On the Cauvery Delta there is a time-lag in water availability. The eastern parts receive the water much later than the western where, in consequence, the farming cycle is considerably earlier. Its large catchment in the Western Ghats gives the Cauvery a steadier régime than most local rivers and its upper course has modern dams equalising the flow and providing hydro-electricity. Padi dominates Cauvery farming, and at Tanjore occupies three-quarters of the farmed area.

TABLE 6

CLIMATIC DATA FOR COASTAL PENINSULAR INDIA

	Bombay	Calicut	Trivandrum	Salem	Madura	Negapatam	Madras
Temperature (mean F. Jan.)	75	71	73	66	69	72	68
Rainfall (inches p.a.) . .	79	120	66	40	34	56	52
% in months June to Sept.	96	73	44	51	38	19	31
No. of months each less than 1 inch.	7	3	2	4	3	3	3
Net rain minus evap. (inches p.a.) . .	14	40	23	−32	−63	−18	−13

The first lowland traversed by the Cauvery after leaving Mysore is the Salem–Erode trough whose dry, poor soil only supports millets, but is has substantial power resources (from the Mettur Dam and the Hagenekal Falls) and large quantities of iron ore. These ores were smelted early last century with charcoal, but heavy industry is impeded by the absence of coal. *Salem* has become a cotton-weaving town on the basis of Mettur and Hagenekal power which also serves textile factories in Trichinopoly, and drives many irrigation pumps on the Coimbatore Plateau, where the natural drainage is well incised and half the cultivated area remains under millets depending on direct rains.

Kerala, isolated by relief from Tamilnad and by distance from the rest of the Subcontinent, is distinctive and homogeneous. The most farmed and densely peopled belt is nearest the sea, where longshore currents have built a complex landscape of lagoons in all stages of reclamation, making a pattern of longitudinal padi-growing troughs separated by slightly higher and sandier ridges, used for coconut growing and settlements. The inner, slightly higher coastal plain is lateritic and mostly under scrub. Inland rises the rainy, forested hills, with rubber, tea and pepper plantations. Kerala has the advantage of some rain even during mid-year so that, aided by a few tanks, rice can be harvested in February–March as well as in the usual September–October. Even a third crop may be collected occasionally. In many districts over 90% of cultivable land is cropped. The local subsidiary is coconut, a response to equability and to the stretches of sandy soils on old beaches. In Travancore the coconut area almost equals the padi. On the inner lateritic soils, tapioca, an innovation of the last twenty-five years, has become common. The lagoon coast permits fishing for local

277

consumption and some Travancore beaches are now being exploited for ilmenite and monazite sands. One of the densest peopled areas of India, some villages have densities approaching 5,000 per square mile. The average Kerala density is about 1,200 per square mile or 2,200 per cultivated square mile. Dispersed population is a feature indicating that water is plentiful and that defence has been irrelevant. Linear settlements along the coast follow the lagoon pattern. Market towns and little ports are numerous, the latter now much silted and a heritage from when the Kerala coast was significant for sailing ships crossing the Indian Ocean. *Trivandrum*, the regional capital, contains less than 200,000 people. *Cochin*, the oldest European "factory" in India, is reviving as a port consequent to the steady import of rice into South India, and its better position (cf. Madras) for contact between Indian Ocean shipping and the Kerala–Tamilnad hinterland.

Tamilnad, while an agricultural region, has many market towns. Most of the countryside is within 50 miles of a town of at least 50,000 people, and there are seven centres each exceeding 100,000.

Madras is the "big city" (about 1·5 millions) owing its standing to the old Madras Presidency, which included the east coast of the peninsula, the Kistna Valley and much of Malabar. It is an eccentrically placed capital to Tamilnad now that the Presidency has been subdivided. On a rapidly silting coast of dunes and lagoons, the port depends on a large artificial harbour built after Fort St. George, an East India Company strong-point and trading focus for all South India. Sprawling, divided by lagoons and river-loops into a series of large open villages scattered round old Georgetown, Madras has been a shipping centre for Deccan and South India trade and focus of migration by South Indians who moved out to form the early labour corps in Burma, Malaya, Fiji and the West Indies. Major railway lines coastwise to Calcutta, trans-Deccan to Bombay and south

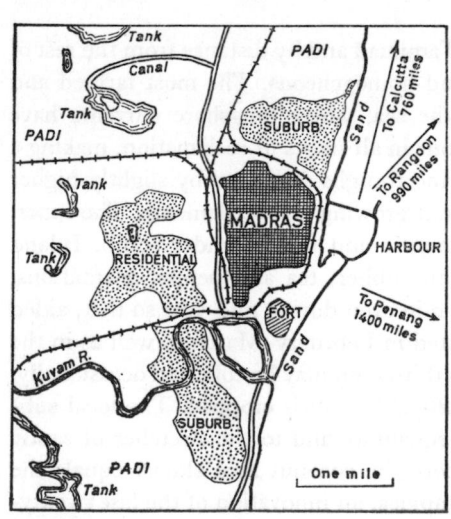

FIG. 87—Setting of Madras City

to Trichinopoly indicate the Madras hinterland, now rapidly changing. Industry was never significant in Madras, which was more exclusively dependent on trade than either Bombay or Calcutta. In addition to a few cotton mills, there are now light industries, craft industries (sarongs and saris) and a tannery based on the large cattle population. Marginal to Tamilnad and to the new linguistic state of Andhra, Madras is the heart of modern Tamil education and culture. *Madura* (365,000) is the classic Tamil–Hindu centre of much pilgrimage, a royal city dating back two or three millennia. It has much cottage industry (weaving, mat work, pottery) and is noted for producing and weaving silk. After prolonged quiescence, Madura is rapidly expanding following electrification and the growth of small factories, many financed from the savings of returned migrants. Located in one of the driest parts of Tamilnad where pressure on farmland is extreme, it has an enormous labour pool which, while an asset in time past, now exposes it to much agitation.

THE GOLCONDA COAST

North of Madras extends the Golconda Coast, the eastern lowlands fringing the Deccan, built of broad deltas from the Penner, Kistna, Godavari and Mahanadi rivers. Inland the structural distinction is blurred where the deltas merge into broad, open Deccan valleys. Its characteristics are complex because the lowlands have been much influenced by peoples entering by way of the Deccan valleys, continuously in touch coastwise during sailing-ship days, and linked with Bengal and Tamilnad. The Penner–Kistna–Godavari Deltas are occupied by Telegu-speaking Hindus in Andhra, a state set up over the last few years on linguistic grounds. The Mahanadi Delta, partly built by the Baitarni and Brahmani rivers, is core zone of Orissa and continued south by a very narrow belt adjoining Vizagapatam where the Eastern Ghats are distinctive and close to the coast. Orissa uses a language more Bengali than Telegu.

The Golconda lowlands have rainfalls of some 45 inches per annum (cf. 125 inches on the west coast) in the typical monsoon cycle to the north and changing to a cycle of October–November maxima to the south. While the deltaic landforms to some extent permit irrigation, the streams from the Deccan are most variable and subject to serious floods and heavy silting. Padi is grown more by direct rains to the north, and almost entirely by irrigation to the south where millets dominate the rain-fed fields. Canal irrigation is usual; tanks occur only towards Tamilnad. Some coastal canals were originally for transport, reflecting the difficulty of landward movement

279

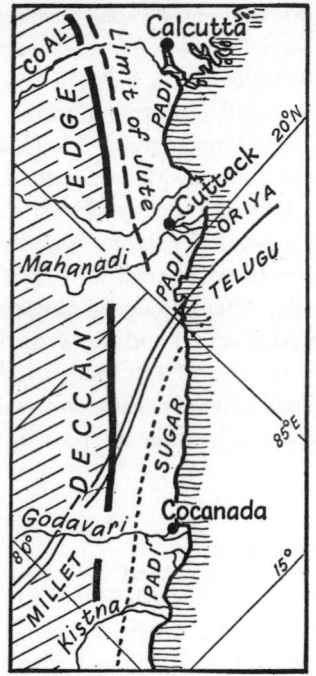

FIG. 88—The Eastern or Golconda Coast: The double line marks the linguistic boundary between Telegu and Oriya; the former is Dravidian, the latter related to Bengali

and the distance of the coastline from the chief zones of population. Rural densities are everywhere high so that the irregularity of water has exposed Golconda plains to major famines, from both floods and drought. Scattered along the coast are little ports now of only local interest because modern shipping must stand several miles off shore, so shallow are the approaches. A few French "trading factories" persisted here until recently. Only *Vizagapatam* (108,000) has up-to-date facilities making use of deeper approaches permitting contact between the railway and steamers. Most of the population is on the inner side of the lowland where stand the bigger towns, such as Bezwada, Rajahundy, Guntar and Cuttack, all over 100,000 each and marketing centres. These towns are linked by a longitudinal railway mostly keeping well inland, a link between Calcutta and Madras with continental lines traversing the valleys across the Deccan to Nagpur and Bombay.

The pressure of local populations and of Deccan invaders upon this belt of unreliable farming has been so great that emigration has gone on for many centuries.

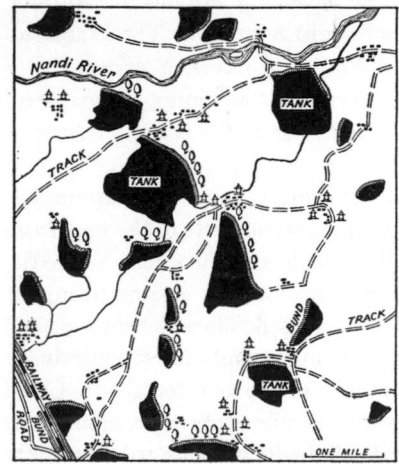

FIG. 89—A tank landscape from a topographic map. Centred inland from Madras, on 13° 9′ N., 79° 41′ E., it shows the arrangement of trees and temples in relation to the bunds of tanks

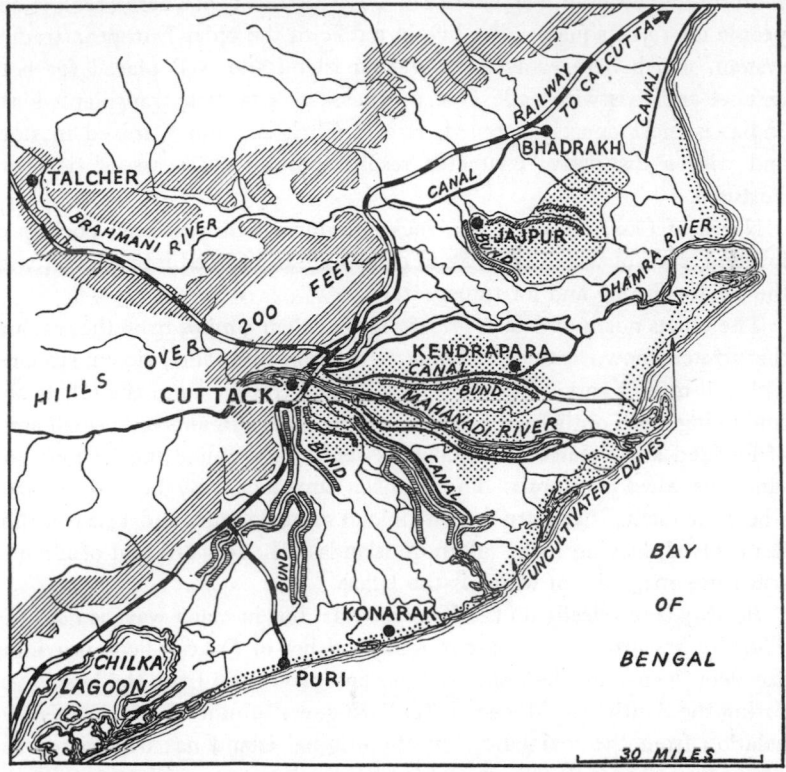

FIG. 90—Detail of the Mahanadi Delta on the Golconda Coast, the bunds marking attempts to limit the effects of flash floods. The stippled areas are those of densest settlement

THE WESTERN COAST

Many features of Kerala are continued northward in a narrowing arm as the steep forested Western Ghats approach closer to the sea. Here the rainy (125 inches per annum), reclaimed-lagoon landscape with padi-farming is prominent. Pressure on the land is great as to the south. Near Mangalore, the Netravati Valley forms a wedge-shaped lowland extending considerably farther inland with low-lying ribbons of cultivation along the streams separated by poor laterised interfluves. The hills are exploited for teak and are the refuge of small primitive tribes. *Mangalore* (120,000 people) has a roadstead for small local vessels, carrying tiles which are an important

281

local trading product. Farther north is Portuguese *Goa* where over 550,000 people on 1,300 square miles live in a relic of the older European trading system, which here evolved around an island site well placed for both defence and coastwise trade. Goa, a renaissance city-state transplanted into India, is most densely peopled, largely Christian, much mixed in stock and with a distinctive character resulting from 350 years of ties with Portugal.

North of Goa, the coast is a rocky platform with scattered pockets of lowland, each of which is isolated, over-built and forced into contact with the sea for fishing and for transport.

The Ghats north of Goa are rarely farther than 5 miles from the sea, and that stretch known as the *Konkan* is high, broken by short, violent streams, with hill masses and scarps both parallel and transverse to the Ghats and containing small outliers of Deccan lava. Konkan contains only small areas of lowland and creates a coastal landscape quite unlike the lagoons and sandspits towards Kerala. The Konkan broadens only behind Bombay where the main Ghat scarp retreats inland some 60 miles and a ria coastline has evolved, leaving rocky off-shore islands at the seaward end of a fan of scarp streams, chief of which is the Ulhas.

Bombay is physically on the Konkan coast but in many ways is not of it. The city has grown on a narrow island outlier of Deccan lava, providing excellent deep-water harbour facilities and protection from the heavy seas during the Southwest Monsoon. Its Portuguese founders sought defensive isolation from the mainland, but the original island has constricted the city's physical growth and set problems of modern communication with the mainland such as only expensive causeways have overcome. Starting as an entrepôt for the Arabian Sea, over the last 250 years Bombay increased its command of coastwise traffic and became an outport when mainland India was nineteenth-century Britain's source of wheat supplies and of Deccan cotton. The greatest fillip to its shipping trade was the opening of Suez prior to which the "Cape" shipping circuits of the Indian Ocean centred much farther south in the peninsula. To become the gateway of India as it is now, Bombay constructed railways from the island to the mainland and through the Ghats, whose abrupt scarp presented serious problems. Water, power and food supplies all had to be brought to Bombay from a distance to supply the shipping and rapidly increasing population, which found itself obliged to establish vertical and elongated settlements in response to the small space and shape of the island. Modern airways have been limited by the same facts. Inevitably the huge trade in raw materials led to Bombay becoming industrialised, starting with shipbuilding under

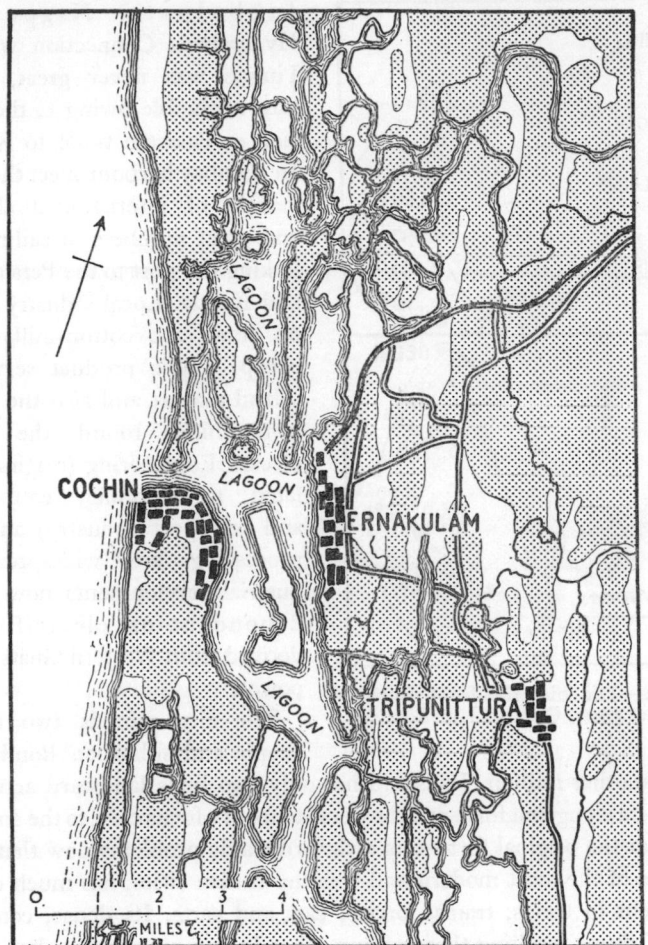

FIG. 91—A topographic map of the Western or Malabar Coast, now part of Kerala State. The stippled area is cultivated land, mostly padi

the Parsees, a minority which went from this beginning to be the innovators of most industrial activity through India (see Fig. 94).

Raw cotton continues to bulk large in Bombay's trade and huge warehouses of it line the harbour, but cotton cloth is now greater in trade volume than the raw materials. Oil seeds and manganese are also exported in quantity. Petroleum, food grains and capital equipment constitute the chief inflowing goods. The hinterland of Bombay reaches to Delhi,

283

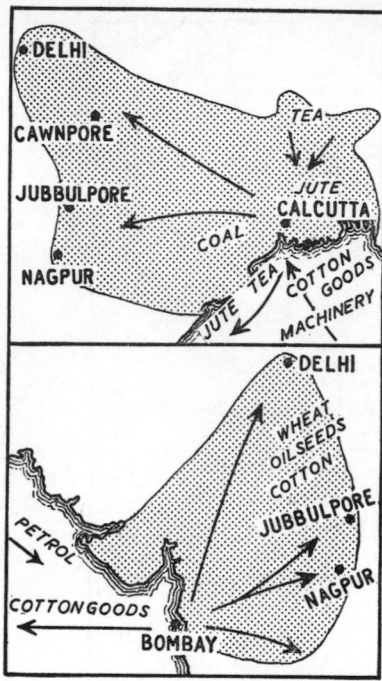

Jubbulpore, Nagpur and Hyderabad. Connection with the Punjab was never great, and is now negligible owing to the diversion of Pakistan trade to Karachi. In Bombay harbour meet the major vessels of international shipping and great numbers of sailing craft linking the port to the Persian Gulf and Kerala. Local industry centres on some 200 cotton-mills whose cheap, coarse product serves the inland market and also the poorer communities round the Indian Ocean. Engineering (originally related to shipping, cotton-mills and transport industry) and food processing are widespread industrial developments now largely dependent on electrification derived from Western Ghats water-power.

FIG. 92—The hinterlands of India's two great ports, Calcutta and Bombay

The city exceeds two million people and suburban Bombay includes another million. Its island has only two links landward across the creeks. Its elongated form and the persistence of a focus close to the southern tip—near the original fort—sets awkward traffic problems now that Bombay, one of the most modern and wealthy Indian cities, has much diurnal movement in trains, trams, lorries, cars and carts. Its dense, congested areas of slums recalling those of any other Indian city, and its boulevards of multi-storied modern flats, epitomise the wide range of cultural and economic standards.

GUJERAT

North of Bombay the Gujerat region fringing the Deccan has quite different landscapes. The Gulf of Cambay separates the low Kathiawar platform of Deccan Lava from the mainland. On the eastern side of Cambay stand *Surat, Broach, Baroda* and *Ahmadabad*, old settlements contolling lines of movement from seaward along major valleys through the Deccan edge into Northern India. This was the core zone of Gujerat which in character, an alluvial plain formed by the Sabarmati, Mahi, Narbada and Tapti, might be considered an outlier of the Gangetic Plain. Rainfall decreases rapidly from south to north, and the risk of failure in the padi-crop is great towards Ahmadabad, which is notorious for famines. Here was for centuries the gateway to India, a function now usurped by Bombay, which has better seaward accessibility so that the many military principalities of Gujerat have long since faded. It is one of India's major cotton-growing regions, stimulated by Bombay's cotton trade last century and result of changing from subsistence to commercial farming. Cotton occupies the greatest area to the north, but rice exceeds it to the south. The countryside is one of large village and adobe and thatch houses clustering on estuarine sandy ridges where there are fresh-water wells. The four major towns are now much industrialised, their strategic significance reflected in their new function as junctions. *Ahmadabad* (nearly one million) is the sixth city of India in size, complex in its cultural outlook and fortifications which show its heritage of the Muslim—Hindu pressures which once went on here. The

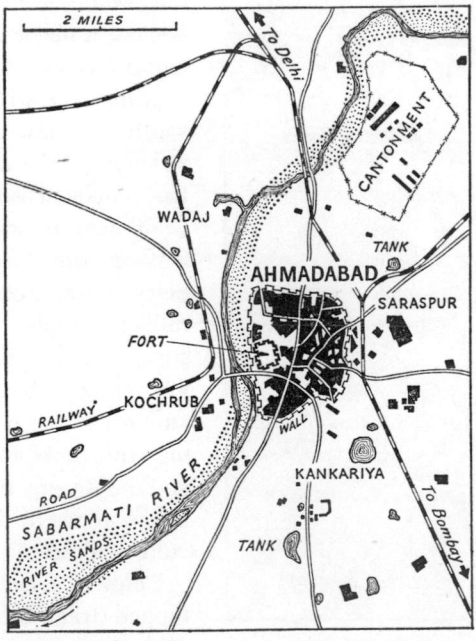

Fig. 93—Topographic map of Ahmadabad, now a major cotton textile centre north of Bombay, but still showing, by its walls, its old importance in historic struggles between Muslims from the west and the Hindus of the East and the Deccan

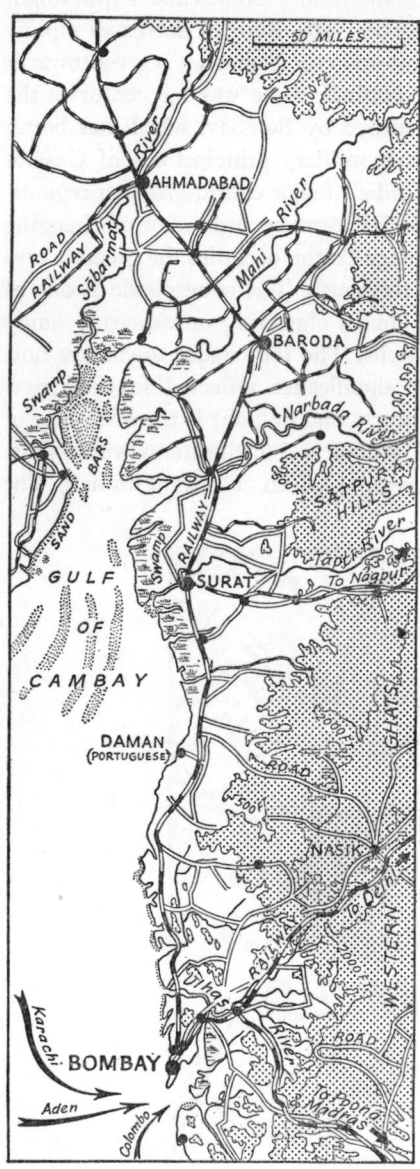

FIG. 94—Gujerat: the western gateway
to northern India

city is now grim with several
hundred cotton factories surrounded by slums recalling the
satanic mills of nineteenth-
century Lancashire. Its cotton-
mills grew up later than those
of Bombay and cheap local
land and labour have helped
Ahmadabad exceed Bombay in
the production of textiles. *Surat*,
the oldest English trading-post
in India (now 250,000 people) is
a lesser textile town noted for
specialising in the cottage production of luxury textiles with
gold and silver threads. *Baroda*
on the Mahi–Nabada doab is
the Maratha focus which has
become a major educational and
cultural centre.

Kathiawar, with the sea to the
south and east and with great
swamps to the north and west,
has remained isolated from development in modern India. For
a long time fragmented into
petty states, it contains over five
million people. About half its
surface is cropped despite the
low rainfall (about 25 inches per
annum) which has to be helped
out with tanks and wells. Wheat
and millet are the main crops,
but in northern districts half the
cultivated area is in cotton.

Cutch is a low island of flat-
topped fragments of sandstone
and some basalts, which is
flanked by water and windborne deposits related to the

tidal marshes and estuaries round it and to the semi-deserts to its north. The landforms relate to old distributaries of the Indus, which now discharge much farther to the west. The Cutch population is small and pastoral; a Rajput colony, it has a critical boundary location between Hindu India and Muslim Pakistan.

CHAPTER TWENTY-TWO

Ceylon

ITS ENVIRONMENT

CEYLON, THE largest island lying off the Southern Subcontinent, has developed on lines with a different twist from those in the adjoining parts of India. An outlying massif similar to the South Deccan, it has several types of crystalline rocks spread round the core of granite mountains which rise in a few places to over 7,000 feet. The northern half consists of low, dolomitic limestone landscapes. The line of little rocky islands of Adam's Bridge in the Gulf of Manar, which in places is only 22 miles broad, indicates the physical link with India. Extensive, dry, coastal plains in Northern Ceylon repeat many landscape features of the Coromandel coast.

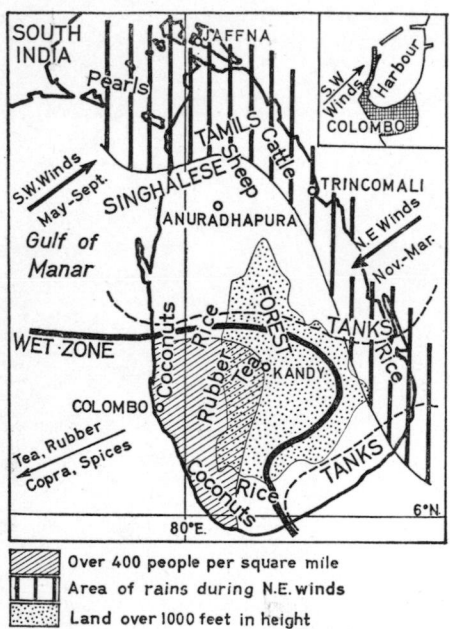

Over 400 people per square mile
Area of rains during N.E. winds
Land over 1000 feet in height

FIG. 95—Ceylon. The heavy line divides the wet zone from the rest of Ceylon; the vertical lines mark the zone which is rainy during the northeasterlies and which is identified with long-settled Tamils, now called Ceylonese

But Ceylon, thrust closer to the Equator than South India, influenced by the seas surrounding it and with a high proportion of mountainous relief, is more equable in temperature and rainfall than Tamilnad. Because only a fifth of its surface is cultivated, much natural vegetation is seen. An evergreen forest covers large areas towards the south and west. To the north and east, lower rainfalls combine

288

XXVII. In Madura, centre of Dravidian Hinduism, the traditional shrine includes an elaborately worked and decorated Wedge-shaped "goparam", a tower-like structure resembling a pagoda, as at this Meenakshi Temple where also the sacred pool of water is symbolic of the vital importance of tank-irrigation in South India.

XXVIII. A Tamil immigrant here plucks tea on the commercially cultivated hillsides of the wet zone in Ceylon and lower down the Singhalese continue their self-contained subsistence farms of padi and coconuts.

XXIX. The spires (dagoba) of regal ruins at Anuradhapura rise above the coconuts and tank-irrigated padi-fields of Dry Ceylon.

with the dry, porous limestone to produce a tangled bush or jungle, which is deciduous under the well-marked régime of monsoon rains. This vegetation has been overcut for centuries, and the effects of prolonged soil erosion are seen everywhere, due to shifting cultivation with an ever-shortening period between successive uses.

Located in the latitude of the trade winds, the weather is dominated by half-yearly alternations of the Northeast Trades and of those southwest winds which are deflected Southeast Trades from across the Equator. While these prevail in the winter and summer respectively, their local effects are complicated by relief rains and by local land and sea breezes so that régimes and rainfalls vary greatly from point to point. Each of the prevailing winds makes its own pattern of "rain-shadows" to the relief. Colombo is dryest in February, the mid-season of the northeasterlies; while Trincomalee has drought in June, during the southwesterlies. The valleys of the central highlands show complex rainfall patterns according to their disposition in relation to the two sets of trades, offset to some extent by the humidity and coolness induced by altitude. The southwestern quarter of Ceylon is significantly called the Wet Zone with annual rains mostly about 100 inches; to the northwest and southeast are localities with less than 50 inches per annum.

LANDSCAPES

Landscapes in the northern half of Ceylon, shown in Fig. 96, resemble the Cauvery delta and the Travancore coast. Local agriculture is based on rice and coconuts grown on the low-lying countryside, which is subject to seasonal alternations of dusty, shrivelling drought and of a muddy, green unreliable wet season. Farming is dominated by water scarcity, and needs the aid of large "tanks" for water conservation and irrigation. Large artificial ponds adjoin most villages. This sector of the island contains the old agricultural economy developed round Anuradhapura whose elaborate tanks and canals, relics of early Singhalese development, lie ruined by war, malaria and silting. Some restoration of the old tanks is going on as part of the national campaign to grow more rice. Padi and coconuts extend in thinning fingers from the north along the narrow fringes of the western and eastern coasts and in inland patches where tanks are still usable. Tank-based farming of a similar type goes on along the dry southeast coastal plain. The bottoms of the narrow valleys radiating from the mountainous middle of the island are also lined with padi-fields, in ribbons distributed fanlike round *Kandy*, the inland capital of historic Singhalese

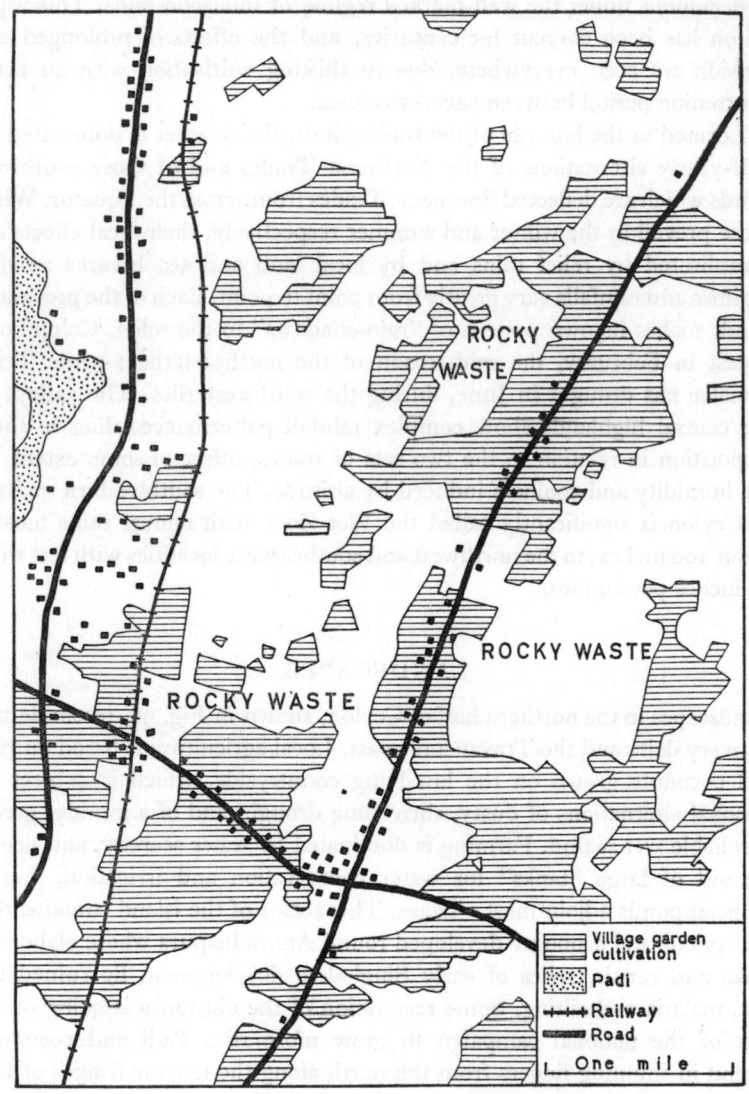

Village garden cultivation

Padi

Railway

Road

One mile

FIG. 96—Topographic map of northern Ceylon, where low limestone relief and low rainfalls create many patches of rocky waste thereby reducing the padi area (east of Anuradhapura)

kingdoms. The east coast is thinly peopled by small padi-farmers and coconut growers, who do part-time fishing inshore.

Ceylon's village landscapes differ from those of South India by the frequency of the Buddhist "pagoda" temple built of limestone and plaster. Centrally to the island, the farmhouses are of wood, bamboo and thatch (rice straw or palm leaves), and have baked clay fireplaces and utensils. These Singhalese farms are traditionally self-contained, well-suiting the simple, vegetarian Buddhist way of life followed by the indigenes whose cotton clothes, once homemade, are of sarong style. Towards *Jaffna*, the long-standing settlement of dark-skinned Tamils from across the strait contains many squat, ornately carved and coloured Hindu temples, marking the racial and cultural distinctiveness of the Tamils, known here as Ceylonese, different in language and religion from the Singhalese who predominate to the centre and south. The Ceylonese rural economy, however, is much like that of the Singhalese. Along the east coast there is a farming and fishing community of dark Muslims called Moors, descendants of seaborne migrants from Malabar and Arabia.

COMMERCIAL FARMING

A fundamentally different economy has grown round commerical agriculture for producing rubber and tea, crops which have brought into use for the first time large, once-forested areas of the Wet Zone, where high humidity and equability create an almost equatorial setting. Tea cultivation was the earlier of these innovations by Western-managed companies exploiting the surfaces, mostly higher than 3,000 feet whose virgin forest soils and cool altitudes reproduced conditions like those of older tea-growing economies in South China and Japan. About the beginning of this century, the rubber tree was also introduced into the Wet Zone, but at warmer levels below 3,000 feet. The higher surfaces on which tea and rubber were planted (as in Fig. 97) presented physical difficulties for transport, which was done by elephants until the present tortuous roads and railways were constructed. A special feature is the system of private aerial ropeways strung above the ground to link cultivated hills to the central "factory" where both tea and rubber have to be processed before leaving the plantations. Round the factory, which is the management and labour centre, a hamlet usually develops.

The commercial crops are both characterised by uniform stands of evergreen plants replacing the natural mixed forest and they involve nearly continuous work through the year. Cultivating tea and rubber

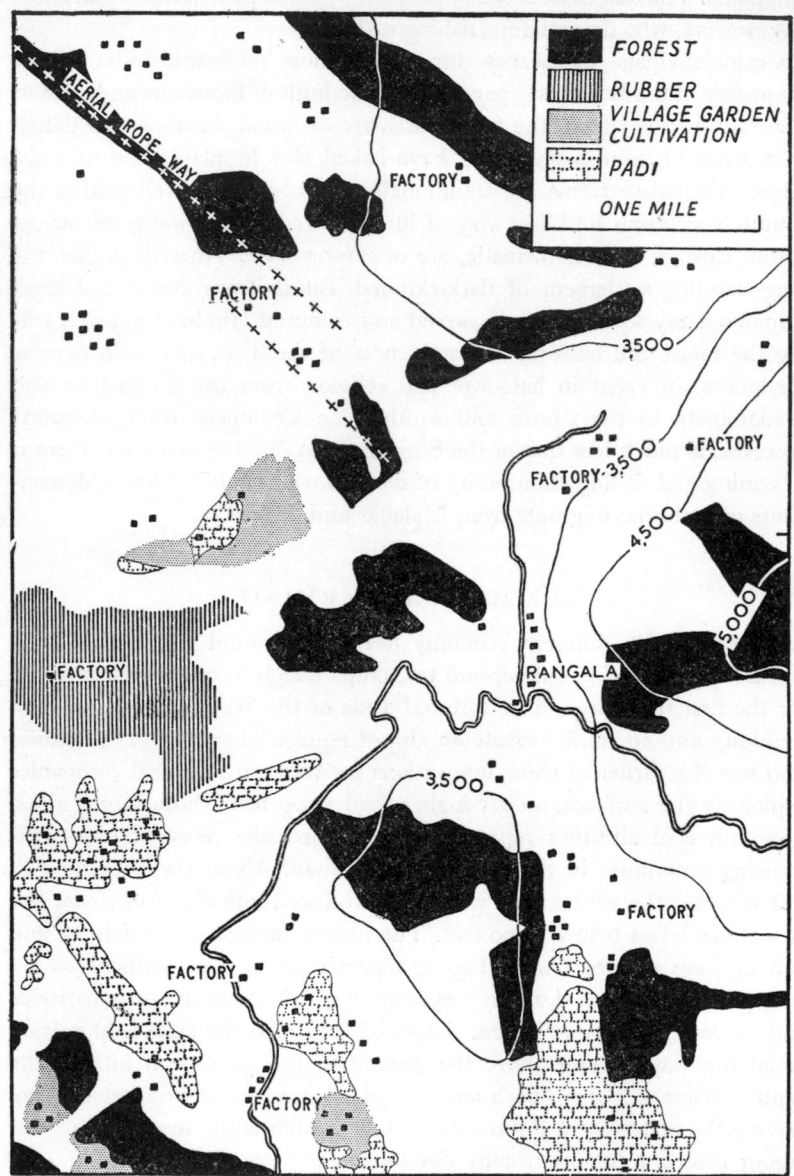

FIG. 97—Topographic map of part of the Wet Zone where tea and rubber occupy the higher surfaces. An aerial rope-way is shown serving a tea factory

commercially was done where local people had not themselves previously farmed and away from their padi-growing areas, thus developing new parts of the country as well as introducing new crops. They were originated by Western planters aiming to trade with the industrial markets of Western Europe and North America. As pioneers in scantily peopled districts, the planters were obliged to bring in labour from South India because local labour was tied to its older economy and régimes. This was the cause of a South Indian immigration, which continued until Ceylon's independence; the plantation workers, mostly Tamils, first came temporarily, and then settled, to form a population different not only by work and by location but also by speech, religion and associations from the Singhalese, who continued their traditional life in the central valleys. The new South Indian immigrants soon formed considerable populations in the marketing towns, which grew up as commerce increased and transport facilitated movement in and out of Ceylon.

TAMILS

There are thus two types of South Indians in the population: the "Ceylonese" Tamils, who had filtered in slowly before the coming of Westerners, settled long enough to have diverged from the customs of South India, living as small-scale, scattered subsistence padi-farmers in the dry, unreliable northern half of the island, with Jaffna as the largest single concentration of them; and South Indian Tamils of recent arrival, forming the unabsorbed wage-labourers on estates and in the towns, little related to other groups in Ceylon and distributed in the Wet Zone.

Thus the different elements of this plural society characteristically live in separate localities and have separate functions, though merging and gradations are occurring. The Singhalese, with whom the British colonial authorities had earliest treaty relations, form an old-style landed aristocracy with a preferred position in modern administration. South Indians are prominent in commercial activities, and show many degrees of absorption as well as internal sectionalisms according to whether they speak Tamil, Malabari or Madrasi. Isolated in the remoter parts of the forest there are groups of dark-skinned Veddhas, the oldest race in Ceylon, living a simple, self-contained life and with a tradition of shifting cultivation and hunting, largely divorced from modern developments.

OVERSEAS TIES

Despite the resemblances to South India, Ceylon continued politically separate from the continent even during the British Imperial period. Minor wars across the Palk Strait took place form time to time, and Ceylon's historic capitals (Anuradhapuar and Kandy) were inland, indicating that their traditional interest was away from the sea.

From the fifteenth century, the Portuguese, Dutch and British succession became associated with the island, coming by sea routes and bringing new emphases to development. The island is placed centrally to routes across the Indian Ocean and a point of convergence for shipping moving round the Indian subcontinent, crosswise between Cape Town, India and China, and between Australia and Suez. *Colombo* evolved with the European connection, internally and externally, as port of call, transhipment port and outlet for tea and rubber and coconut products from the Wet Zone. Its harbour is man-made. The trade winds prevailing over Ceylon create violent on-shore seas so that its coasts are rounded off by waves forming either rocky cliffs or fringing sandbars which, while aiding primitive fishing to some extent, impeded the growth of modern harbours for ocean-going vessels. Thus Colombo became a major international port only after the construction of protective sea walls; its position in relation to the Suez Canal was incidentally advantageous rather than the basis of its importance (see Fig. 95).

The Indian Ocean trade centred round Ceylon brought it many contacts and accounts for its present mixtures of people. Additional to the Singhalese and Ceylonese, Arabs, Bengalis, Parsees from Bombay, Burmese, Indonesians and Malays, Africans and Chinese may be met in the streets, and there are long-standing mixed strains such as the Burghers, descendants of the Dutch who were in Ceylon until early last century.

The east coast is without effective overland connection, and is isolated landward by thinly peopled, forested heights and also isolated seaward for several months a year when the violent northeasterlies hinder shipping in the shallow waters. *Trincomali*, its one natural, deep-water harbour, has neither good overseas aspect nor productive hinterland, and has now lost its function as a naval dockyard. *Jaffna* has a lagoon-type harbour used by a few vessels trading to South India. *Mannar*, the small ferry-port for connection with the Indian railway system, handles only a light traffic; trade connections between Ceylon and India are by way of the large steamers using Colombo.

Ceylon's rivers are short, swift and erratic, unsuitable for transport and not yet controlled effectively for irrigation or power. Apart from minor maintenance work in Colombo, industrial activity is insignificant, not least because there is no local fuel apart from wood for domestic use. Padi, the staple food, occupies $1\frac{1}{4}$ million acres and coconuts, largely for local use but permitting some copra exports, another million acres. Padi yields are low because fields are so dependent on the unreliable rains and tank storage is inadequate, and because of disinterest. Holdings are small and much fragmented. The clean-rice production of 390,000 tons per annum falls far short of the national requirement, so that much rice must be imported from Burma. Tea and rubber, the crops of the higher levels in the Wet Zone, each occupy a little over half a million acres, to produce 135,000 tons of tea and 90,000 tons of rubber annually. Graphite (for pencils and nuclear plant) and gems are mined from the crystalline rocks not far from Kandy, and ilmenite sands are being worked near Tirukkovil and Pumodai on the east coast.

Over a third of Ceylon's 9 million people live within a belt roughly 100 miles long and 15 miles broad along the southwestern coast (the Western Province), to which Colombo (half a million people) is roughly central. This population is mostly rural, but includes ten small coastal market towns each containing 40,000. Another quarter of the population is scattered in patches and ribbons round Kandy, and a further million people live round Jaffna. Outside these zones, settlement is very sparse with much empty, wooded country between the villages.

Part V

Economic and Political Geography

CHAPTER TWENTY-THREE

The Economic Geography of Monsoon Asia

CONTAINING 850 million cultivated acres, half the world's farmed land, Monsoon Asia ranks as the global region with the highest proportion of cultivated to available land. In part this is necessitated by the millions of mouths and a consequence of millions of pairs of hands.

THE PATTERN OF AGRICULTURAL PRODUCTION

On the basis of information supplied to the United Nations Organisation, a quarter of Asia's arable land is under rice, an eighth under wheat and another eighth under the coarse food grains (maize, millet and sorghum). Nearly 80% of the farmed area is in grains, and much of the rest for beans, soy, peanuts and vegetable oil crops, the protein elements in Asian diet. Cotton, the main non-food crop, occupies less than one out of every forty arable acres. In 1956, cultivation of all kinds led to a regional production of nearly 130 million tons cleaned rice, 40 million tons wheat and 60 million tons coarse grains. Of the massive production of staples, detailed in Table 7, little left the countries of origin; the only local food grain exported (largely from Burma and Siam) was rice, amounting to barely a fortieth of the product. Food remains largely in domestic use, a consequence of farm self-containment, which explains why internal trade in staples is a minor fraction of the product and why they rank smaller in the national commerce than the area they occupy might suggest. In India, for example, it has been estimated that only 27% of the cereals produced move from farms into commerce. Sugar, largely from cane, is the chief commercialised food-crop: the annual out-turn is 9 million tons (half in India), leading about 1·7 million tons into international trade (over half from the Philippines). In the equatorial countries, native coconut production enters trade as coconut oil or copra, and there are some plantations of it; yet the traded quantity (1·3 million tons oil-equivalent in 1956, two-thirds from the Philippines) is less than half what the small, isolated holdings produce.

While widespread, fishing does not appear reliably in Asian national data because, like subsistence farming, its produce goes only partially into commerce. Japan, with most commercialised fishing, produces nearly 5

TABLE 7

CEREAL PRODUCTION, 1957

	Rice cleaned		Wheat		Maize		Millett Sorghum		Cereals per cap. as % of 1938	Rice prod. lb. per cap.
	million acres → *million tons*									
	acres	tons	acres	tons	acres	tons	acres	tons		
Chinese Mainland	83	58	67	24	122			57	87	199
Korea, South	2·8	2·2	0·31	0·16	—		0·57	0·1	72	190
Taiwan	1·9	1·6	0·05	0·04	0·03	0·011	0·03	0·008	80	342
Japan	8·3	10·4	1·5	1·4	0·13	0·1	0·15	0·1	90	203
Philippines	7·5	2·5	—		3·0	1·0	—		110	201
Vietnam, South	7·9	3·0	—				—			501
Laos	1·5	0·34								430
Cambodia	3·5	0·7			0·11	0·05				335
Thailand	13·2	4·8			0·03	0·2			82	480
Burma	9·9	4·4					0·38	0·03	72	441
Federation of Malaya	0·97	0·49	—				—		90	172
Northern Borneo	0·6	0·1								197
Indonesia	17·2	7·8			6·8	2·6			87	196
Ceylon	1·2	0·5					0·1	0·01	106	114
India	74·2	34·2	31·3	9·9	10·0	3·2	87·8	16·7	96	155
Pakistan	23·1	8·0	12·4	3·9	1·1	0·5	3·1	0·5	82	208

million tons annually and is the only Asian participant in Pacific whaling. Indian Ocean coasts are less heavily fished than Southeast and East Asian coasts.

The non-food products are cotton, rubber, jute, tobacco and tea in that order, in total about 8 million tons annually. These crops, analysed in Table 8, occupy less than 8% of the cultivated area and, grown entirely commercially, enter at once into local trade and move into international trade, as shown in Table 12. The area under these crops has declined during the last twenty years, not accompanied by increasing yields, so that productions have been static or declining despite the incentives of war and industrialisation. Deccan India, the North China Plain, the Yangtse Plain and West Pakistan produce half the region's cotton, which totals only about 20% of world supplies, though the plant is of Asiatic origin. Malaya, Ceylon, and Indonesia contain almost all the rubber acreage, Bengal and East Pakistan the jute, Mindanao the hemp, and Assam, Ceylon and Southeast China the tea. Tobacco is a widely dispersed crop for domestic use, but the superior quality for export is a speciality of Java and the Philippines. Table 8 shows how restricted these crops are. Their total varies from year to year, the vagaries of climate and biotic environment still having such importance that in 1956, for example, India's cotton acreage rose 8% above the previous year, but flood and pests lowered production by 14%.

Silk has ceased to be a major Asian fibre, owing to wartime disruption and artificial fibres. Rearing silkworms makes a labour demand which restricts it to cottagers in China, Japan and Indochina. Japan is now the world's chief producer, of about 40,000 tons in 1955 as against China's 5,500 tons, and also chief silk weaver—183 million yards in 1955.

FURTHER AGRICULTURAL DEVELOPMENT

Governments of Asian countries all have schemes for developing their agriculture, not least due to the new powerful farm vote. They aim to increase production, to increase the average consumption, to improve the standard of living and, in some places, to secure better and more efficient distribution of land. The environments here present many obstacles to greater farm production, whether by intensifying existing farms or by extending farming. Increasing the farm yields, already attempted for many years, has proved to be a slow process because it requires developing better strains of seeds to make fuller use of the ecology, educating farmers in more efficient methods and, in many places, capital works for irrigation and

TABLE 8

MAJOR AGRICULTURAL PRODUCTS (NON-CEREAL), 1957

	Soy & grd. nuts	Sugar	Tea	Jute, hemp	Cotton	Roots, pots, yams	Rubber ('000 tons)	Copra (mill. tons)
	million acres / million tons							
Chinese Mainland	31·8 / 11·8	0·6 / 0·9	0·7 / 0·014	—	15·0 / 2·3	22·0 / 10·8	—	
Korea, South	0·7 / 0·14	—	—	—	0.15 / 0·01	0·24 / 0·64	—	
Taiwan	0·4 / 0·15	0·24 / 0·9	0·12 / 0·02	—	—	0·6 / 2·8		
Japan	1·0 / 0·52	(beet) 0·06 / 0·98	0·12 / 0·08	—	—	1·1 / 6·8	—	
Philippines	0·06 / 0·01	0·6 / 1·5	—	Hemp 0·045	0·1	0·5 / 0·9	—	1·1
Vietnam, South	0·07 / 0·02	0·08 / 0·02	0·02 / 0·004	—	—	0·12 / 0·24	74	0·03
Cambodia							32	
Thailand	0·03 / 0·21	0·32 / 0·07	—	—	0·1 / 0·01	—	140	0·02
Burma	1·14 / 0·3	0·09 / 0·2	—	—	0·3 / 0·01	—	13	—
Federation of Malaya		—	—	—	—	—	703	0·12
Northern Borneo	—	—	—	—	—	—	67	0·4
Indonesia	3·4 / 0·71	0·35 / 0·87	0·4 / 0·07	—	—	1·1 / 2·9	742	0·65
Ceylon	—	—	0·58 / 0·19	—	—	0·03 / 0·05	102	0·32
India	13·6 / 4·7	4·9 / 2·0	0·8 / 0·3	jute 1·7 / 0·82	20·4 / 0·84	1·0 / 3·6	25	0·23
Pakistan	—	1·25 / 0·17	0·078 / 0·025	1·4 / 1·0	3·4 / 0·31	0·14 / 0·28	—	—

transport. Maladjustment to the present ecology, particularly when due to prolonged over-use, needs a slow cure. Educating the isolated, often illiterate farmers is slow. New works face conflicting claims on national capital. Extending the farmed area may be done by reclaiming land gone out of cultivation, but the pressure of Asian population has been heavy for several centuries, so that farms have already been pushed beyond the limits of reliable return with present facilities. Towards the Equator there are empty areas where new rice-lands might be pioneered *if* migration was unrestricted, transport existed, disease controlled—and so on. The Indonesians have under their own administration large, accessible areas with farming potentialities, and high-density zones whence migrants might come; but with facilities and incentives, the Javanese are not extending vigorously. Nationalist policies prevent such areas being available for farming and settlement by other nationals. Movement of overcrowded Japanese, Chinese or Indian farmers to other potential padi-lands in Cambodia, Sumatra, Mindanao, Celebes and Borneo would cause an international crisis.

Lands which have gone out of cultivation form substantial acreages not far from large concentrations of people. They are where, by deforestation, excessive exploitation, erosion and similar destructive processes in India, China and Japan, farming has been rendered impossible by indigenous techniques. Reclamation is easier to the extent that it is accessible from crowded areas, yet is costly and not immediately beneficial in proportion to the works necessary. It offers marginal relief rather than a massive solution to long-standing rural congestion. Reclamation from the sea is already done where feasible, and little further extension can be expected.

INTRODUCTIONS FROM OUTSIDE ASIA

The first half of this century saw great agricultural changes by the introduction of crops or systems then novel to Monsoon Asia. Spectacular developments centred on rubber, jute, tea and sugar-cane. Cotton, once only grown by small farmers for home spinning, was transformed by an innovation of method; that is, by growing it for commerce and buying the family foodstuffs. Cotton was also extended on new farmlands created by poldering parts of the Yangtse Plain and by irrigating in Sind. Rubber was a commercial innovation from Brazil, enabling Western planters to bring equatorial forest into cultivation and to attract migrants to new areas of Malaya, Sumatra, West Java and Borneo. Jute was also a plantation development, enabling the wettest lands of Bengal to be brought into use.

Sugar, an old innovation on large estates in the Philippines, was elsewhere mostly an intermittent crop on small-sized farms. Tea and coffee growing were highly commercialised from introduction to little-used hillsides of Ceylon, Assam and West Java not far from densely peopled, food-growing localities. Tea originated in Southern China, where production was from bushes grown marginally on small food-growing farms; the Chinese output has for years been less significant than that in India and Ceylon, whither tea was transferred on large western monocultivated estates. Commercial tobacco, brought to large estates in the Philippines from America by the Spanish, was introducted by Dutch planters on virgin land behind Medan. Asian smallholders cultivate a little for domestic use. Most copra in trade is from little plantations rather than from kampongs, where Asians grow what they use. The oil-palm has recently been introduced from West Africa to large commercial plantations in Malaya and Sumatra.

Commercial farming on new lands by foreigners has been commoner than farms evolving to commerce from the self-contained system. Innovations, despite their success in the past, do not appear to be taking place any more, possibly due to political risks in labour, markets and financing. Extension and change in Asian agriculture often hinge on conditions other than domestic ones, whether economic or political. Rubber production and acreage have become fairly static partly because the tree needs time to mature, but more because the production of synthetic rubber by the heavy industries of Europe and North America has catered for the still-expanding world rubber consumption and the natural failed to expand. Further sugar-cane production is partially hindered by expanding beet production in Russia and Western Europe. Synthetic fibres deter more cotton growing, though the efficiency of production outside Asia seems largely responsible for the reduction within it.

LESS EMPHASIS ON FARMING

Despite much discussion of and political interest in farm developments in Ceylon, Taiwan, Pakistan and the Philippines (countries where agricultural projects absorb most of the funds for national development), agriculture is producing a lessening proportion of the total national product and other developments are producing faster. Asia's farmed area has increased over the last generation, but has not maintained the regional *per capita* food production. Malaya, Borneo and the Philippines have each failed to maintain food productivity in relation to their population, and Burma, Japan, South Korea and Vietnam have decreased their areas under cultivation.

Monsoon Asia in 1956 was producing nearly 10% less cereals *per capita* than before the Second World War, and rice is rationed in India, Pakistan and Ceylon. A major wheat exporter until 1910, India has become a net food importer. The scale of Asia's food deficit is indicated by the fact that in 1956 alone foodstuffs worth over U.S.$850 million were imported by the region in addition to about U.S.$200 millions-worth sent as gift from the U.S.A. to Cambodia, Taiwan, India and Pakistan, Korea and the Philippines (see Table 13). While Asia's population has increased about 39% during the last twenty years, its cereal production has increased by 16%. Since national schemes for agricultural expansion have shown little sign of substantially adding to the food potential, pressure to make use of virgin areas still in Southeast Asia must be steadily building up.

So far there has been little success in establishing large-scale and mechanised commercial farms for food in tropical Asia comparable to the commercial and mechanised wheat-farms in Australia, Central U.S.A. and the Argentine. Pioneering of this kind might take place in the drier margins of the region, in western parts of the Indo–Gangetic Plain, in Deccan India and beyond the Great Wall of China—if irrigation became available. While waterworks to this end are going on in the Himalayas (as at Bhakra–Nangal), in the Mahanadi and Damodar valleys of the Deccan and in parts of the Chao Praya Plain they meet a very small fraction of the need.

At the same time, the breakdown of self-containment and the emphasis on commercial farming causes internal movement of agricultural products to be increasing, while not always reflected in exports or in diminishing food imports. India and Japan have the highest reported ton-miles of freight on their railways. The annual freight on Chinese railways is two and a half times that on India's railways, though the latter have twice the length. The freight per unit of railway length is now 30% greater than in 1950 for the whole region. During the past decade the numbers of commerical road vehicles has doubled or trebled. In their national development plans, Cambodia, India, Burma and Indonesia, aiming to make commodity production more flexible, each spend more on transport schemes than on any others.

Despite the pressure of population on Asian farms, chemical fertilizers are little used, a reflection of self-containment as well as of low commercialisation. Japan, as might be expected, is the greatest consumer of fertilizers—at the rate of 77 lb. *per capita* in 1957 when by the same standard Taiwan used 45 lb., Ceylon 6 lb., China 3 lb. and India barely one pound. Expressed in relation to farmland, Japan was then using 515 lb., Taiwan 130 lb., Ceylon 181 lb. and China 9 lb. per cultivated acre.

THE PATTERN OF INDUSTRIAL PRODUCTION

A contrasting picture shows in industrial production. Because their populations are gravitating to the towns and because industrialisation affects national prestige, Burma, India, Pakistan, Thailand and the Philippines show a rising proportion of their national product to be from manufacturing. Only Japan shows a reverse trend.

Mining extraction has increased in each national economy except India and Malaya. Mainland China makes mining and manufacture the chief target of its Five Year Plan. The quantitative effects vary considerably, as in Table 9. Comparing with 1938, in coal-mining India (with 350,000 miners) has increased by 30%, Japan is equal, and Malaya and Indonesia

TABLE 9

MAJOR MINERAL PRODUCTION, 1959

	Coal (mill. tons)	Iron Ore (mill. tons)	Tin ('000 tons content)	Crude Oil (mill. tons)
Chinese Mainland . . .	123	?	9·8	1·4
Korea, South . . .	2·4	0·18	—	—
Taiwan	2·9	—	8·4	0·002
Japan	51·7	2·3	1·0	0·3
Philippines	0·2	1·3	—	—
Laos	—	—	0·6	—
Thailand	0·1	—	13·7	—
Burma	—	—	0·9	0·4
Federation of Malaya . .	0·2	3·0	66·2	—
Northern Borneo . .	—	—	—	5·5
Indonesia	0·7	—	28·1	15·5
India	44·1	4·1	—	—
Pakistan	0·5	0·02	—	0·3

dropped by half. Iron-ore output has doubled in Japan, risen by half in India (which has 80% of Asian iron reserves) and the Philippines, and diminished elsewhere. The Deccan is still the world's chief mica producer. Tin ore (until recent restrictions) had increased slightly in Indonesia and by about half in Malaya. Oil outputs since 1938 have increased some seven times in Northern Borneo and by half in Sumatra; Burma has dropped to about a quarter of its production. Japan maintains production from its Niigata fields, West Pakistan has brought new wells into production and China with Russian help is expanding output in West Kansu as well as exploring Szechuan and Sinkiang. Nuclear power and jet engines, demanding new metals, are stimulating existing Asian mining (i.e. graphite from Ceylon and Korea) rather than creating new mines. Monazite sands for thorium are worked on the Travancore coast, and titanium ores from the Deccan are exported to Europe and the U.S.A. Tungsten is still mined in Burma, Korea and Thailand, while South China's output is moving into Russia. Columbite (for toughening jet steels) is a by-product of Malayan and Billiton tin mining. These activities involve small volumes and do not point to any major change in the pattern of Asia's mining.

The chief manufacturing industries are analysed in Table 10, which shows the main one to be cotton textiles. India and Pakistan, the largest raw cotton producers, produce a third more cloth than in 1938, the expansion being fastest in Pakistan (six times greater over the two decades). Japan's rebuilt mills are back to prewar output. Cotton cloth, the pro-cessed article most widely used by Asians, enters all national development plans though the quantities may only be a small part of the regional pro-duction, now about 12,500 million square yards annually, 40% from India, 24% from Japan. In this decade, Taiwan has multiplied its weaving by fourteen to 141 million square yards. Mainland China, weaving less than prewar, claims to turn out 4,000 million square yards, about 33% of Asian production. In jute manufactures (sacking), the total Pak–Ind production is now barely to pre-partition volume, but fast expanding in Pakistan and declining in India.

Artificial fibres have been quickly adopted in Asia and suit its cheap markets. Since these fibres derive from heavy industry, their production has been limited to Japan and India. Japan has returned to second place among world artificial yarn producers with an out-turn of 450,000 tons of rayon and acetate, and 25,000 tons nylon-type in 1957, when also it was leading producer of artificial fibres for blending with cotton and wool. India has only recently appeared as a rapidly expanding producer of artificial yarn. Paper totalling 4 million tons is manufactured in Asia,

TABLE 10

INDUSTRIAL ACTIVITIES, 1959

	Railway freight (mill. ton-miles p.m.)	Comm. motor vehicles ('000)	Cotton cloth mill. sq. yds.	Steel (mill. tons)	Cement (mill. tons)	Electricity ('000 mill. kWh)
Chinese Mainland .	16,700	?	5,700	8·4	9·5	28·0
Korea, South .	280	20	132	0·02	0·5	1·6
Taiwan . .	240	9	148	0·12	1·05	3·1
Hong Kong . .	8	5	650	—	0·14	0·9
Japan . . .	6,400	480	2,645	14·0	17·2	91·0
Philippines . .	26	79	10	—	0·7	1·4
Vietnam, South .	11	15	—	—	—	0·2
Cambodia . .	8	5	—	—	—	0·05
Thailand . .	127	37	48	—	0·5	0·3
Burma . . .	84	22	5	—	0·04	0·2
Federation of Malaya —Singapore .	58	44	—	—	0·2	1·6
Indonesia . .	135	70	56	—	0·9	0·9
Ceylon . . .	39	27	5	—	0·08	0·3
India . . .	9,400	230	4,500	2·2	6·5	14·2
Pakistan . .	850	24	489	0·01	1·0	1·0

Japan accounting for 2·5 million tons annually, against India's 120,000 tons. Cement, of major importance for the projected roads, buildings and public works, has become an expanding industry, especially in Taiwan, Thailand and West Pakistan. The greatest producers in the total of 30 million tons annually are Japan (43%), China (22%) and India (17%).

Indicative of its heavy industrial development, Japan is the only country in Monsoon Asia with a large production of chemical fertilizers, amounting to nearly 3 million tons in 1957 when other Asian countries together produced only about one million tons.

Electric power is fast expanding, mostly derived from coal or oil, but

Japan generates three-quarters of its electricity by water. Regional generation has almost trebled over 1948–58 to 126 million kW., greatest increase occurring in Pakistan, Thailand, Hong Kong and Ceylon. These increases have so far been for urban use: the tiny "city-state" of Hong Kong produces as much electricity a year as the whole of the populous country of Pakistan, The *per capita* kilowattage for 1957 was 900 in Japan, 330 in Singapore, 280 in Hong Kong, 220 in Taiwan, 150 in the Federation of Malaya and less than 25 everywhere else.

The iron and steel production figures epitomise the low level of heavy industry. In 1957 the region altogether produced 20 million tons of steel (less than Britain's output), two-thirds in Japan and a quarter in China. Much effort is going into smelting; Japan has had to reconstruct its war-damaged plant; India has expanded output 45% since 1947: China's production is mostly from Manchuria, using ex-Japanese plant restored with Russian help.

All Asian states except Japan have far to go before they reach the mature levels of industrialisation known in Europe and America. For 1956 the *per capita* coal out-turn in China was one-thirtieth and of India one forty-fourth that of the U.K. The steel production *per capita* for 1957 was 18 lb. in China and India and 370 lb. in Japan, as against 950 lb. in the U.K. Even the cotton cloth out-turn *per capita* is low by western standards— Japan, China and India producing a sixth, a fifth and a third respectively of the U.K. figure. Asian industrial installations appear new, and the climate permits them to be open and slight in structure and seemingly more makeshift than their European or American counterparts.

PRODUCTION, POPULATION AND POSSIBILITIES

These varied national productions may be put into perspective against their populations by examining the gross value[1] *per capita* (the total value of everything produced by farming, mining and manufacturing divided by the population). The variations for 1956 within the region were wide: the Federation of Malaya led with a *per capita* product worth U.S.$215, and the Philippines with U.S.$185. Ceylon, South Korea and Taiwan had

[1] Where money values are quoted, they are converted into U.S. dollars of the time so as to simplify interpretation by using a gold-base currency. In 1958 a U.S. dollar was roughly worth in local currencies: 500 South Korean hwan, 26 Taiwan yuan, 6 Hong Kong dollars, 355 Japanese yen, 34 South Vietnam piastres, 3,600 North Vietnam dong, 34 Laos kip, 34 Cambodian riel, 2 Filipino pesos, 21 Siamese baht, 3 Malayan dollars, 12 Indonesian rupiah, 5 Burmese kyat, 5 Ceylonese rupees, 5 Indian rupees, 5 Pakistani rupees.

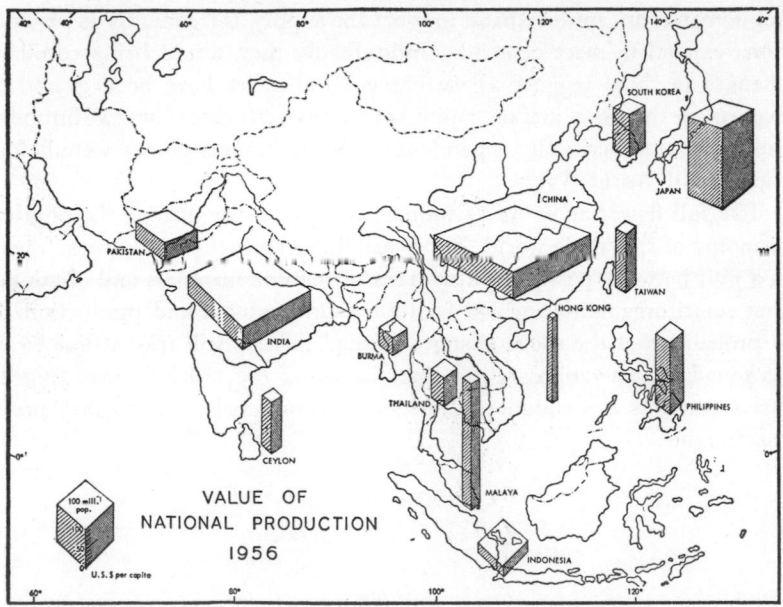

VALUE OF
NATIONAL PRODUCTION
1956

FIG. 98—Productivity in relation to population in Asian countries. The columns
have bases in area proportional to population, and heights according to *per capita*
production in U.S.$

from 100 to 120 U.S.$ *per capita*. Thailand and Mainland China had
productivity of about U.S.$70, followed by India, Pakistan and Burma
producing nearly U.S.$50 per person, Indonesia ranking least with
U.S.$26.

Small though their present industrial product is, China and India have
man-power and natural resources which might enable them to indus-
trialise to the level already reached by Japan, the ultimate result of which
is not foreseeable, but the effect on world economy could be violent.
Given organisation and peace, great changes could come by 1980 and lead
to new patterns of concentration in these countries and new regional
relationships. The change could affect internal transport, and might
remove that incohesion now a feature of most states, altering the balance
of power internally and externally. China might establish in its outer
regions industrial complexes comparable to those Russia has created in
Siberia, which was once"Outer Russia". Similar industrialisation in India
might give rise to cut-throat international rivalry between Asian powers,

yet demands are apt to expand to meet the supply as frequently as productions expand to meet demand. Undoubtedly they would bring corollary changes in those regions whose present industries have been geared to exports for the Asian market, and it is possibly fortunate that few European industries are as critically dependent on Asian markets as they were before the Second World War.

The full flowering of Asia's industrial growth may change the political economy of the whole world. But possibilities are not probabilities. There is a gulf between possessing resources of men or materials and obtaining that social organisation which facilitates development and production. It is probable that the social changes needed in Asia will take a time to be reckoned in generations rather than in years; the task of converting all Asian peasants to a commercial or even a communal economy may prove insuperable.

CHAPTER TWENTY-FOUR

National Trade Movements

THE EXPORTS OF Asian countries are largely of agricultural raw materials, as follows from the nature of their economies. They are analysed in Table 12, and by no means move exclusively to industrialised countries for processing. In order of bulk (and therefore of transport needs), rice ranks first of such exports (over 3 million tons), sugar second with 1·9 million tons, rubber third and tea fourth. Raw-cotton exports have shrunk to barely 200,000 tons annually. Rubber and tea go largely to markets outside Asia, sugar only partly so and rice largely to Asia. Of mineral exports, crude oil involves by far the largest quantity (18 million tons), iron ore second (3 million tons) and tin third (about 100,000 tons moving to Europe and the U.S.A.). Only India and Japan export many processed goods, particularly cloth for other Asian countries. Cement moves from Japan and Taiwan into Asian markets. About half Asia's exports move through Suez. The exports from some Asian countries are dominated by one or two commodities. Rice is over 75% of Burma's export; Malayan and Indonesian exports are each at least 50% rubber; and Thailand's export comprises 50% rice. Raw jute and cotton together form 95% of Pakistan exports, and coconut products nearly half of the Philippines exports. National export value *per capita* varies from as little as U.S. $3 for India to nearly U.S. $220 for Malaya, but is mostly U.S. $25 or less (compare with U.S. $150 *per capita* for Britain).

Asian imports, analysed in Table 13, are more varied and consist overwhelmingly of a miscellany of manufactured goods and the heavy equipment and machinery for capital works. Inflowing food, once only to commodity specialists like Ceylon and Malaya, now goes to Indonesia and South Korea which a generation ago were self-contained. India by restricting imports has caused capital goods to account for 40% of its inflow, which includes much food. The total regional import drawn from other Asian countries averages a third of the whole, from Europe and the U.S.A. a half. Inflow from Russia has been a trickle through Suez to India and Indonesia, and a larger movement overland into Outer China, Manchuria and Peking.

The regional trade is much influenced by government to government

TABLE 11

EXPORT VALUES, TONNAGES AND DESTINATIONS, 1959

	Total Export value (in mill. U.S. $)	Total Export value (U.S. $ per capita)	Tonnage Load estimated at ports (mill. tons)	Direction			
				To Asian countries (%)	To West Europe (%)	To North America (%)	To East Europe and U.S.S.R. (%)
Chinese Mainland (1957)	600	1	?	41	48	—	?
Korea, South .	21	1	0·04	69	14	17	0
Taiwan . .	151	15	1·3	67	4	6	0
Hong Kong .	604	215	2·0	45	17	13	0
Japan . .	3,222	35	9·6	30	11	30	1
Philippines . .	574	23	7·4	22	19	56	0
Vietnam, South .	63	5	0·5	31	54	10	0
Cambodia . .	55	12	0·3	34	28	26	0
Thailand . .	326	15	2·0	59	9	18	0
Burma . .	205	10	1·9	73	10	1	14
Fed. of Malaya— Singapore .	1,343	166	10	35	32	12	7
Northern Borneo	350	295	5·5	25	45	10	0
Indonesia . .	858	9	14·2	46	27	19	1
Ceylon . .	354	37	0·4	10	44	11	0
India . . .	1,294	3	8·9	16	38	20	5
Pakistan . .	295	4	0·9	24	53	11	5

financing arrangements or aid, sometimes as trade credits, sometimes as gifts, sometimes for personnel. From mid-1955 to early 1958 the U.S.A. has given aid of this kind worth U.S. $2,134 million to non-Communist Monsoon Asian countries, and Russia and China also provided U.S. $464 million.

TABLE 12

AGRICULTURAL PRODUCTS EXPORTED, 1959

Quantities and Proportions

(million tons and percentage of production)

	Rice (clean)	Sugar	Tea	Rubber	Cotton (raw)	Veg. Oil	Coarse fibres
Taiwan . .	0·16 (10%)	0·74 (63%)	0·04 (27%)				
Philippines .		0·91 (60%)				coconut 0·54	hemp 0·12 (90%)
Vietnam, South .	0·17 (7%)			0·074 (100%)			
Cambodia . .	0·2 (31%)			0·03 (100%)			
Thailand . .	1·05 (22%)			0·16 (100%)			
Burma . .	1·6 (38%)			0·012 (100%)			
Federation of Malaya				0·52 (100%)		coconut 0·23 palm 0·05	0·023
Northern Borneo				0·06 (100%)		0·05	
Indonesia . .		0·03 (3%)	0·035 (43%)	0·74 (100%)		coconut 0·019 palm 0·11	0·125
Ceylon . .			0·17 (85%)	0·09 (100%)		coconut 0·09	
India . .		0·08 4%	0·2 (60%)		0·067 (8%)		jute 0·83 (100%)
Pakistan . .			0·005 (25%)		0·066 (22%)		jute 0·8 (78%)

TABLE 13

IMPORTS FOR 1959 BY TYPE AND BY SOURCE

	Total value (U.S. $mill.)	Type				Source			
		Food (%)	Raw materials (%)	Manufactured goods (%)	Cap.* Eq. (%)	Asia (%)	Western Europe (%)	N. Am. (%)	Eastern Europe and Asia
Chinese Mainland (1957) .	533	?	?	?	?	7	14	0	75
Korea, South .	297	14	13	48	15	7	4	89	0
Taiwan . .	245	2	45	12	35	46	8	39	0
Hong Kong .	899	22	16	48	14	53	19	10	0
Japan . .	3,361	15	63	9	13	20	9	41	1
Philippines .	519	13	9	40	38	27	13	54	0
Vietnam, South	218	10	9	56	23	32	42	26	0
Cambodia .	62	7	11	58	22	49	41	9	1
Thailand .	394	9	11	40	37	51	29	18	1
Burma . .	201	4	8	40	48	52	34	4	7
Fed. of Malaya —Singapore	1,316	22	20	45	12	59	26	4	0
Northern Borneo .	240	18	51	19	10	78	15	3	0
Indonesia .	439	21	10	39	29	40	33	15	1
Ceylon . .	430	30	12	38	24	38	33	18	0
India . .	2,019	4	16	19	44	14	42	23	4
Pakistan .	333	3	15	40	42	22	39	31	2

* Includes machinery, vehicles.

CONTINENTAL EAST ASIA

While *China* does not provide much detail of its internal trade (the 1957 ECAFA report noted that railway freights and coastwise shipping had declined), the returns from other countries provide evidence of a substantial flow out of China notwithstanding the difficulties of currency and barter deals. In 1956 other Asian countries were absorbing about U.S. $380 million of Chinese products (food specialities and raw materials), and supplying in return about U.S. $120 million, mostly Ceylonese rubber, Burmese rice and mixed manufactured goods from Hong Kong. Hong Kong was leading trader in Chinese products, and Japan ranked as second largest importer of them. A two-way smuggled trade takes place in South China. Rapidly growing trade with Soviet Russia is said to account for 80% of China's trade; little of China's bulky produce can move overland, but Russian equipment (40% of the inflow) evidently comes via the Transiberian Railway. Administered exclusively on an inter-government basis, trade with Russia and its allies is difficult to relate to ordinary trade. The publicly reported agreements between Communist governments for 1956 included the following exchanges with China, quantities unknown:

Chinese wheat, edible oil, tea, flax exchanged for Albanian copper and tobacco; Chinese minerals, tea, animal products and industrial materials for Bulgarian fertilisers, agricultural machinery, tobacco, textiles; Chinese steel, machinery, edible oil, tea, silk for Egyptian cotton; Chinese soy products, tea, silk, eggs, glue for Finnish paper, paper machinery, copper, steel boilers; Chinese ores, metals, raw chemicals, fibres, tea, edible oils, hides for Hungarian agricultural and communications machinery, instruments, dynamos, vehicles, textiles, petroleum products; Chinese iron ore, asbestos, wool, hides, tea, hemp, cotton for Rumanian generator and well-drilling equipment, tractors, oil-tanks, petroleum products; Chinese agricultural, mineral and handicraft products for Russian machinery, technicians, metallurgical, chemical and electric plant; Chinese sulphur, mercury, soda, rice, tea, wool, hides for Russian machine tools, drilling and building equipment, cranes, pumps, diesels, generators, instruments, iron; Chinese vegetable oils, silk, hides, tin, asbestos, graphite for Yugoslav tobacco, agricultural machinery, chemical products, cotton cloth, medical supplies. Manchuria's soy-oil export appears to have faded out.

Chinese cotton crops continue to be large (1·4 million tons in 1957) and mostly retained for domestic manufactures, its cloth output now ranking second largest in Asia, concentrated at Shanghai, Wu-Han, Canton and Peking. China's coal out-turn, about 9 million tons annually from Kailwan, Fushan and Fushin, and 7 million tons annually from Huainan and Tatung, is now Asia's largest, enabling an increasing production of steel and electricity. The need for foreign currency to finance developments is thought likely to induce China to force the pace of its exports which now only trickle out, mainly through Hong Kong.

North Korea does not publicise its economic position. Its heavy industry, established originally by the Japanese on the basis of the large coal and iron production, is being restored and hydro-electricity from the Yalu is used extensively for textiles. Migration south of the border in the disturbed early 1950s caused internal labour difficulties.

North Vietnam enters little into trade. *South Vietnam* is exporting a little rice, but like all Indochinese countries its rice surplus has shrivelled to an unprecendented low. Only 5% of South Vietnam rice is exported.

South Korea is expanding its cotton-mills and making its agriculture more commercial. Both South Vietnam and South Korea have low export values *per capita*, sending largely to other Asian countries. They are producing cereals much more slowly than their populations increase, the *per capita* decline being greatest in Korea.

Hong Kong has trade flow without basis in local raw materials. Its trade is entrepôt, about half with other Asian countries and a fifth with Europe. China alone supplies a fifth of what goes into Hong Kong. Its small-scale industries, including many cotton piece-goods, are a response to its free-port transhipment trade and to refugee labour from the mainland. Its imports (U.S.$925 million in 1957) much exceed its exports (U.S.$570 million in 1957), the greatest item of inflow being rice for local consumption and re-export. Hong Kong and Singapore are complementary entrepôts for the South China Sea.

INSULAR EAST ASIA

The region of Insular East Asia continues to increase its already high levels of food production. *Taiwan* and the *Philippines* are still food exporters, the latter having raised its *per capita* cereal out-turn chiefly by maize. An eighth of Taiwan's rice and three-quarters of the sugar of both Taiwan and the Philippines go to export. Taiwan's sugar and Philippines hemp have diminished area since the Second World War. The arrival in Taiwan of wealthy entrepreneur refugees from China has led to speedy industrialisation in part to service the refugee Nationalist army. Its coal is now intensively mined for increased steel, cotton cloth and electricity outputs. *Japan* dominates Asian industrial activity by any criterion: it leads in number of commercial vehicles used in industry and farming, as well as in steel, cement and electricity production; it has third place (after India and China) among Asian cotton-cloth producers. The export flow from these states, greater than from any other region in Monsoon Asia, is composed of primary agricultural products together with manufactures from Japan: it totalled U.S.$3,000 million in 1956, of which Japan alone was responsible for 84%. Japan's heavy industry, while no longer unique in Asia, includes the only major shipbuilding, originally for its own bulky commodity trade and now partly for ships to sell to other nations, including those of Europe; Japanese costs are much the same as in the shipbuilding yards of Britain, but the rate of delivery has been faster. Taiwan and Japan both send most of their outflow to other Asian countries, while the Philippines, which leads world trade in copra and hemp, sells half its exports to the U.S.A. Taiwan and the Philippines absorb substantial food imports from the U.S.A., whose grain surplus for some years has been used to support those nations. Much of Japan's expanding export is in miscellaneous capital equipment in demand by Asians; the boom arising from reconstructing its own economy has been perpetuated as other Asian countries sought similar equipment. Such Japanese exports compete with those of Europe and North America, traditional sources of capital goods.

Japan is absorbing large quantities of wheat and sugar ($2\frac{1}{4}$ and $1\frac{1}{4}$ million tons respectively in 1956), its rice imports being small considering that rice is the Japanese staple; eating habits are changing because in 1956 the price of wheat per ton landed in Japan was half that of imported rice. Two-thirds of Japan's inflow consists of raw materials, iron ore, raw fertiliser, cotton, timber. Taiwan has a large import of fertilisers and petroleum. The Philippines chiefly absorb consumer goods. Half the regional inflow comes from North America and a third from Asia.

CONTINENTAL SOUTHEAST ASIA

In Laos, Cambodia and Thailand, rice continues to increase in acreage and production. In Burma it has substantially declined, *per capita* production being less than two-thirds that of 1938, the greatest cereal deterioration in Asia; yet Burma exports 47% of its rice as against Thailand's 24%. Rice is no longer the chief item of Indochinese export values. Only Thailand has notable other production, having increased its outputs of tin and rubber (largely from Kra), which are exported crude. In this region, industrialisation has not gone far: Thailand's railway mileage and freight have been substantially increased and cement production has started. Fuel resources in these countries are limited and their coal mostly lignitic, hence their electricity production is among Asia's lowest. Burma's oil output has not been restored to prewar levels. Continental Southeast Asia exports about U.S.$660 million annually, over half going to other Asian countries and consisting of rice, a trade which involves much shipping. Burma and Thailand have little mercantile marine, the former registering only four vessels of over a thousand tons each, the latter seven; much rice moves overseas in Chinese sailing junks. Over 10% of Burma's exports for the years 1955-7 were to Russia. The regional *per capita* value of exports is high, that for Thailand being two-thirds of Japan's.

Consumer goods form half the regional inflow, capital goods a fifth. Half the imports come from other Asian countries.

INSULAR SOUTHEAST ASIA

Indonesia differs from Malaya and Northern Borneo by its separated parts with contrasting developments. The region is now food deficient, Indonesia least so as a whole, though Kalimantan and Sumatra are worse than average. Net food production has decreased in Northern Borneo and increased in Malaya and Indonesia, though not keeping pace with population increase. Indonesia has substantially lessened its maize acreage and increased its root foods. The three territories produce for export rubber and varying proportions of tea, coffee, sugar and vegetable oils. Palm oil from Malaya and Sumatra are new and unique in Asia, yet totalling only 200,000 tons annually so far. The chief exported vegetable oil is coconut, the equivalent of 300,000 tons being shipped in 1957. Once one of the world's major sugar exporters, Java is decreasing its acreage and only 16% of its sugar goes into export which at 165,000 tons for 1957 is a third that of Taiwan. The Indonesian rubber export exceeds the Malayan, but partly flows through Malayan ports. Of tin, Malaya produces twice as much as Indonesia, both countries exporting to Western Europe and North America, and now self-resticted for price control. While coal is diminishing, petroleum from Outer Indonesia and Northern Borneo has greatly increased, the production of 21 million tons crude in 1957 being double that for 1938: the Seria field accounts for about one-quarter, the rest coming from Sumatra and Kalimantan. None of the countries is significantly industrialised. Still a major exporting region, Southeast Asia accounted for 23% of all Asia's exports in 1956. Malaya leads Asia in *per capita* national production, and is the second most valuable exporter among Asian countries, its *per capita* outflow (excluding Singapore) exceeding five times that of Japan. Half the total regional outflow goes to Europe, a third to Asia and the rest to the U.S.A. The commodities are bulky and need considerable shipping capacity, partly accounting for the great concentration of sea traffic through Singapore, where routes of Southeast Asian seas converge. Normally the total gross registered tonnage of vessels calling at Malayan ports each year exceeds that for Japanese ports and is two and a half times the tonnage entering Indian ports. Food imports are expanding but the greater regional inflow is of manufactured consumer goods, much from Japan, with textiles increasingly drawn from India. A substantial import both of consumer goods and capital equipment comes from Western Europe.

SOUTHERN ASIA

Recent increases in cereals (in acreage and production) achieved by much effort in both India and Pakistan still leave them slightly lower in *per capita* production than before World War II. In the same period Ceylon has greatly improved its local food supply, while being far from self-sufficient. Pakistan and India have become dependent on U.S.A. food surpluses imported in large quantities. The parts of Pakistan are sufficiently complementary to make its food position as a whole much like that of India, though East Pakistan is exclusively "wet tropical" and West Pakistan "dry tropical". India has a great area under groundnuts, and is still expanding both its tea and jute acreages, while Pakistan is diminishing those commercial "Western" crops. Pakistan is increasing its cotton output, India decreasing it. From Pak–Ind about 40,000 tons of hides are exported annually. The Deccan provides India with minerals, of which Pakistan has little. India's coal output is now about half that of Japan, and its iron ore production (concentrated at Asansol and Jamshedpur) leads all Asia, exceeding 4 million tons annually. West Pakistan is bringing in a little oil from new fields on its northwestern borders and India has new oilfields in Upper Assam. India and Pakistan are Asia's only substantial cotton exporters, the former sending out 13% of its product and the latter half, but their combined production is a million tons annually—which is less than half that of U.S.A. and two-thirds that of China. Ceylon contributes about a sixth of the rubber in world trade. India's internal trade is largely by rail, Ceylon moves most goods by road. India surpasses Japan as cotton-cloth producer, but its heavy industry produces only a fifth as much steel as Japan and less than half the cement. India exports to other parts of Asia and to Africa about two-thirds of a million square yards of cloth, chiefly the inferior grades, a seventh of its output. India is rapidly increasing its electricity, but the three South Asian countries combined generate only a seventh as much electric power as Japan. Their combined exports have a value about that of Japan's but *per capita* the exports from India and Pakistan are among the least in Asia. Despite the long land boundaries, the outgoing trade of India and Pakistan is largely seaborne, only about 5% moving overland and made up largely of trade between themselves. Ceylon's fairly diversified commercial agriculture (rubber, tea, copra and spices) gives it a high export per person. Of the outflow, about 60% from each country goes to Europe; Ceylon and India export considerably to the rest of Asia. Ceylon in recent years was occasionally exporting more value to Russia than to Asia.

The inflows to India and Pakistan have been substantially exceeding outflows for some years. Half India's imports are capital equipment and similar goods, drawn largely from Europe and North America; in 1956 imports from Russia were barely 1% of the total. Manufactured consumer goods are 60% of Pakistan's inflow, largely from Europe and North America, but 39% is from Asian countries, particularly Japan. Food is a high proportion of Ceylon's imports notwithstanding the success in increasing rice production over the last decade. Asian sources are therefore prominent for Ceylon's imports, only a third coming from Europe which supplies consumer goods in competition with Japan. Total imports of Southern Asia countries are about two-fifths from Western Europe, a fifth from Asia, and 13% from North America.

CHAPTER TWENTY-FIVE

Political Geography of Monsoon Asia

IT IS NECESSARY now to consider how the setting and the content of Monsoon Asia affect those administering the countries in deciding on policies for their own citizens and for their relations with other states, particularly in estimating what power they command to implement domestic and external policies. This appraisal of the region's political geography relates not only to the present pattern and balances of material influences within the countries and in relation one to the other, but also to the changes taking place in their domestic organisations and in conditions outside the region.

Asians have been participating in a tremendous upheaval during the last hundred years, as a result of which the framework of their states has altered drastically, the grouping of peoples changed and new ties and links established amid a widespread social readjustment. Some changes have been implemented with local violence, as in China, Indochina and Indonesia; others came peacefully and more generally in the course of trade and education. The last hundred years have seen ideas and techniques transform whole countrysides and the way of life of millions of Asians at a speed and to a profundity probably without precedent in the region's history.

ASIA LAST CENTURY

In 1850, China and Japan were virtually sealed off by their "Bamboo Curtain" round feudal empires, then at a stage of development resembling the Roman Empire in decline. Many of Asia's powerful cities (including Shanghai, Singapore, Tokyo and Karachi) were then scarcely more than villages if they existed at all. Thousands of Asian settlements were isolated from their own capitals and from the rest of mankind to a degree now unbelievable. India and Pakistan were then controlled by a single British private company, and Indonesia by a Dutch company. The combined population of Southeast Asia was probably less than that of modern London. In Asia there was not a single mile of railway. From Baluchistan to Japan not a dozen miles of hard-surfaced road existed. It took more than six months to get from Singapore to London and six weeks from Singapore to Japan. The total annual external trade of Monsoon Asia appears to have been no more than could be carried in half a dozen of the ocean-going steamers plying there by the hundred on any single day in the 1950s. Every article produced locally was hand-made. Swords, spears, bows and arrows were the basic armaments of the innumerable chieftaincies and principalities which were the Asian political units of that time.

A HUNDRED YEARS OF CHANGE

Since then the governments of Britain, U.S.A., France, Netherlands and Germany have at different times established administrative colonies of different extents and types over most of the region, the last being their occupation, at the end of the Second World War, of Japan, which had itself become a colonial power like them. This colonising (Fig. 99) swept the region like a political and cultural tide, and was backed by modern governmental and mercantile organisation and by the industrial equipment of the Western World, both of which were so powerful that nothing local could withstand them. By now that overpowering tide has receded almost completely: in 1960 only Portugal retains all the territorial fragments it held in 1850. In place of the political colonies there are left more than a dozen "succession" states with independent governments which have an acknowledged equal voice in relation to other countries of the world such as no earlier Asian country had had. Japan for a few years included in its empire all Eastern and Southeast Asia. China has undergone two internal revolutions, seen waterborne foreigners establish "treaty ports" and concessions on its coast and relinquish them, been administered by the Japanese for seven years and become a close ally of Soviet Russia. Here political experimentation has gone on as a result of which all the countries have modern, Western-type elective constitutions, including several monarchies (Japan, Siam, Cambodia and the Federation of Malaya). Massive migrations of Asians have occurred, leading permanent settlers to previously unused places. Millions of Chinese now live in Manchuria and Southeast Asia, millions of Indians in Burma and Malaya; Indonesians migrated to their Outer Islands and into Malaya. Japanese went as settlers and as administrators into Manchuria, Taiwan and Korea and into the trading towns of Southeast Asia, and then in 1945 withdrew to their original islands. Inside the Asian countries there has been rapid urbanisation. In the rural areas, large populations of Burmese, Siamese and Indochinese shifted to new rice-lands within their own borders. Millions of acres of new land have been brought into cultivation, sometimes for economic plants never previously seen in

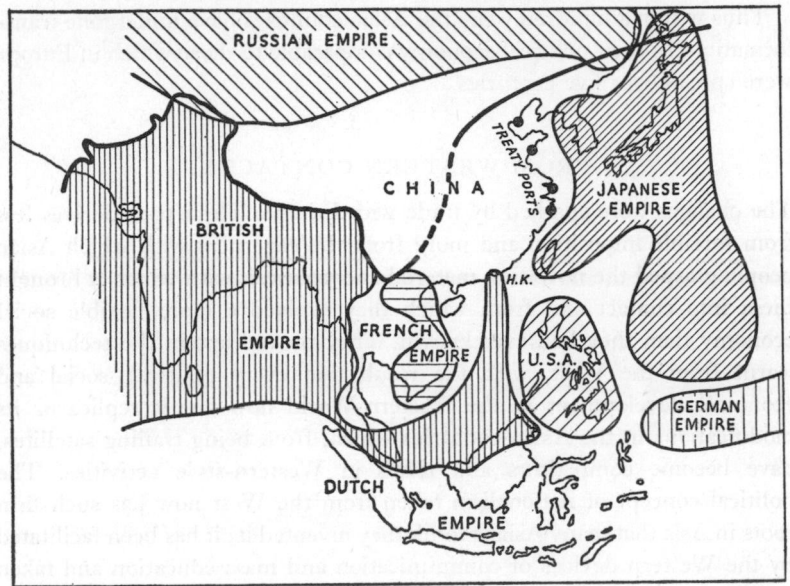

FIG. 99—Colonial Empires in Monsoon Asia (1910)

the region. Every mining industry of significance in Asia grew up during this hundred years. Japan's large-scale industrialisation, adopted simultaneously with an expanded agriculture, achieved a success so spectacular that Japan's modernised navy could defeat the Russian fleet decisively in 1905 and its military power challenge for several years the combined resources of Britain and the U.S.A. From being an exclusively agricultural region, selling only raw materials, Asia moved into manufacturing, at first in Japan, then successively in Manchuria, India and China. The cloth output of China alone is now two-thirds that of U.S.A. The commercial economy of the Western World came into play, creating domestic strains in Asia's self-contained farming economies on the one side and bringing into existence large Asian trading communities on the other. Hand in hand with urbanisation came modern hygiene and medical practice, helping to cause very rapid population increases, so that today the region adds annually to its already overcrowded countrysides some 25 millions; this is roughly the equivalent of adding a new Spain each year or a new Russia every decade. Each Asian country now has railways, air services, broadcasting stations and newspapers and every device for communication among its own people and with foreigners.

323

Thus within a hundred years the Asian countries have undergone transformations in their political economy comparable to those which in Europe
were spread over five centuries.

FROM WESTERN CONTACTS

The changes were sparked by trade with Europe. Their pace derives less
from forcible imposition and more from the eagerness with which Asian
people grasped the novelties, material and political, with which it brought
them into contact and from which they evolved a more flexible social
economy than they had ever known. They proved apt in the techniques
learnt from the West, with the result that every political, social and
economic development in the Western World now has it replica or its
modifications in the Asian countries which, from being trailing satellites,
have become competitors and rivals in Western-style activities. The
political concept of nationalism taken from the West now has such firm
roots in Asia that many Asians think they invented it; it has been facilitated
by the Western devices of communication and mass education and taken
the form, not so much of that nostalgia centring on tradition and literature
which is chiefly the basis of Western nationalism, but more of the attitude
best summed up as "Anything you Westerners can do, we can do for
ourselves" and far more racially biased than in present-day Europe. It is
thus a forward-looking, economic type of nationalism; only Japanese
nationalism has a touch of that traditionalism evident in European nations.
By and large, the Asian nationalists look to Western patterns of development, in which sense local politicians have been revolutionary in their
societies rather than looking back to the Asian past. Hence the drive to
Westernise seemed never so powerful as when the Western colonial
administrators left the Asians independent. Education, helped by the
newspaper, has greatly aided the spread of ideas which have produced the
new political economies so that, while in 1850 it may be doubted whether
as many as a million Asians were literate in their own languages, the
number of Asians now with a working literacy in English alone probably
exceeds the population of Britain, additional to the greater number now
literate in their own languages. Communications, trade and education have
contributed much to Asian nationalism and have in turn led to regionalist
movement of several kinds under such titles as "Sumatra for the Sumatrans" and "Andhra for the Telegu-speaking people". Those same means
of communication, however, have also served to show that the content of
the regional writings and literature offers little that is helpful to the process

of modernisation and economic advancement or to the cohesion of the new independencies. Hence it is that English became the lingua franca of modern Asia.

DOMESTIC STRAINS

Because every Asian state now has an elective government, political actions are influenced by their agricultural populations in the first place, and then by the smaller but concentrated and vocal communities in the towns. Each country thus shows domestic political strains arising from inherited agrarian difficulties and from varying degrees of advance achieved in its farm economy from place to place. Each state has regions modernised by trade or by industry, located side by side with regions where life centres still on self-supporting little farms insulated from the national economy. There are major tensions at voting time between region and region in this respect, showing sometimes as tension between the generations in one region. The political administrators are frequently more versed in Western political economic theory, biased to industry, than they are in their domestic economies, heavily weighted towards agriculture. It gives rise to politicians more skilful in discussing and manipulating the machinery of international affairs than they are with that of home affairs, where the friction of diverging economies in quick-moving and irregularly trans-formed groups is of a kind not present in the maturer Western countries.

How to even out domestic strains of this kind in the political economy is a problem with the Asian nations of such difficulty and complexity that some politicians attempt to divert public attention towards external issues, however subsidiary these may be to the national interest: for this reason it is advisable to look carefully at the boundary problems of each state in turn.

POVERTY AND EXTERNAL TIES

While recent political activities in Asia have arisen often from objection to Western administrators, there remain strong economic links with Western Europe and North America which continue to have great significance and show clearly in Tables 11 and 13. Many Asians during the colonial phase were misled into believing that their countries were "rich" because they saw some foreign firms achieve success in local commerce. The Asian faces the reality that local resources, while grossing large, are smaller *per capita* than in the European and North American countries. As indicated in

Chapter 23 and in Table 14, Malaya is the wealthiest territory of Asia in proportion to its population, but its 1956 production *per capita* was only a third that of Britain and a fifth that of the U.S.A. Indonesia, the poorest Asian country that year, had an income per person only 3·5% that of Britain and 2·5% that of U.S.A. Domestic poverty is so generally a characteristic of Asian states that they bristle with plans to alleviate it, which brings them at once into relation with the rest of the world, seeking by direct purchase or by loan, privately or on a government to government basis, the large quantities of capital equipment which expansion, development and modernisation of their agriculture and industry necessitates. This need, made more acute by high rates of population increase, establishes trade ties in the same directions as recent "colonial" political ties, with the difference that the Asians now seek to establish it from their side. For the time being these needs for things from outside represent a dependence often differing only in name and not in pattern from the earlier political dependence. Procurement of national needs is hindered by the small part of national income which enters into government revenues for public purposes. Thus the Pakistan government has a revenue equal to only 6·5% of its national product, India 9% and the Philippines 10%, as against the comparable figures of 20% and 29% for the U.S.A. and Britain respectively. The revenue of a Communist state is not strictly comparable because the state acts as domestic entrepreneur, but China's government revenue now is 31% of the national product. The internal strains set up by this aspect of Asian poverty are the more difficult to deal with because in the minds of electors there continues an idea that government can be a universal provider. That view grew when colonial governments could draw upon metropolitan resources to develop a colonial territory. The independent "succession" governments can expend for national improvements and public works only funds they can raise internally by taxation. An internal tension arises as the Asian governments press heavy taxes on their demonstrably poor electors, even if the purpose is to improve the public facilities. Asian domestic politics must continue under a strain for some years because their national product is so small that every effort to add new capital equipment must severely reduce the current standard of living. Few parties can say this to Asian voters until after elections; it has been stated unequivocally in China and more recently become explicit and evident in India. The physical problems of extending farming are overwhelming now that the limit of cultivability by present techniques has been reached at many points. Merely to keep pace with the birthrate is a major task, in face of population increases so fast that they can nullify plans for redistribution, resettlement and reintegration before they are implemented.

URBAN INFLUENCES

Asia's closely compacted urban populations are more accessible, more easily educated and less involved with traditional methods than the farmers. They have become acquainted with the facilities of Western life, with drainage and medical services, electricity, public transport, cinemas and newspapers and trade unions. The towns are where vocal political pressures develop best and where cultural diffusion is fastest. Those of Asia contain the best and the worst of innovations from Europe and America, often adjoining relics of an older Asian society and older cultural practices. Much conspicuous consumption goes on, of goods like those anywhere in the West, sometimes imported, sometimes locally imitated. Great blocks of flats, cars, dresses, foods, refrigerators, and air-conditioners exist together in streets where bullock carts ply, houses are of wood and thatch, women may go veiled, and where there are Oriental slums, more diseased, congested and poverty stricken than any now left in Europe or North America. The towns, expanding fast as they receive new populations unabsorbable in the countryside, are thus a kaleidoscope of variety and intermixture over a wide range of distance and time, East meeting West and old meeting new, with the net effect of confusing or obliterating traditional loyalties and ties, stimulating needs, provoking tensions of dissatisfaction about wide differences in level of living, as well as fostering endless party groupings to bring about yet further political change.

Many national treasuries are near-bankrupt. It is not merely a consequence of the inherent poverty of resource: it arises from the disconfidence normal to times of speedy change without domestic cohesion and to fear of expropriation. War and revolution share the responsibilities everywhere, together with over-spending in the exuberance of first independence. In most countries there have been currency changes which make uniform evaluation of economic data difficult, and in some countries, official controls lead to great margins between governmental and "black market" exchange rates.

DISINTEGRATING AND UNIFYING INFLUENCES

There are thus many cross-pulls in the political units. Administrative colonisation worked to unify into the new boundaries places which had often not previously been politically incorporated and have linguistic, racial and economic distinctiveness even now. After the colonial administrations departed, separatist tendencies appeared, the break of Burma and Pakistan from India and away from the pattern (of unifying all three) attempted by the British administration is the extreme example; French Indochina broke into the separate countries of Cambodia, Laos, North and South Vietnams, and Taiwan separated from China as well as from Japan. Inside several Asian states there are regionalist tensions—as between the two parts of Pakistan, between the Ganges Valley and South India, between Luzon and Mindanao, and between the Outer Islands and Java. Further internal strains arise from plural societies due to undigested migrations, as between indigenous Malays and their immigrant Chinese, between Siamese and their Chinese, and between local and mainland Chinese now living together on Taiwan.

Against these disintegrating effects, some unifying trends are at work. Three out of five Asians have governments which are members of the United Nations; one out of three Asians is within the British Commonwealth; ten Asian nations have received economic aid from the U.S.A., six from Russia; the form of Communism identified with the Chinese sets a racialist tie from Tibet to Manchuria and from Peking to Jakarta and has led to a more massive and extensive imperialist structure, albeit loosely organised, than any during the last millennium. Burma, Pakistan, India and Ceylon use different rupee currencies fixed at the same exchange rate to sterling (p. 308) and three Indochinese succession states act similarly. It is possibly inevitable that unifying tendencies will persist, by military, diplomatic or economic means, because some succession states have a smallness which weakens them in international affairs.

LANDWARD INFLUENCES

After a thirty-year absence from the scene, the Soviet Union has reappeared as a political influence in Asia where many Asians falsely think it to have taken no part in either the colonial phase or in the war against Japan. But it is not the first appearance. In the first decade of this century, the Russian Empire was pressing into Asia via the Transiberian Railway as a contender with other European countries for colonies. In Manchuria, Russians arrived too late; their administration was forestalled by the large-scale Chinese settlement and their power in Eastern Asia was eclipsed when their navy was summarily sunk by the Japanese in 1905. In its period of overland colonial probing, Russia continually provoked the land-hungry, militant hill tribes on the Northwest Frontier of India. In area, Russia is the largest European power still colonising in Asia, and its resumed imperialist pressures are in much the same places as before—but more intensive and more significant. Russia now has powerful new industrial centres in Central Asia (round Kuznets and in Kazakhstan), where nuclear weapons and rocket projectiles are developed and tried out; the arid wastes which are so generally the border zones of Russia may now be quickly traversed by planes and their "buffer" value is almost lost; the extension and duplication of major railways ties the margins of Monsoon Asia more strongly to Russian industrial centres, providing trade and communication lines not only between Central Asia and Vladivostok, Manchuria and Peking but also southward, where new lines reach to the border of Turkmen and Uzbek, within 250 miles of West Pakistan's railway terminus. Russian political influence is now felt more strongly because education and modern communications make it possible to contact Asian minorities from a distance. The radio and the newspaper can readily exacerbate the cross currents of feeling within the Asian countries, where poverty places all governments in dilemmas and where there is already the domestic weakness of many languages and religions, new constitutions and the heritage of regionalism, revolution and guerrilla war. Russia is now beginning to supply capital equipment for Asia, a trickle of which moves into China and India, though the continued difficulties of landward access must be recurringly restictive.

This political pressure upon the Asians from overland can be exaggerated. For practical and economic reasons, Asian countries will continue to have strong and numerous economic and political ties with Europe and America, contact and trade with which continue to be massive if only because they produce plenty of what Asians want now. Large-scale regular shipping is still the most efficient way of moving what Asia needs and what it can supply in return. The Asian countries are also traversed by the world's major airlines, moving quickly and regularly to Europe, America and Australia; there is no comparable movement within Central Asia. Europe, America and Australia have access to the regional radio sets, newspapers and cinemas, and can likewise exert influence at a distance.

They can induce greater effects with these means, owing to the educational links at institutions within the region where English is a common medium for teaching. Asian politicians have largely been educated in Western style, and inherited the Western form of governing authority which they understand better than those from Central Asia. Having campaigned against Western colonies, these politicians appear opposed to European and American practice and outlook more than is really the case. At the moment their political and economic policies are geared to European and American nations, which are still their chief suppliers and chief customers.

ASIA IN THE NUCLEAR AGE

Today the Asian nations must be appraised by a new standard of political strength—nuclear power, atomic weapons and rocket missiles. While scientific and technical education exists in most Asian countries, so far only Japan has anything approaching the technical, industrial and financial capacity for establishing nuclear industries, whether for peaceful or military purposes. None of the Asian nations has added an idea to aviation or is producing modern aircraft in quantity. Their commercial and military equipment is invented and made elsewhere. At the same time these countries are great potential users of nuclear generators of electricity because so many lack other power resources. Asians have expressed a moral attitude to atomic power stemming from the fact that the first atomic bombs were launched against Japan. How longlasting that attitude will be depends on whether it is a defensive pose against the thought that the Western World continues to be technically further advanced than Asia. Most Asian countries now have the major weakness of lacking the means of ordinary armament production; in one sense that ceases to be a drawback if the development of nuclear weapons invalidates any kind of defence. The Asian nations are all weak in the face of rocket missiles and nuclear weapons, yet that high proportion of people in the widely dispersed, self-contained farm economy could prove a factor for survival in a world war of atom bombs in which the urbanised Western powers might end with their cities and their machinery of organisation wiped out, leaving the Asians of the "pocket handkerchief" farms as the dominant surviving group. It is right to recall that, notwithstanding Asia's demonstrable weakness politically, militarily and economically, its people form a greater proportion of the world population than was the case at the time of inventing the steam engine and it is always possible for them to buy, borrow, beg or assemble atomic bombs, nuclear warheads and all the missiles.

CHAPTER TWENTY-SIX

Political Geography of Asian States—1

WE WILL NOW consider the power of Asian states, with special attention
to the balance of their parts, their domestic unity, their potential and their
border conditions. Table 14 gives critical data for each state, and Fig. 98
demonstrates their proportions in population and productivity.

CHINA

As a country, China of the Mainland ("The People's Republic of China")
has the North China and Yangtse Plains with the longstanding outlying
settlements of Szechuan and Canton, as its core zone, densely peopled, massively productive agriculturally yet without surplus. Surrounding this
concentration of people and resources, are extensive hilly or mountainous
and semi-arid areas extending thousands of miles into Central Asia, parts
of which are irregularly or sparsely settled and irregularly developed,
screening the core zone from landward approaches and restrictive but not
prohibitive to landward extension, of settlement and cultivation This more
difficult "Outer China" has been persistently colonised by Chinese, sometimes briefly, sometimes only in small patches. The colonisation of that
part of the screen which is now the Manchurian Plain early this century
was speedy and spectacularly successful: a flood of Chinese farming
immigrants overwhelmed the Manchu nomadic tribes which had from
there harassed the North China Plain for centuries; the Chinese settled on
land, which proved more fertile than elsewhere in Northeast Siberia.
China has more recently undertaken administrative colonisation by
extending into Tibet, Inner Mongolia and Sinkiang, where their suzerainty
had been intermittent. These inner Asian colonies are of the type normally
thought of as Western; Chinese officials there control and police people
who neither by speech, culture nor economy resemble metropolitan
Chinese. Postwar expansion of this type has given China a boundary with
India in the Himalayas and with West Pakistan and Afghanistan in the
Pamirs.

The great colonial screen round China Proper (the original twenty-two

331

TABLE 14

DEMOGRAPHIC FACTS OF NATIONAL POWER

	Area (thou. sq. miles)	Arable Area (% of total surface)	Population (mill., 1959)	Population increase % since 1937	Density (persons per sq. mile)	Nutritional density (persons per cult. acre)	Gross domestic product, 1959 (U.S. $ per capita)
Chinese Mainland (1957) . .	2,450	11	660	44	273	3·1	63
Korea, South .	41	24	23	53	575	5·5	54
Taiwan . .	15	10	10·2	85	704	3·1	98
Hong Kong . .	0·4	1	2·9	150	6,615	1,130	269
Japan . . .	154	16	93	32	621	6·8	334
Vietnam, South .	129	9	13	49	22	5·1	132
Laos . . .	96	2	1·7	53	17	7·1	33
Cambodia . .	71	12	4·9	61	69	2·1	71
Philippines . .	121	26	25	60	196	1·4	216
Thailand . .	206	10	22	51	104	2·1	99
Fed. of Malaya— Singapore . .	53	15	8·3	75	158	1·8	305
Northern Borneo	32	2	1·2	45	14	1·4	300
Indonesia . .	612	6	90	34	146	3·4	26
Burma . .	272	12	21	31	78	1·1	53
Ceylon . .	24	18	9·6	69	396	3·2	126
India . . .	1,210	38	403	32	333	1·7	57
Pakistan . .	391	23	87	30	221	1·7	50

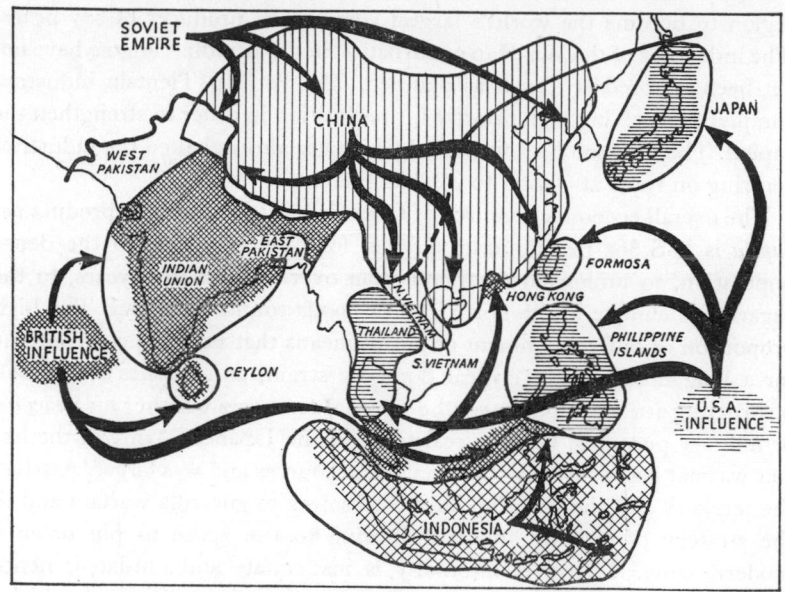

FIG. 100—Political influences in Monsoon Asia (1958)

provinces) has repeatedly fallen from Chinese control in the past, some-times under virtually independent war lords or regional dictators exploiting the isolation from the central government in Peking or Nanking. The advent of radio and the aeroplane has reduced the regional isolation, yet there is so far little more economic interlocking with the core zone by trade and by transport than was the case several centuries ago. Outer China has terrains physically suiting road and railway development, and Russian aid is being used to evaluate its economic minerals but the landward colonial screen suffers from aridity, high relief, extremes of heat and cold and the long-standing cultural conflict between the horse and the plough, the nomad and the oasis. While capital works, transport and mining might transform the Outer China economy quickly, Sinkiang and Tibet consti-tute protective screens also for Russian Siberia where there are nuclear testing grounds. The low-potential of the vast skirt round China holds only slight prospect for relieving the core area, where the majority of Chinese live and where domestic problems are serious.

China's heavy industries are chiefly round the Manchurian coalfields, a heritage of Japanese colonisation there. The Japanese also greatly extended Manchurian rice growing (despite the short summer), and caused the region to become the world's largest commercial producer of soy beans. The industries of the Wu-Han conurbation in the Middle Yangtse have not yet been restored at Tayeh as planned. The Peiping–Tientsin industrial complex is receiving high priority for restoration in order to strengthen the capital. The Bamboo Curtain round China has almost halted the industries centring on trade at coastal towns like Shanghai.

The overall economic resource of China is low (the domestic product *per capita* is U.S.$65 per annum, half that for Ceylon) owing to the dense population, to prolonged disorganisation over the last fifty years, to the vagaries of climate to the north and of floods round the Hwai. The high proportion of self-containment on farms means that isolation can continue for a long time without critical domestic strain, and implies a tradition obstructing attempts to harness the national resources whether for peaceful or military purposes. Chinese resistance to the Japanese Army in the last war was not based on using their natural resources and was largely passive; the territory and the tradition lend themselves to guerrilla warfare and to the strategy of evading and withdrawing to use space to pin down a modern army. Transport internally is inadequate and outdated, hence much effort is now going into it; railways and roads are few and vehicles scarce. The waterways are unmodernised and less useful today than they were centuries back, a consequence of silting, broken banks and little organised maintenance. Weakening the national cohesion is the presence of large groups in the skirting zones to the south, west and northeast who do not speak standard Chinese. Communication is further impeded by high rates of illiteracy which the present government hopes to overcome by the radical solution of romanising the old character-language which has always taken so long to learn. Regionalism finds expression in the tradition of opposition and resistance to central government controls, whether at Peking, the eccentric capital created by Genghis Khan, or at Nanking, the more central capital set up by the first republican government. China's success in the Korean War (1950–2) was incidental, the powers really engaged being Russia, supplying and reinforcing the Chinese, and the U.S.A. supplying and enforcing a policy of the United Nations.

The sprawl of China works against cohesion, and its political potential is the less for the absence of modern internal links between its regions. A major natural facility is the hundreds of miles of complex waterways along the Yangtse and through part of the North China Plain.

Ties and links across the landward boundaries of China are slight, chief being the lines across Manchuria leading to the Transiberian Railway. The movement of aeroplanes across the negative border belts between

China and Russia is slight compared with comparable flows between the rest of Asia and the rest of the world. The Amur River is the China–Russia boundary for a considerable distance, and its valley is one of convergence rather than separation. On the Siberian side, the Amur is paralleled by the Transiberian Railway and by roads; on the Manchurian side the transport network is more open and transverse to the line of the river. Migration across the Amur has so far always been more from the Siberian side and contrary to the dominant pressure of populations.

Migration of Chinese overland towards the southwest, to Yunnan and Tonkin, has gone on for centuries, though rarely leading to military situations; so that the ways through the forested mountains of the border country to Burma and Thailand and the hills of North Vietnam must be thought of as pressure zones even though no major transport or economic facilities exist there—apart from the old French Kunming–Hanoi Railway which while never a commercial success, underlines the closer link between Yunnan and Vietnam than between Yunnan and China Proper.

China is the greatest colonial power in the Asian World in yet another respect. Millions of Chinese from the core zone have moved overseas to the "island palisade", to Taiwan, to Continental and Insular Southeast Asia where now live 12 to 15 million South Chinese migrants in all stages of becoming domiciled. They have migrated to the Pacific islands and to the Americas. They have there evolved a way of life which leaves them dominating trading activities in many of the receiving countries. They form large majorities in foreign towns, and in Malaya and Thailand are so numerous as to create plural societies. This pattern, developed in the last seventy-five years, forms an overseas colonial screen to the Chinese mainland, and provides a means to undermine indigenous non-Chinese governments. The overseas Chinese are Cantonese, Hokkien and Hakka; they do not use standard Chinese as their mother-tongue, and are often educated in non-Chinese languages so that they are almost as divided among themselves as the Chinese of the mainland. Like all expatriates, they often look to China as their homeland, which most of them have not seen for many years, if ever, with that nostalgia which gives them nationalist feeling running counter to the nationalisms of the countries where they now live, an embarrassing situation for the governments of Malaya, Thailand, Indonesia and the Philippines.

Militarily China's assets consist of enormous manpower, much dispensable space and the "aid from a distance" represented by the large influential overseas groups. In some ways China is an agricultural slum, with the inheritance of social and rural difficulties arising from a hundred years of administrative disintegration and revolution. It has little industrial development in proportion to its needs and size, and has negligible armaments production. It has no navy. It depends on allies for aircraft and weapons. Its offensive power is small unless drawing upon the productive capacity of Russia, Japan or U.S.A. In defence its farming community can remain undisturbed even if blockaded or deprived of transport, but its lightly built, congested cities are readily vulnerable from the air. Its industrial installations, located mostly to the north, are at once eccentric to the core zone and accessible to foreign attack.

KOREA

North and South Korea are separate states which, following an international war (1950–2) which was partly a civil one and partly a continuation of the Second World War, succeeded Japan's oldest mainland colony covering the whole of the peninsula.

North Korea is a satellite of China and Russia which, to create a "buffer state", maintain its internal economy, now considerably unbalanced by being separate from what had been the complementary food-producing region of South Korea. The boundary at the 38th Parallel runs athwart the transport lines which once handled the exchange between the industrial north and the food-producing south; it marks no major linguistic or historic border.

North Korea has the junction-town of Pyongyang as its capital, located central to the western belt of mineral production and industrial population, and orientated towards Antung and Manchuria, to which it is linked by road and railway. Extensive unpeopled forested mountains separate the west from the Hamyong district to the east, where there is an electrified industrial development for textiles and light goods, orientated towards Vladivostok and having the advantage over that Russian port of being always ice-free.

South Korea, containing the densest and largest population on the peninsula, was an intensive rice-growing region fostered by a colonial administration primarily to supply metropolitan Japan. It resembles in many ways the Japan of the Inland Sea in its small landscapes of double-cropping for wet rice, and it also has some industrial development, cotton textiles now being prominent. One of its chief foci has always been Pusan, the harbour nearest Japan, once much used as ferry port for travelling overland between Japan and Manchuria. Today its political capital is Seoul (Kyongsong), an historic capital close to the new border where tension persists. Because continuous farming and settlement is to the west and round some southern bays, centrifugal influences operate, aggravated by the opposing interests of Pusan and Seoul. The small territory, bursting with long-standing land problems and no longer well balanced economically in relation to neighbouring territories, faces the instability of being a buffer state to Communism on the north and of resisting renewed association with Japan, its traditional market and nearest non-Communist neighbour. That it was the stage for a China–Russia war against the United Nations in 1950 indicates the political implications of its position and its weakness of being unable to provide even defensive military strength from within. Continued interest in this agricultural region by the Japanese appears inevitable owing to the internal food difficulties of Japan and to the fact that South Korea and South Japan are in many ways analogous.

JAPAN

Differing from other Asian countries by never having been colonially associated with any Western nation, not even having permitted them treaty ports, Japan has been occupied from outside only following defeat in 1945. Until then, indeed, Japan had become one of the powers colonising Asia, and consists today of the island-group which acted as metropolis of its short-lived but extensive overseas empire. It possessed Taiwan from 1895, Korea from 1905 and Manchuria from 1932; it acquired a great sprawl of West Pacific islands during the First World War, occupied the core zone of China by 1938, and extended to the Indian and Australian borders by 1942, when its forces occupied all eastern and southeastern Asia except for Yunnan and Szechuan. Japan's naval-mindedness is unique in Asia, a reflection of its island setting.

By far the most industrialised Asian state even though it resisted contact with the West until 1854, it has factory installations comparable to those of Britain without having permitted its agriculture to lag. Its food resources are large, intensively produced in a manner more horticultural than agricultural, well-organised and scientifically and economically efficient, its rice yield ranking highest in Asia. The strain of its very dense population on a mountainous territory only 16% of which is level enough for cultivation, formed part of the background of its expansionist phase and constitutes a major imbalance now that so many Japanese have been repatriated. It is still developing Hokkaido, the least-settled and least-farmed of the main islands, where a long, harsh winter sets limits to intensifying the farming. American postwar aid has facilitated speedy recon-

MONSOON ASIA

struction on most modern lines of its domestic industries, which were severely bombed despite the protective screen of broad oceans. No longer carrying its burdens of heavy military and naval expenditure, Japan has a high national productivity (over three times higher *per capita* than India), and ranks as the chief manufacturing and trading country in Asia, as well as the only one comparable to the industrialised states of Europe and North America.

The core zone for both its industrial and agricultural activities is to the south from the plain round Tokyo westwards and round the Inland Sea as far as the coal mines and heavy industries of Kyushu. Here are six major industrial cities of over a million people each. Half the population of Japan is urban. Well-knit by close railway networks on each island and by highly organised coastal shipping, its parts have interlocking economies arising from a fully commercialised agriculture, much inter-regional and inter-island trade and a close relation between rural and industrial areas. These features make Japan the Asian state of greatest cohesion, modernised in its processes of farming, industry and trade, but maintaining traditional discipline. Its people are homogeneous, accessible to one another, highly literate, educated more than other Asian nations and socially minded. Its nationalism resembles that of European nations, and the continuity of the emperor through the social and political changes of the postwar period signally marks the identification of the Japanese with their state. Far from self-contained, the country generates an inflow of raw materials and an outflow of processed goods, as in the case of Britain. The development of trade unionism and a democratic constitution has to a large extent eliminated its old asset of very cheap labour, so that its costs of production are high and it has to compete on comparable terms in this respect with manufacturing rivals elsewhere. Japan's spectacular recovery from a war which was most destructive to its wood-built towns and light factory installations as well as to its sphere of interest, indicates its vitality as a state. Its ability to challenge successfully for several years the combined industrial and military power of Britain and the U.S.A. demonstrates its strength and its capacity for producing its own war equipment if need be and the capital equipment for industry. At the same time, the defeat evidences its vulnerability when over extending its resources spatially and in alliance with Asian nations less well-knit politically and economically than itself. Japan can withstand isolation to some extent because its farming system is still most varied and productive, but its huge urban industries are no more nationally self-contained than those of Britain.

The population densities of Japan are exceptionally high (608 per square

338

mile), and the density per cultivated acre (6·7) is the highest in Asia. These facts constitute a national incentive to develop overseas outlets for trade and people. The possibility of a spillover of Japanese to other parts of Asia is always present, the only emigration outlet at the moment being South America, whither a continuous trickle of Japanese is moving. On the other hand, even at the height of their imperialist expansion Japanese were reluctant to move overseas in numbers large enough to make any difference at home.

Japan has no serious boundary conditions, not least because its limits are new and maritime. Close enough to the mainland to be vulnerable to continental attacks, basis for its long-standing suspicion of Russia, its core zone is more open to the Pacific than to the mainland, for attack and for supply. Japan's natural resources are not geared to military and naval objectives, but its potential in this respect has been proven and we cannot doubt its ability to respond quickly, effectively and intelligently to challenging conditions. Its ties postwar have been militarily, politically and economically with U.S.A., and more recently, as supplier of manufactured goods and equipment to South and Southeast Asia. Its proximity to the Chinese Mainland must attract its industrialists consistently to the raw materials and market there, the present obstacle being a political one which can quickly change. The modern position in this respect repeats a long standing pattern. The difficulties of government to government trade with China are reinforced by the growing rivalry between industries in Manchuria and Japan, and Japanese resentment at the loss of their Manchurian installations. Because Japanese lean heavily on their fishing industry for protein food, they are attracted to the coastal fisheries off Eastern Siberia, so much closer to the Asian markets than to the main Russian concentrations several thousand miles inland. Russo-Japanese competition for the fisheries could become intense here and also in Sakhalin, which has a producing oilfield originally developed by the Japanese. There is a tradition of at least fifty years of Russo-Japanese friction in Northeast Asia.

For the time being Japan has no armament of any size. It has the equipment and ability to produce them and can revive the power its navy had in 1942. Its defence from mainland pressure at the moment turns on Okinawa, a large island between Kyushu and Taiwan, now exclusively a U.S.A. base and dependent on trans-Pacific supplies, unable even to supply itself with food. On this island an irridentist movement could develop.

While Japan is the only Asian state with enough science and technology to be a possible maker of nuclear bombs and rockets, it was the only territory to experience atomic bombing, and its public has an intense moralist attitude to those devices. Its need for fission power turns on considerations of declining coal resources, particularly now that Japan has no access to the coal of Manchuria which was a vital part of its prewar economy.

TAIWAN

Intensively developed by the Japanese for fifty years until 1945, yet still three-quarters forested, Taiwan has a government which was that of the "National Republic of China" until the "People's Republic" took over Mainland China. It is a succession state to the Japanese, rump of the Nationalist Republic and separate from China, whence most of its people derive. Two elements are present in the Chinese population; the Nationalist Government and the refugees, military and civilian who came with it, largely from Central and North China; descendants of those Hokkien and Cantonese farmers who settled in West Taiwan before or during the Japanese Occupation. Since the hill tribes are small, the long standing Hokkiens and Cantonese are in practice the indigenes, now administered by newcomer refugee Chinese. Internal tension on this score has shown from time to time.

In 1945 the outflow of rice and sugar from the island ceased to go to Japan, which had developed the economy to that pattern. Sugar has resumed movement towards Japan. The presence of a Chinese army and of refugee entrepreneurs from Shanghai and Canton has stimulated Taiwan industry, which now produces fuel and steel but not enough for a modern army, depending for this on external supply. The island now has a greater national population density than Japan, and its population per cultivated acre is as great as in China, so that the rice surplus has greatly diminished.

The core zone is the western agricultural plain, which has many small towns well linked by railway and road lines The eastern mountains are little developed. Taipeh (the Japanese Taihoku), the capital, is located to the far north, more significant for its air base than as a port owing to its inland location on a silting river. It has sea and air connections with Hong Kong, Manila and Honshu.

In a sense the island is besieged by the Mainland, but neither Chinese governments have large naval forces, so that the Taiwan Strait acts as a moat and is little used by international shipping. Local friction arises from Taiwan claims to a few islands close to the Fukien coast. The present stalemate situation could continue for some time, because as a separate self-governing state Taiwan has a political strength probably greater than Malaya or Ceylon. The national trade ties are largely with Asian countries, except that half its imports are from U.S.A., consisting largely of fuels and heavy equipment for the new industries and armed forces. Taipeh is part of the entrepôt of Hong Kong, which is used in common by Taiwan and China.

PHILIPPINES

The Philippines, a succession state to the U.S.A. colonial administration, still shows a cultural distinctiveness derived from the Spanish, whose colonial administration ended in 1898. Unique as a catholic state in Asia, the Philippines has Spanish place-names in Luzon, the core area of this archipelago state. On that island production and population are greatest, compacted on the plains round Manila, a capital created by the Spaniards. Another densely peopled and productive zone is the Visayan island group between Luzon and Mindanao, focusing locally on Cebu. Mindanao is thinly peopled by Muslims and little developed, resembles Borneo rather than Luzon and is only loosely knit into the national economy. Luzon is the main food-producing island, and Manila functions as entrepôt for the islands—supplying them with rice and handling the sugar, copra and tobacco which they export to U.S.A. Producing considerable gold, iron and chrome ore, the islands are themselves without fuel resources and have little manufacturing part from a few cotton factories. The military potential of the state is therefore slight. Isolated by distance from the Asian mainland, its present trading and political links are away from Asia and across the Pacific; base facilities are still maintained there by U.S.A. Ranking fourth highest in Asia in domestic production *per capita*, the Philippines sprawl over considerable distances which operate against concentration of interests. Several economies and languages exist yet do not give rise to significant regionalism, probably because its inter-island shipping and exchange are better organised than in Indonesia, for example. Postwar Hukbalahup guerrilla activities made use of the communication awkwardnesses and the considerable forested hills yet did not indicate separatist or racial differences so much as a political tradition recalling the South American republics. Luzon inherits agrarian problems from the Spanish form of land use, which no longer suits the dense populations of today. The Muslim minority in the south has not for years caused domestic strain. South Chinese have immigrated into Luzon over many years and form an influential minority in trading centres. Although some have been there

341

long enough to become almost Filipinos, the Chinese group is resented for its economic power, and further immigration from China is forbidden. Until 1945, Japanese settlers were present in the towns and round Davao where they ran the hemp industry. Relations with Japan have been uneasy since the war, and Japanese manufactures are locally seen as a threat to Filipino efforts to establish factories.

The Philippines boundaries are all maritime. No boundary tension exists with North Borneo, Indonesia or Taiwan, its nearest neighbours. Without either military or naval strength of its own, Luzon is so placed that its potential as a base must be involved in crises occurring on Taiwan and China, or China and U.S.A.

*   *   *

Burma, Thailand and the Indochinese countries resemble their insular neighbours in political lay-out. They have core zones which are continuously farmed, closely settled, reasonably well knit by light boats on streams and canals and linked to the rest of the world by transport and commerce. Each also has round its core a "screen of forested space", thinly peopled, farmed only in irregular patches, scattered among forested mountains and economically negative, having little transport connection within themselves, with their core zone or with international trade. These outer or skirting zones have less than 3% of their surfaces cultivated, so that local tribes and groups maintain a way of life as isolated as any on the tiny islands of Indonesia. Movement by modern transport through the skirting zone is overwhelmingly difficult, as was demonstrated in the Second World War when attempting to move supplies through Burma to Yunnan and through Assam to Upper Burma. On the other hand, to aeroplanes as well as to groups able to live on the land, these spaces are wide open and have two-way possibilities, like the sea which can link or isolate island communities. Boundaries set in the skirting zones have only the physical awkwardness to prevent movement across them, and have little military defence. Thus the core zones of Burma, Thailand and Vietnam are like islands set within a space where any group may pass; the space is physically at once ideal for guerrillas and illegal immigrants, and an insuperable obstacle for a modern army. The outer zones are both vulnerable and strong; they can facilitate a guerrilla approach to the boundaries and to the core zones; they can prevent an army moving to defend or to attack.

THAILAND (SIAM)[1]

Thailand retained its independent monarchy through the period of European colonisation, less by demonstrating its own strength and more by conveniently insulating the rival interests of the French in Indochina and the British in Burma and Malaya. What was left to Thailand of its historic domains was fairly homogeneous, fringe groups having been largely absorbed into the surrounding colonies. Hence Thailand is more cohesive as a state than most of the other states around it, and domestic regionalism is not characteristic. Its core zone is the aggradational plain of the Lower Chao Praya roughly below Nakorn Sawan and focusing on Bangkok, the eccentrically placed capital which is the only modern and significantly commercial town in the state. On that plain rice is produced by a fairly evenly distributed population in padi-fields which extend continuously over large areas, working a simple one-crop economy and linked by shallow waterways of distributaries and man-made drainage canals. The rest of the country is thinly peopled and patchily cultivated amid large empty areas of forest and bush.

Its northern border runs across the ends of the East Tibetan ranges, where Shans and other hill peoples live in isolation; local people freely move across the Burma–Thai border, but the only trans-border commerce is along a pony caravan route, focusing on Cheng Mai, a fortified hill town and end of the railway line from Bangkok. Both sides of this northern border are worked for teak, which floats south by streams in the wet season. Otherwise the economy both sides of the border is negative. The Mekong River from Pak Ta to Chieng Kan became the Thai–Laos border in the Second World War, and then restored to its present Dai Laung watershed position. East of Korat, the Mekong is the boundary running lengthwise round Eastern Thailand. Although traffic along it is small and seasonal, the Mekong acts as a line of local convergence from both sides. The poor savannah plateau of Korat tilts towards the Mekong border; river transport around Korat is negligible, and roads and two railways link it firmly to Bangkok so that little moves towards the Mekong margin. The western Thai border runs along the steep, thickly forested watershed of the skew ranges of Kra. Several tracks cross it, the important one being along the Upper Kwe Noi valley, which provided an historic invasion route between Bangkok and Moulmein. This is not a boundary of tension today;

[1] The government has in the last twenty years alternated the official name between "Thailand" and "Siam".

the culture and economies either side are similar. Far to the south the Malay–Thai border lies on similar watersheds, well south of the linguistic and religious divide. From South Kra rubber and tin flows across the southern boundary, which is linked by railway and coastwise shipping to Malayan ports. Several thousand Siamese Muslims move south into Malaya each padi harvest. Kra contains considerable numbers of Chinese, who dominate tin and rubber production.

The southeastern border with Cambodia has little economic movement across it, yet it is a boundary of dispute; with Japanese help, it was pressed back as far as Tonle Sap for several years. The railway from Bangkok is discontinuous and ends near the border.

Thailand has laid out transport in a way intended to induce national cohesion and defend it. The railways north to Cheng Mai, northeast to Vientiane and Ubon across Korat, east towards Cambodia and south through Kra to Penang and Singapore, supported by feeder roads, make for strong national ties. Further cohesion comes from the Buddhist practice of requiring young men to stay for a year or so in a monastery for education in the tradition. The armed forces are elaborate, even though entirely dependent on outside equipment (the country has no heavy industry), and also makes for integration. Thai concern about Chinese pressure from the north is long-standing and not the result of recent developments in China, with which Thailand does not share any border. Political efforts to control the large Chinese population has been sustained, firmly pressing them to naturalise and reduce their identification with China. Though the official estimate of their number has been given as 3 million, these Chinese could be appearing more Thai than they actually are. Chinese are still prominent in trade and commerce, but are increasingly Thai-educated.

Thailand has received much postwar aid from outside, and Bangkok has become the headquarters of an economic arm of the United Nations. The state plays a major international role, due to its seniority as an independency and its position as the main rice-exporting country. Its economic strength could become an attraction to other Asian countries, but the national cohesion has been such that the territory has escaped internal guerrilla war such as has plagued the countries round it since 1946. Its political life centres on Bangkok; the occasional *coup d'etat* marks the inflexibility of its electoral system rather than instability in the country.

BURMA

No longer connected with the British Commonwealth, Burma derives its boundaries from the earlier British administration, which extended the state to an area never unified by Burmese kings. Its core zone is the spindle-shaped agricultural zone from Mandalay (capital of the old Burmese kings) along the Irrawaddy to the Delta, with an offshoot into the Sittang Valley. In the core zone is a high degree of homogeneity in speech and culture, Buddhism and the early kingdoms of Mandalay and Pegu being the foundation of the modern nationalist concept. To this uniformity the light but extensive boat transport on the Lower Irrawaddy and the Sittang contribute. North and west of the core rise densely forested mountains forming the Arakan divide, thinly peopled by scattered clans differing in speech, religion and way of life from the valley people; some came overland from Eastern Tibet, others from Assam. No migration of modern Indians has come across the Arakan watershed despite the possibilities suggested by the Ledo Road from Upper Assam, which was built for military operations from India against the Japanese in Burma during the Second World War. The million or so Indians who were in Burma until 1941 had come by sea from Madras and Bengal early this century while Burma was administered from India, and predominated as traders and artisans. About half of these retreated with great losses overland to India in 1941. The Indians ran Burma's railway and river-boats, and they were considered by the Burmese to be a serious domestic problem when they became rural landlords and moneylenders. East of the core zone and extending beyond the lonely Salween Valley are the several large clans forming the rural community of Shans, different from both Burmese and Arakan hill people and culturally related to Thais. Their small farms of rice, tea and fruit are scattered irregularly through the highlands each side of the Thai border, which is no cultural divide. North from here the Burmese boundary is contiguous with Yunnan, the southwesternmost province of China, whence from time to time Chinese have tended to drift into Burma. Here runs what is left of the Lashio–Kunming Road, which before 1941 was the supply route for the Chinese Nationalist Republic besieged there. Of Southeast Asian countries, Burma has the longest boundary with China. Large colonies of Chinese are settled in Rangoon; they came by sea but could be of subversive value to support an infiltration from Yunnan. The eastern boundary extends south from the Shan Highlands roughly along a watershed separating the narrow Burmese provinces of Tennasserim and Moulmein from the Thai coast of the Upper Kra Peninsula; the cultural differences either side are slight, but there is a history of national pressure here. The skew valley of Kwe Noi was used by historic armies of Thailand and Burma and by the Japanese army, but it has no road or railway and no trade movement—the economies each side are competitive rather than complementary.

Burma has no land boundaries which cross active routes of goods or people. Greatest strain is at the Shan–Yunnan border, where Chinese pressure has been increasing and where it is alleged demarcation was never agreed.

While Burma's population is not large, there is considerable regionalism because localities are not firmly linked together either by education or by trade except along the Irrawaddy: Buddhism is however a strong common bond. In the Pegu Yoma and along the Sittang is the substantial Karen group, mostly Christianised and speaking a distinctive language; they have shown vitality and unity among themselves in sustaining armed resistance against the first independent Burmese governments in Rangoon, the capital which is eccentric to the country as a whole. Inevitably exploited by Communists, the restlessness of Karens and others who resist Rangoon underlines the loose association of clan-organised people in this large territory which was never previously united. Another distinctive group is the non-Burmese "Arakanese Muslim" population settled round the port of Akyab, which is not only remote from Rangoon but also has close trade and religious associations with Bengal and East Pakistan.

Thus, while seemingly simple in form, Burma is far from cohesive, the language troubles being worsened by limited trade, low level of economy and poor inter-regional communications. Industry is almost non-existent. The life is largely rural, based on rice growing, the export of which has become the sole basis of the national economy. Its food export and its position bring Burma into contact with rice-deficient India, yet there is a heritage of resentment against Indians who settled in the country under the British administration.

Political pressure from Burma is inconceivable in its depressed domestic condition, which could continue at the present low level for a long period of time without causing a crisis at home or abroad. The country lies off critical lines of trade developments; less shipping uses Burmese ports than those of any other Asian country. However, there are still potential rice-lands in Burma which could become attractive to Indian or Chinese governments whose food position is weak and whose capacity to pioneer for rice has been demonstrated. Militarily the Burmese from their own resources could not resist penetrating actions by either Indians or Chinese and the country could once again become the battle-ground between East Asians and Southern Asians.

VIETNAM

Although a postwar constitution was agreed for an independent Vietnam stretching from the Red River Delta to the Mekong Delta, the elongated territory quickly divided at about 17° N. The older Tonkin principality became a separate northern unit, the North Vietnam Republic, a satellite of China which had provided military support to the Red River Delta guerrilla forces. Since partition the lack of cohesion even in the north shows further by subdivision into "autonomies" of Thai–Miao hill clans to the southwest (resembling the clans of Laos and Thailand) and the Tho–Nan clans to the northeast (related to hill clans in South China). The coalfield of Along is slowly reopening for export to South China. External trade associations have diminished, reflecting the closed economy of the delta and the domestic preoccupation with longstanding agrarian problems and a population still increasing while the practical limit of delta farming has been reached.

The Republic of South Vietnam includes the coastal belt east of the Annam Mountains and the outer lobes of the Mekong Delta. Consisting of the old provinces of Cochinchina and Annam, it was settled during the French period by millions of Tonkinese migrants (also called Annamites) from the Red River. Further migration southward took place when the partition began to crystallise. Pioneering and immigration are thus a feature of the south which continues to be the most commercialised Indochinese state. Saigon, once capital of all Indochina, is now the capital of South Vietnam and the chief exporting centre, although its flow of rice has greatly decreased due to greater internal consumption, loss of hinterland and weakening of organisation.

The boundary between the two Vietnams at the 17th Parallel is crossed by road and railway lines constructed by the French to weld north to south yet never inducing great trade movement. Separatism had been showing earlier, the old kingdom of Tonkin having great density and long history, the south being newer and consisting of people with less roots and local identification. In religion, speech and domestic customs there is little difference between north and south except degrees of modernisation and radically different constitutions. Neither parts of Vietnam retain political or economic links with France.

North Vietnam, which has about 100,000 Chinese in its population, has a long history of ties with South China and movement between the two is less difficult than movement to the south or to the interior. The similarity of economies has inhibited trade exchanges with China. The peoples scattered from the Red River to the Si-kiang have much in common racially, linguistically, religiously and economically—more so than South Chinese have with the core area of their own state.

South Vietnam, while still probably the wealthiest of the Indochinese states, is weakened by the boundary separating it fiscally from the rice trade of Cambodia. It has about a million Chinese in its urban and commerical life. While cohesion within South Vietnam is slight, its people differ in language, history and religion from the Cambodians further inland. Since the distributaries of the Mekong are the only trade routes out of Cambodia, the northwestern border is open and weak, subject not only to economic pressure but also to a racial pressure by Vietnamese drifting towards Cambodia and by Cambodians claiming historic rights to the whole Mekong Delta.

Saigon, while roughly central to South Vietnam, suffers from loss of hinterland. Its good port facilities attract to it the overseas trade for Cambodia and Laos, so that it may in practice maintain something of its original function as commercial forces for all Indochina. As an international airport, it has lost custom to Bangkok.

CAMBODIA

Created in 1954 as a constitutional monarchy, Cambodia is the modern continuation of the historic state of Khmer which, additional to its linguistic unity, provides a traditionalist background to its nationalism. Independent of France and of the succession states to its east, its widely dispersed, exclusively agricultural population includes a few non-Cambodian clans in the forested hills, some Vietnamese near the delta border, and a quarter of a million Chinese in its market towns. With large areas of available land, its farming people are scattered and cultivation is discontinuous even in the core zone round the lake Tonle Sap and along the Mekong. Inland waterways are the links for people and trade. The railway from Pnom Penh to Borey is little used: the road to Saigon carries less trade than the waterways. Pnom Penh, the capital, located where the lake joins the Mekong, is focus of native craft moving between Laos, the delta and the lake. Rice and dried fish, basis of the national economy, move along the waterways for external trade by way of Saigon. Resentment against dependence on this foreign trading centre finds expression in the plans to create a Cambodian port at Kampong Som, now a fishing village on a bay across the Cardamom Hills. A scarp boundary separates Cambodia from Korat to the north, then runs conventionally across the broad well-farmed lowland near Borey to continue as a watershed boundary in the Cardamoms. The lowland section here is disputed: Thais claim linguistic and historic basis for a boundary much farther to the east and for a few years during the Second World War shifted the line east to Tonle Sap and south to near Stung Treng on the Mekong. The boundary with South Vietnam crosses all the water routes to the sea and leaves in Cambodia those large western plains of tributaries draining into the Mekong at the confluence towns of Kratie and Stung Treng. The boundary with Laos is crossed by the Mekong and still much disputed. No modern military strength can be claimed for Cambodia, and the simple economy, largely based on monocultivation by small farmers depending on outflows through South Vietnam is precarious. The state, though characteristically inert, inherits traditional friction and economic rivalry with Thailand and with Laos, and its rice potential is an attraction to other Asian neighbours.

LAOS

Laos is more thinly peopled and lightly developed than other Asian units outside Borneo. The small kingdom centres on an isolated mountain-girt confluence at Luang Prabang far to the north, where a fan of tributaries converges from the east side of the Mekong, and extends to the south along a corridor lying immediately east of the Mekong. Cut off by difficult forested heights north and east, only caravan routes link Laos with Yunnan and North Vietnam—except for the poor road from Vientiane to the Gulf of Tonkin. Its small rice surplus moves south along the Mekong for export by way of Pnom Penh and South Vietnam. A short, difficult and entrenched section of the Mekong acts as a boundary with Burma and only one caravan route traverses it. Farther south the Mekong is at once the lifeline of Laos and its boundary with Thailand: roads and two railways linking the Thai side to Korat and Bangkok but there are no modern ties on the Laos side. Little more than a large valley-chieftancy, Laos has a population containing all the types of hill clan common in South China, Yunnan and North Thailand; the Thai type predominates in the country as a whole. The irridentist possibilities are many. Little economic or political vitality is apparent due to lack of transport and education. The state can neither defend itself nor mount actions against its neighbours. Its commercial potential is low, but politically it buffers Thailand from the Chinese communist colonies in North Vietnam and Yunnan.

CHAPTER TWENTY-SEVEN

Political Geography of Asian States—2

SINGAPORE, HONG KONG AND MACAO

As POLITICAL UNITS Singapore and Hong Kong are city-states too small to be economically self-sustaining. They are overwhelmingly Chinese by population and depend on entrepôt trade with foreign areas. Both have modern highly organised port facilities which enable them to maintain *per capita* incomes higher than anywhere in Asia. Each is untenable militarily, yet has domestic reasons for continuing distinct from the mainland; Singapore's Chinese population is divorced in outlook, language and economy from the Malay-dominated political life of the Federation; Hong Kong's Chinese are refugees from the régime on the mainland. More international in their associations than their respective mainlands, both are by shipping and airways as much tied to the industrial economies overseas as they are to neighbouring agricultural states.

Singapore, now independent, yet with somewhat less people than Hong Kong, which is still British-administered, controls no part of the mainland but depends on it for water and some garden stuffs; it could not exist without an easy economic association with the mainland. Hong Kong includes Kowloon, a portion of the mainland larger than the island itself and held on a lease which expires in 1997. The population and trade of Hong Kong bestride the strait between the island and Kowloon and it would appear impossible for the dry, unproductive, urbanised island to continue its economy if politically separated from Kowloon.

Macao remains a Portuguese colony of negligible economic and military significance. It persists as a kind of satellite to Hong Kong with which it has regular ferries and close economic contact.

FEDERATION OF MALAYA

The latest of the succession states is a federation at the southern end of the Kra Peninsula. Created in 1957 with a national economy in good order, the Federation of nine constitutional monarchies (with sultans or rajas) and two ex-colonies of Penang and Malacca, is grouped under a central government at Kuala Lumpur half-way down that western coastal plain

350

which is the national core zone. One monarch is elected by the others to head the Federation. The complexity of the constitution reflects that of the political economy.

The core zone contains the rubber, tin, rice and vegetable-oil producing districts, linked by roads and a railway continuing south to Singapore and north to Bangkok. Singapore and Penang handle the exchange of raw materials and foods which enables the Federation to achieve the highest national productivity *per capita* in Asia. Three-quarters of the surface is unused, the eastern side being little developed.

The Federation is an extreme type of plural society. Indigenous Malays, a strict Muslim community related culturally to Indonesians, form 49% of the population (1957), Chinese 38% and South Indians 10%. Malays monopolise rice-growing lands and dominate the rural areas, the administration, the police force and the army. Chinese are the artisans, shopkeepers and entrepreneurs in rubber, tin and commerce, and total three-quarters of the urban population. Indians are in the rubber plantations and the towns. Chinese guerrillas fought the British and Malay administrations for ten years before independence, and then until early 1960. The internal division is thus more pronounced than in neighbouring countries, and education has not yet operated long enough or intensively enough to establish a nationalism integrating these contrasts. The racial and cultural differences between Malays, Chinese and Indians are accentuated by their separate economic interests, so that a remarkably compartmentalised national structure exists. On the other hand, the high average income provides means and incentive for cohesion, even though the elongated form of the country works against it. Pressure on the land does not really exist, so that there is opportunity for extended development. Of the two boundaries, the northern one with Thailand is a terrain of severe physical difficulty, running over forested mountains and through swamps to the sea. Commerce moves along the railways crossing each end of the border, and serves the plantations and mines of South Thailand. Many Malay-speaking Muslims live on the Thai side of the border, and until 1909 Thailand held the three Malay states immediately south of the border, briefly resuming possession of them during the Second World War. Only a few thousand Thais live south of the boundary. The possibilities of this mountainous border are indicated by their use for access and escape by Chinese guerrillas over recent years. The Japanese military used the eastern end in Kelantan as point of attack in 1941. To the south, the boundary through the Johore Strait is crossed by a causeway carrying a great volume of trade along arterial road and railway to Singapore.

351

The military forces of the Federation are Malay-manned. The townspeople are Chinese and Indian, the guerrillas have been Chinese. The forces cannot be equipped from local industry. Its communal sectionalism and high productivity cause Malaya to be of special interest in various ways to the neighbouring governments of Thailand, China and India. Language and religion give Malays points in common with Indonesians though the cultural similarity has not led to practical ties so far. Malaya and Indonesia are rival producers of similar commodities traded to the industrial Western World and trade links between the two have been created by foreigners and largely handled by Chinese in both territories; Chinese traders in Malayan ports deal with Chinese in East Sumatra and West Kalimantan to ship produce to Europe and America and to import for retail in the local markets. Malaya has a divided interest in Singapore. Malayan Chinese traders are attracted by the practical facilities of its port and banking system; Malays are repelled by the economic and political possibilities that Singapore's Chinese could augment Chinese in the Federation to overwhelm the Malays.

Malaya's central position in Southeast Asia has value for a political power able to make use of it but the Federation does not now have the material basis for exerting such power and the risk of becoming a colony of China is clearly considerable.

INDONESIA

Succession state to both the Dutch and Japanese administrations, Indonesia assumed independence after a long guerrilla action which left it as bankrupt as postwar China. Now a unitary government, it started as a federation of the islands, recognising centrifugal tendencies arising from its parts spread across three thousand miles of sea. The archipelago had never been unified under a single government until the Dutch achieved it and they themselves only brought the whole territory under one control in 1907.

The metropolitan island is Java which is the most productive and the most populous island but only the fourth in size. Internally it has large almost unused mountain areas, mostly to the south, and a densely peopled farming belt along the north coast with extensions into valleys among the central volcanoes. Even Java is not homogeneous in speech, three major languages continuing in use. Much of Java still follows the self-contained economy, accounting in part for its resilience during social breakdowns. Hilly West Java had extensive commercial plantations for rubber, coffee, tea and cinchona. Its administrative capital varied in the postwar years between inland Jokjakarta (capital of an historic principality) and coastal Jakarta, the latter having been commercial focus and administrative capital throughout the Dutch period when it was called Batavia.

The major Outer Islands, Kalimantan (South Borneo), Sumatra, and Celebes are racially, linguistically and, on some islands, religiously different from Java. Their distance apart must be noted; Jakarta is almost 900 miles from the nearest port on Celebes, a slightly greater distance from Medan, chief commercial town of Sumatra, and 600 miles from Bandjermasin, the capital of Kalimantan. By sea, Palembang, Medan and Pontianak are nearer to Singapore than to Jakarta, and much of East Indonesia is nearer to Manila and Darwin than to Jakarta. Despite the aeroplane, the bonds between Java and the Outer Islands are weak, worsened by the present lack of shipping and by the domestic restriction on trade in petroleum, rubber and tobacco, copra and timber, which move to markets outside Indonesia. Here resentment against the old colonial administrations tends to become resentment against administration by other strangers and the basis for a claim to regional self-government as opposed to administration by the Javanese in Jakarta. The Outer Islands have large unused areas and have received a trickle of Javanese settlers, not enough to open them up in a big way or to relieve the pressures in Java itself, yet sufficient to irritate some indigenes. Further weakening to inter-island ties is the presence of over 2 million Chinese residents who have assumed what was originally the Dutch role in the trading systems. Most towns have substantial Chinese trader groups, which in East Sumatra, for example, establishes a closer working link between them and their fellow nationals across the strait in Malaya than between Sumatra and Java. Little inter-island exchange goes on because they produce similar foodstuffs and their industrial raw materials go to foreign markets.

Since the parts of Indonesia so loosely associate, regional civil wars have several times occurred. This tendency to subdivision does not fatally disrupt life in Java. Nowhere is Indonesia industrialised enough to produce either domestic goods or capital equipment for its large needs. East Sumatra and East Borneo petroleum are a foreign development and goes to markets elsewhere. Little local manufacturing arises from Padang coal or Billiton tin.

The positions of Sumatra and Kalimantan facilitate trade ties with Singapore, which in turn offers the facilities of free trade, easy currency exchanges, wide choice of freighting and a Chinese population sympathetic to other Chinese who run the inter-island shipping. The Japanese administration of the 1942–5 period used Singapore as capital of both

Malaya and Sumatra. It is to be noted that the Outer Islands have little cohesion within themselves. The Indonesian political economy leaves plenty of room for the poverty-stricken, congested populations of Java to move into unoccupied, potential rice-growing areas in Sumatra, Kalimantan and Celebes. Until 1941 the Dutch attempted to induce such migration, with only slight effect. That pioneering interest which drew Burmese and Thais to their deltas and Indians and Chinese by the million into the empty areas of Southeast Asia was not repeated among Indonesians, who had greater opportunities and greater domestic pressures.

With a lower *per capita* national production than any other Asian state and slight national coherence, the political power of Indonesia is low and without sign of change. For military purposes, whether offensive or defensive, its own resources are negligible, but its dense population of self-contained farmers in Java, even though so disorganised, has shown it can disrupt administration by guerrilla war. Its international boundaries include some of possible tension. Near Singapore, a boundary runs along the deep-water channel which handles a major concentration of international shipping. The boundary in the South China Sea loops northwards to include the Natoena and Anambas Islands, round which moves shipping between Singapore and Eastern Asia. The Kalimantan boundary with the little-developed colonies of Sarawak and North Borneo runs along an inaccessible watershed uncrossed by trade or communication lines. Across Central Timor, Indonesia shares a boundary with a Portuguese colony where recent oil explorations have begun to attract attention to a previously negative area. The easternmost border consists of narrow seas beyond which lies Netherlands New Guinea; Indonesians have stated a claim to this (which they name Irian), though the traditions, history, languages, religions and cultures are not Indonesian. The corollary claim to Australian East New Guinea (Northeast New Guinea and Papua) is so far only implicit.

NORTHERN BORNEO

The three British administrative colonies of Northern Borneo in present form date only from the Second World War. They are politically separate from one another, and come into association only by air services or small coastal vessels. Footpaths and light craft on the rivers are the only domestic communications and internal trade movements are very small.

North Borneo (a political name in contrast to Northern Borneo, the regional name) was administered by a chartered company until 1941. Its economy centres at a few harbours on a dangerous coast, where Chinese traders handle a little rubber and forest products. Jesselton, the capital, is a British creation, largely peopled by newcomer Chinese arriving by way of Hong Kong, and retains a makeshift pioneer air. Round it spread a few rubber plantations suffering always from shortage of labour. The interior is an equatorial forest containing a few self-contained tribes. North Borneo has little contact with either Filipinos or Kalimantanese.

Brunei is a Malay sultanate peopled by a few thousand long-standing immigrant Muslims living around an estuary where they once depended on self-contained rice-growing. They are culturally distinct from the forest peoples, but no longer have any direct links to Java or Malaya. The state derives large revenues from the Seria oilfield on the shallow coast so that its political economy recalls that of the "oil sheikdoms" of Arabia. Militarily indefensible, the field has the attraction of being the largest producer near China and Japan. It is isolated by swamp forest from the Brunei settlement and links almost exclusively overseas, drawing labour from Hong Kong, Singapore and India.

Sarawak was purchased from British "white rajahs" who ran it privately until 1941. Forest covers most of its large area where tribes of many types are the indigenes, some with a simple hunting-and-collecting economy and reachable only by footpath or by canoe, others equally isolated in a self-contained rice-growing economy (i.e. the Kelabits). Small areas around the few coastal and river towns are peopled by immigrant Malays and Chinese, who work rubber, pepper and copra holdings. The capital and main market is the river port Kuching, which has sea and air links with Singapore and Jesselton.

These colonies are so lightly developed and thinly peopled that they have no political strength of their own. They are little involved with Asian affairs, off the track of world-trade streams, and interesting chiefly as areas of potential where Chinese and Malay immigration is occurring.

INDIA

As a nation, the Union of India approximates more closely in size and in economy to China than to any other Asian country. Its lay-out as a nation is, however, radically different; its less-peopled space is roughly central to a triangular population pattern. The lightly peopled Deccan lies between the dense population belts in the Ganges Plain, the Malabar Coast and the Coromandel Coast. While the Ganges Plain is conspicuously the broadest and most productive of these belts, it has not been the sole nursery of Indian culture and economy (as was the case with the core zone of China).

Its size now makes it dominant in Indian affairs, but the other population belts are not mere outgrowths from it; large Dravidian populations from mid-Deccan southwards and eastwards are anthropologically, linguistically and historically separate, and there are several million negrito people also on the Deccan with a way of life far different from that of "Hindustan" on the Ganges Plain. The peripheral pattern of settlement and development in India, combined with major linguistic differences between the parts (the constitution formally recognises fourteen different Indian languages) and large religious minorities (it contains more Muslims than there are in West Pakistan, 6 million Sikhs and 8 million Christians), set a trend towards regionalism which finds expression in strong, linguistically distinctive state governments which succeeded the principalities and maharajarates of long history. The national government of this union of fourteen states and six other "unions" resembles a federation with its capital at New Delhi which, while central to the Indo-Gangetic Plain as a physical whole and on a site long associated with concentrations of military power in the north, is most eccentric to the Union and removed from the national population and economic concentrations. To some extent this is offset by its inheritance of a fairly elaborate converging railway system, supplemented by an extensive network of domestic air services.

To the centrifugal tendencies inherent in these patterns, which recall those of Iberia and yet have the scale of the U.S.A., is added the self-containment of farms and regions arising from the traditional self-supporting economy, from the inertia of low productivity *per capita*, and from the desperately low productivity per acre. Much of the Indian surface has been exhausted by prolonged farming unameliorated by fallowing or manuring. Apart from its cottonweaving, dispersed along the Ganges Plain and over the Deccan to Bombay, India's industrial power is small and mostly concentrated behind Calcutta, thus adding another eccentricity to the national layout. Only lightly urbanised and not homogeneous culturally, the nation is made up of large but inert groups, preoccupied now to invigorate its agriculture and promote its industries, and heavily committed to capital works for irrigation. Mass education techniques, attempted in India for the past century, are being intensified to facilitate that national cohesion which comes from literacy. Hindi, the speech of the Middle Ganges, is technically the official language of the Union, whose territory has never had a common language except English, which still dominates public life and is used for all official purposes, though it is planned to convert to Hindi within the next ten years or so. Not yet in a position to maintain itself with modern armaments, India is without a large-scale navy or mercantile marine. Its military organisation, taken over directly from the British in 1947, is small in proportion to the size of the country, but has twice been effectively in action under its own control—to force Union on Kashmir and on Hyderabad State.

India's border to the north runs along the Himalayas, which form a linguistic and cultural divide as well as being a major natural barrier, so that it is without local tensions even though it separates India and China, Asia's largest nations. There is little coming and going across the serried ranges. The old maharajarate of Kashmir beyond the northwest mountains fringe is where the Hindu and Muslim cultural worlds overlap, and where there is a well-trodden, old caravan route from the Punjab into Tibet, as well as the headwaters of streams of critical importance for irrigation in the East Punjab plains. In Kashmir, a virtual state of war has existed between India and Pakistan, India now holding the territory whose future has still technically to be decided by the United Nations. Down in the adjoining lowlands, India's border runs through the Punjab, directly cutting across some Indus tributaries and the railways along which much grain and cotton once moved into India. This was a bitterly contested boundary at the time of partition and the scene of a mass migration of millions of Muslims retreating from India and Hindus retreating from Pakistan. The boundary continues out across the undisputed Thar Desert to the swamps of Cutch. In the Punjab the religious and political boundary runs within a few miles of Lahore, the wealthy commercial focus of inland West Pakistan, disrupting its old trade ties and leaving the seeds of possible crises. This same area is the centre of Sikhism, a religion focused on the holy city of Amritsar a few miles on the Indian side of the border, whose 6 million followers persistently claim status independent of India. This makes for additional tension.

East Pakistan has a complex boundary with India, also drawn on a religious basis and assuming a form which leaves only a narrow "railway corridor" (resembling the Polish Corridor) at the foot of the Himalayas to link Assam to the rest of India. The boundary elsewhere runs across the lines of commercial movement along the rivers and railways, separating the older jute-growing areas in East Pakistan from the jute-weaving factories of West Bengal, the tea of the Assam Hills from the international markets of Dacca and Calcutta, and the rice surplus of East Pakistan from its traditional markets in the cities of Eastern India. There was much migration across these boundaries in 1947. Assam's boundaries with Burma are along forested mountains and without tension. Portugal retains a few thousand square miles of scattered little territories and islands along India's west coast, strongly Catholic and relic of the earliest European association with Asia. The main Portuguese centre is at Goa where tension has developed several times in recent years.

As a power India has both people and industries able to sustain a landward action now that some planes and vehicles are assembled in the country. It is accessible seaward for attack and for receiving supplies: none of its mountain boundaries provide lines of easy movement for military supplies. Its domestic cohesion is slight, but India has food enough to withstand blockade and facilities for internal guerrilla activity. It has no boundaries with Russia, though Kashmir comes close to the zone where Chinese, Pakistani and Russian territories are in conjunction round the difficult Pamir Knot. Over the last century or so and despite the political changes since the Second World War, India's economic outlook has been overseas, its heaviest trade being with Britain and U.S.A., the latter having recently become a major source of grains for Indians. The world's chief air routes between America, Europe and Asia, pass over India which is thus much woven into international relations though it has no history as a sea power.

As consequence of its dense population and of the old ties with the British Commonwealth, large numbers of Indians have migrated overseas. Several million are now scattered through Ceylon, Lower Burma, Malaya, East and South Africa, Fiji and the West Indies. Political issues arising from these migrants have already appeared in Ceylon, Burma and Malaya, though the risk is less because the groups are small minorities; they can be a pretext if not a cause for Indian pressure overseas.

Nepal (capital Katmandu) and Bhutan (capital Punaka) are principalities of self-contained, little-developed, thinly-peopled agricultural valleys north of India and in the Himalayas. They are so isolated on all sides that they retain a degree of independence from India, but now recognise its "special relations" in their affairs. Both states are buffers between India and Tibet, and therefore possible contact zones between India and China, but there is little transmontane traffic or trade between them and their neighbours. No significant routes cross them; the rough caravan route from India to Lhasa is by way of Kalimpong, which lies in a 'corridor' of India between Nepal and Bhutan.

PAKISTAN

Pakistan is an unusual state. It originated in 1947 with Islam as the criterion of its separation from India when the British administration was

358

leaving the Subcontinent. Its territory is in two parts separated by 1,500 miles of India, each part distinctive in economy, language, racial characteristics and history. Diverging interests of the parts have already proved a severe domestic strain, yet neither part has moved towards abandoning its conception of independence from India. East Pakistan, a Muslim enclave surrounded by Hindus, has a simple economy based on rice and jute growing, much moving directly into commerce; its only industry is the string of jute-weaving factories newly built near the regional capital at Dacca as part of the policy to divert jute from the Indian mills across the border. West Pakistan, smaller in population but far greater in area, is more complex; there is the ancient wheat and cotton country of the Punjab, centring on Lahore far to the north; the sheep country of the dry central zone and Baluchistan; and the modern commercialised, Nilotic irrigated belt along the lower Indus. Karachi, the first national capital, and Rawalpindi, the new capital further inland, are as difficult to reach from some parts of West Pakistan as they are from East Pakistan. From Karachi to Dacca by sea is roughly the distance between London and New York, and by air to that from London to Athens. Apart from the Lahore mills, Pakistan had no industrial plant at the time of independence, and has been hard pressed to install even maintenance factories since. It has negligible mineral resources: active drilling for oil goes on in the west and there are hydro-electric possibilities to the north of West Pakistan.

Pakistan has that trend to regionalism evident in India. Its high population densities are aggravated by spatial division and low national productivity. Karachi and Dacca still support thousands of poor Muslim refugees from India, and they form socially difficult squatter groups where not yet absorbed into these cities which expanded so rapidly and so haphazardly to serve their new functions. West Pakistan has a military tradition, partly arising from the numerous poor tribesmen of the Northwest Frontier and Baluchistan, partly from traditional employment in the British Indian Army. There is little basis for national cohesion apart from Islam, which has shown itself, however, able to fuse a little-educated people. The country has poor, over-extended transport facilities internally and no industry able to equip modern armed forces. The enclave position of East Pakistan establishes political risks, not least because the boundaries cross trade routes. West Pakistan has a buffer position between India, the Arabic World to the West and the Communist World of Central Asia. Although nowhere contiguous with Russia, it is separated only by a narrow range in Afghanistan along the Upper Oxus. From its own resources Pakistan could not withstand or mount thrusts across the Hindu Kush. It may even be questioned whether from its own resources of men and materials Pakistan could defend its parts against India or against guerrillas from across the Afghanistan border. The territory is isolated by difficult desert mountains from the main part of the Arabic World, and has an outlook different from that of most Muslim countries. Among the Muslim states, however, Pakistan ranks second only in size to Indonesia; West Pakistan alone is 50% more populous than Egypt. Karachi has considerably entrepôt trade through the Persian Gulf, and its raw cotton exports move mostly through Suez. Pakistan's relations with Western Europe and U.S.A., turning on its need for capital equipment and its substantial assets at the time of independence, have been close and better than those with India. Its attitude in the latter direction has been resentful and particularly bitter regarding Kashmir. In the postwar phase Karachi, which inherited most elaborate port facilities, has become one of the world's major air junctions; on it converges a fan of airways from many parts of the Middle East in one direction, and in the other from many places round the Indian Ocean and Pacific Ocean.

CEYLON

Ceylon resembles Taiwan in proximity to the mainland, in size and in population; politically its position is radically different. Over the last thousand years, it has never been part of India and even in British colonial times was not administered from the mainland. Ceylon's modern associations stem from its centrality within an ocean of heavy shipping movements and in many ways they are stronger with parts of the world other than India. Western Europe dominates its trade relations, apart from the rice imports from Burma.

Ceylon's compactness and productivity make for a strong political economy and it inherited capital reserves built up in the Second World War, when the island profited from being chief headquarters for Indian Ocean forces. Its gross domestic product *per capita* is more than twice that of India and ranks fifth among Asian nations, yet the island has considerable room for extending its agricultural specialities. Overwhelmingly a farming state, its agriculture is fairly diversified. Its commodity production for export has not paralysed local food production. Ceylon shares with the Philippines the uniqueness in Asia of having a greater cereal production *per capita* now than it had twenty years ago.

Its core zone spreads round Colombo, the capital, international harbour and commercial hub, where within less than a hundred miles radius three-quarters of the national agricultural lands lie, food and raw commodities being well interdigitated. Here the network of roads is close and the zone, now influenced by modern commercial production for tea, rubber and copra, is also the historic territory of the indigenous Singhalese for whom the hill town, Kandy, was a regal and religious capital. The rest of the island is thinly peopled and patchily developed, except in a narrow, northern coastal fringe where subsistence farming goes on. Jaffna, to the extreme north, is the largest of many coastal settlements isolated from the core zone and giving rise to little trade. The surrounding seas are frequently violent and coastwise trade is negligible. Mannar, the ferry port for South India and linked by rail to Colombo, handles the small traffic between the island and South India.

Consequent to its overseas trade and its expanding opportunities, Ceylon has attracted many people from the surrounding area. Old colonies of Hindu Tamil farmers from South India are spread round the north coast. Having developed on lines different from their forebears across the strait, they identify themselves with Ceylon and are called Ceylonese. The core zone is the region of the Buddhist Singhalese, who have a language and literature of their own. Among them have moved this century a large population of new immigrant Tamils, originally the plantation workers and more widely spread as artisans and labourers. They show divergence from the Ceylonese of the north. A further large southwestern group is Muslim, known locally as "Moors" but of South Indian, Javanese and Arab stock. A distinctive mixed community also exists, relic of the long Dutch, Portuguese and British associations.

Thus a distinct plural society exists, with religious, linguistic and occupational differences. Internal frictions between the sections have arisen owing to divergent views on national language and education now that the British departure has altered the status of the English language. Until recently the Singhalese were given priority in the civil service because they were the indigenes with whom the British had established the original political relations. The voting system of the independent constitution has enabled South Indians to press for removing that preference and for Tamil to be at least recognised as a national language. The possibilities of an Indian irridentist movement are evident. Boundary tensions have not developed in the Palk Strait.

Critically placed in relation to the shipping routes across the Indian Ocean and also with some importance for world air routes, Ceylon has no military strength of its own. Unlike India, it makes no attempt to build even a defensive force, and the British navy has relinquished the dockyard at Trincomalee.

Book List

THE AUTHOR ACKNOWLEDGES with gratitude that the materials used in this book have been drawn from many of the appended works which are the definitive geographical works on various parts of Asia.

Lengthy studies readily available in English and giving more specialised detail about parts of Monsoon Asia are:

CRESSEY, G. B. *Land of the 500 Million* (China). McGraw-Hill, New York, 1955.

DOBBY, E. H. G. *Southeast Asia*, Sixth Edition. University of London Press Ltd., London, 1958.

SPATE, O. H. K. *India and Pakistan*. Methuen, London, 1954.

TREWARTHA, G. T. *Japan*. University of Wisconsin Press, Madison, 1945.
Statistical data are best obtained from:

UNITED NATIONS. *Economic Survey of Asia and the Far East* (Bangkok) which appears annually and contains co-ordinated and digested economic facts not readily available in any other form. It is retailed in Britain by H.M.S.O. Exploration and developments of Asian oil are reported most fully in *Petroleum Press Service*, available monthly in London.

The following are more detailed studies in order of sequence in this book:

EAST, W. G., and SPATE, O. H. K. *The Changing Map of Asia*. Methuen, London, 1950.

Development of Upland Areas in the Far East, Volumes I and II. Institute of Pacific Relations, New York, 1949.

LEE, J. S. *The Geology of China*. Murby, London, 1939.

BUCK, J. L. *Land Utilization in China*. University of Chicago Press. 1937.

RODGERS, A. "Manchurian Iron and Coal Industry", *Geographical Review*, 1948.

TODD, O. J. "The Yellow River Reharnessed", *Geographical Review*, 1949.

GINSBURG, N. S. *Economic Resources and Development of Taiwan*. Insistute of Pacific Relations, New York, 1953.

WU, YUAN-HI. *An Economic Survey of Communist China*. New York, 1955.

LATTIMORE, O. *Inner Asian Frontiers of China*. American Geographical Society, New York, 1940.

CHEN, C. S., "Land Utilization in Formosa", *Geographical Review*. New York, 1951.

362

CHEN, TA. *Population in Modern China*. University of Chicago, 1946.

DAVIS, S. *Hong Kong in its Geographical Setting*, Collins, London, 1949.

ACKERMAN, E. A. *Japanese Natural Resources*. University of Chicago Press, 1953.

EMBREE, J. F. *Suye Mura*. University of Chicago Press, 1939.

Japan, Overseas Economic Survey. Board of Trade, London, 1952.

LOCKWOOD, W. *The Economic Development of Japan*, Princeton University Press, 1955.

McCUNE, G. M. *Korea Today*. Harvard University Press, 1950.

MALAYAN JOURNAL OF TROPICAL GEOGRAPHY. University of Malaya, Singapore, 1953–8 (particularly for field-surveys).

PELZER, K. *Pioneer Settlement in the Asian Tropics*. American Georgaphical Society, New York, 1945.

PURCELL, V. *Chinese in Southeast Asia*. Oxford University Press, 1951.

ANDRUS, J. R. *Burmese Economic Life*. Stanford University Press, 1947.

BROEKE, J. H. *Evolution of the Netherlands Indies Economy*. Institute of Pacific Relations, New York, 1946.

STAMP, L. D. "Irrawaddy River", *Geographical Journal*, London, 1940.

SPATE, O. H. K. "Burmese Village", *Geographical Review*, New York, 1945.

SPENCER, J. E. *Land and People in the Philippines*. University of California Press, 1952.

ROBEQUAIN, C. *Economic Development of French Indochina*. Oxford University Press, 1944.

BRUSH, J. "Iron and Steel Industry of India", *Geographical Review*, New York, 1952.

BROWN, J. C., and DEY, A. K. *India's Mineral Wealth*. Oxford University Press, 1955.

DAVIS, K. *Population of India and Pakistan*. Princeton University Press, 1951.

WADIA, D. N. *Geology of India*. Macmillan, London, 1953.

ANSTEY, V. *Economic Development of India*. Longmans, London, 1952.

SPATE, O. H. K., and ENAYAT AHMAD. "Five Cities of the Gangetic Plain", *Geographical Review*, New York, 1950.

SPATE, O. H. K., "Partition of the Punjab and Bengal", *Geographical Journal*, London, 1947.

SYMONDS, R. *Making of Pakistan*. Faber, London, 1950.

FARMER, B. H. "Agriculture in Ceylon", *Geographical Review*, New York, 1950.

FARMER, B. H. *Pioneer Peasant Colonisation in Ceylon*. Oxford University Press, 1957.

Index

Place entries are in roman type and subject entries are in *italic type*. A page reference printed in *italic type* indicates a map or diagram. A page reference printed in **bold type** indicates that there is a photographic illustration facing that page.

Onga River, 160
Onggin, 141
Optical goods, 152, 155
Orakzais people, 225
Ordos, 29, 130, 135
Orissa, 74, 264, 271, 272, 279
Oriya, *266*, 268, *280*
Osaka, 102, *143*, 147–54, **160**
Otsu, 150
Otsunomiya, 155
Oudh Plains, 253
Oxen, 108, 122, 128, 131, 180, 219, 234, 238
Oxus River, *225*, 226, 359
Oyashiwo current, 41

Pacific Islands, 335
Pacific Ocean, 27, *102*
Padang, 179, *199*, 211, 353
Padi, 61–3; Ceylon, **289**, 289–93, 295; China, 100–3, 116, 117, 122, 137, 141; Continental Southeast Asia, 178, 180–5, 187–96, **192**, 343, 344; India, 219, 235–7, 249, 251, 265, *267*, 275–281, *283*, 285; Insular Southeast Asia, 200–15, **208**; Japan, 147, 151, 162, 163; Philippines, 169–74; Taiwan, 165
Padi, Dry, 208, 213, 214
Pak–Ind, 218. *See also* Subcontinent
Pak Ta, 343
Pakistan, 242, 358–60; *Products*, 257–60, 299–*309*; *Trade*, 311–14, 319, 320, 326
Pakistan, East, 247, *249, 333*; *Products*, 181, 235, 245
Pakistan, West, 260, *333–5*; *Political*, 327–9, 331, 346, 356–60
Paknampoh, 185, 187, 195
Pakokku, 195
Palai Hills, 274
Palaung people, 180
Palawan, 168
Palembang, *199*, 205, 211, 353
Palghat Gap, 274
Palk Strait, 274, 294, 361
Pamirs, *23*, 24, 28, *225*, 331, 358
Pampanga, 172, 173
Panay Islands, 168, *169*, 171
Panjnab, 258
Paotow, 131
Paper, 129, 142, 163, 253, 306, 315

Papua, 354
Parachinar Pass, *see* Kurram Pass
Parsees, 283, 294
Pasak River, 185, 196
Paseroean, 179
Pasir PG, *204*
Pastoral farming, 45, 58–61, *63*, *67*, 238, 260
Pat Desert, 259, 261
Pathan people, 225
Patiala, 258
Patna, 239, 240, *251*, 252, 253, *272*
Paya Lebar, *204*
Pearls, 288
Pegu, 185, 195, 345
Pegu Yoma, *177*, 182, 184, 194, 346
Pei-kiang, 115, *119*
Peiping–Tientsin complex, 334
Peiyuakiri, 185
Peking, 38, 82–4, 96, 103, 105, 111–14, **112**, 131, 135, 139, 140. *See also* Peiping–Tientsin complex
Peking Grid, 135
Penang, *197*, 198, *201*, 204, 210, 344, 350, 351
Pench, 272
Pengarga, 270
Pennar River, 279
Pepper, 188, 192, 208, 211, 212, 214, 215, 277, 355
Peshawar, *225*, 226, 231, 240, 261
Peshawar–Delhi Highway, 258
Petroleum, 71, 129, 305–7, 311, 315, 317–19, *355*; Continental Southeast Asia, 181, 185, 188; India, *223*–229, 241, 283, *284*; Indonesia, 205, 211, 215, 353–5; Japan, *143*, 159, 160, 339; Philippines, 166
Philippines, 27, 36, 93, 167–74; *Political*, *333*, 341, 342; *Products*, 120, 298–308, 326; *Trade*, *309*, 311–17; *Chinese*, 168, 335, 341, 342; *Dutch*, 303; *Japanese*, 143, 167, 342
Philippines Trench, *23*
"*Piccotah*", 234
Pigs, 59, *60*, 128, 180, 192, 193, *223*
Ping River, 178, 195
Pinghsiang, 126, 127
Pingting Gap, 139
Plantations, 67, 185, 202, 205, 208, 277, 302, 303
Pnom Penh, *176–7*, 190–3, 348–9
Podsols, *46*, 48, 162

INDEX